KORDAN

The Wizard

Story By David Nos
Music and Lyrics by David Nos/Bob Agner

Overture

Published by

RebelBooksPress.com
A division of The Jersey Tomato Press, LLC

ISBN: 979-8-9875536-0-2

Front cover design by David Nos with Adam Nos

Manufactured in the United States
First Edition

Dedication

Bob and Dave would like to dedicate this book and accompanying music to:

Dave's sons: Matt and Adam

Bob's son: Jeff and his wife MaryAlice

And we wish to give extra acknowledgement to:

Dave's wife Kimberley for her support and allowing us to use her marvelous vocal talents for the songs in our story.

Bob's wife Kelli for her complete support and positive feedback to all our combined endeavors.

And a special shout out to Matt's wife Chelsea, who came to the table at the last minute and loaned us her voice to help complete the final song so we could present our work to the publisher.

Bob and Dave are most grateful and appreciative for the support and trust shown to us.

We love and thank you all.

Preface

Welcome to Singing Stories™. This is our unique offering to help enhance your reading experience by adding another layer – songs.

Throughout the book musical links will be available so you can listen to a song specifically written for that segment of the story. For the E-books you will have a direct link you can click. For the paperback book reader, we've supplied easily accessible QR codes which will take you to the songs.

So, turn on your speakers, sit back, read, relax and listen. We hope you enjoy the story and music as much as we did creating it for you.

For more information go to www.singingstories.net or

Kordanthewizard.com

DISCLAIMER: All songs are stored on remote servers. While we don't expect issues, servers do go down. We cannot guarantee 100% up time. If you find you cannot access the song(s), please wait. The server should return to normal shortly. We strongly suggest that you save the song(s) to your hard drive for your convenience allowing you to listen at any time.

Table of Contents

PROLOGUE

The solitary hooded figure walked slowly through the dark forbidding forest. In the distance, the low rumble of thunder could be heard yet the figure did not hasten the pace against the advancing storm walking slowly, even deliberately, deeper into the dark.

Suddenly a bolt of lightning lit the forest like daylight revealing, if only for a moment, the cloaked-hooded figure. The individual's stature was tall and slender. The light showed quite clearly the ashen staff being held by the left hand.

A gust of wind blew the hood from the head revealing the male countenance and slight beard. His eyes pierced the dark as if nothing could keep them from seeing. His physical appearance seemed slight, but that did not belie the power and strength that seemed to emanate from him and the staff he wielded.

He spoke, "VENIRE," or was it another clap of thunder? From deep within the shadows, he saw his quarry approach. It was Ningthus the Giant.

"Who calls me?" boomed the Giant.

"My name is not for you to know," spoke the man. "What you need to know is why I am here…and that is to tell you to leave the farmers' crops and livestock alone!"

"I will do as I please," laughed the giant, "including crushing you like an insect, little man."

"I think not," said the figure.

The giant hearing mockery in the man's voice became enraged and charged forward. The man raised his staff and spoke in clear audible tones which seemed to rise above the heavy air.

"Mutatus Lapis!"

The giant fell in mid stride. He had completely turned to stone.

The man walked to the smooth, granite figure which lay on the ground and tapped it with his staff.

"You may now know my name since you can no longer find power with it. I am Kordan, the Wizard".

Chapter 1

ALICANTH

Alicanth couldn't remember the last time a thunderstorm had scared her – kept her awake. But tonight's encroaching storm felt different. She couldn't smell the moisture in the air, the thunderclaps were louder and felt like they were right over her room. Yet the approaching storm looked some distance away. And the lightning, normally white and bright enough to light up the whole valley, had a green cast that did not look natural.

Despite her misgivings, she was thankful for the storm. "This will keep the farms and livestock safe from Ningthus," she thought. He never seemed to attack and raid the farms during inclement weather. She had only seen the giant one time when he had wandered near the castle. He stood 12 feet tall with a full beard down to his round protruding stomach. He had a bulbous nose that bore the scars of many battles and large elephantine ears. Actually, he looked quite comical if it were not for the deep-set jet-black eyes that could pierce holes with their stare. Her Father's army had confronted him at that time and the soldiers and guards drove him back; their arrows and catapulted rocks did little to harm him. They quietly spoke of his evil intentions. Despite the thoughts of thunder, lightning, and giants, sleep took her to a restful place where she did not stir again until morning.

The sun's rays broke through the window of Alicanth's bedroom moving slowly across the floor towards her bed. As the gray of night left the room the face of the sleeping young lady slowly became visible in the light. She was beautiful. She had deep-red hair and piercing green eyes which complimented her soft freckled complexion. She stood 5'4 inches tall and had a slender but well-proportioned frame. She was strong-willed, something which her father fostered. Since he had no male heirs to his throne; he prepared her to be Queen.

She was well liked, even loved throughout the kingdom. She was kind and did her best to protect and help the people, treating them more as equals than subjects. It wasn't uncommon for her to see someone walking in the road during one of her rides and stop to walk and talk with them like they were close friends.

At 18, she was still single and though there were many suitors vying for her hand, she just smiled and politely refused. She was in no rush. Her father put no pressure on her; he knew his daughter would marry when she was ready.

In the meantime, she would learn about the problems with the kingdom. Most were internal and she let her father deal with such things as Ningthus and other unpleasantries. As fate would have it, her father was at peace with the surrounding Kingdoms. He was an honored and respected King – a man true to his word.

By the time the sunlight had reached her face Alicanth was awake. She rose quickly, dressed, and headed to the stables so she could take a morning ride. She enjoyed this immensely, especially after an evening storm. Everything always looked so fresh. As usual her two guardians were there to accompany her. They had saddled and prepared her horse and were awaiting her arrival.

The three rode from the castle at an easy gait. Alicanth loved her father's land. It was beautiful and the people kept it well. The two guards, Darien and Kir, rode silently behind her – far enough away to give her privacy, but close enough to spring to action if necessary.

The guards had been Alicanth's protectors since she was a baby. It was a personal request from the King. "You two are the bravest and strongest of my army. I am not asking you to be nursemaids, I'm asking you to protect the future of my kingdom. I will ask no others, because I trust you with my life; I know I can entrust hers to you."

They accepted and rarely left her side since that day. They did their job well and to be sure she loved them both with all her heart and treated them as her uncles. Each man knew he was her favorite.

The day was beautiful - the morning crisp - the air

clean. As Alicanth and her companions left the castle, she could see the people dotting the fields as they began their day working the land. She knew many by name and returned greetings as they respectfully rang through the air. "Good morning, Princess." "Good day," she brightly responded.

She was clearly enjoying herself. These rides always made her feel closer to the people and the land. As she looked ahead, she could see a lone figure walking slowly on the road moving toward her. The figure held a staff and was covered completely by a robe and hood.

The guards, aware of their charge, changed positions Darian moving to the front and Kier bringing up the rear with the princess safely between them. They felt no danger, but precaution is always the wise choice. Their pace slowed as they approached. All would have proceeded as if nothing had happened except for the figure's lack of acknowledgment for the passing royalty.

"Stranger," said Kier, "In this realm we stop and pay respect to the royal princess when she passes."

"I meant no disrespect," said the stranger, "but I am weary and have traveled far with little sleep. I am making for King Timor's castle to have audience with him."

"And is my father expecting you sir?" chimed the princess. "The King is busy and sees no one without prearranging it."

"No, my Lady, he is not expecting me...yet. I am ahead

of my time. But it matters not, he WILL see me!"

The stranger bowed at the waist straightened, turned, and slowly walked past the entourage making his way to the castle. The princess stared in disbelief as the figure slowly distanced himself from her. "My father will take care of this," she thought and galloped off to finish her ride.

Chapter 2

TIMOR

Timor was a well-respected King. In fact, he was known throughout all the kingdoms as "Timor the Just." It was a title he earned at a very young age. At seventeen, his father King Fadron died suddenly, leaving the young prince to rule and fend for himself. One other nearby kingdom saw what they felt was an easy chance to expand their own realm and attacked Timor's kingdom. When the first wave arrived at his castle, the young king was seen dressed in his battle armor standing with his troops vowing to remain with his men to the last man.

King Godrin's army attacked without warning, but he found Timor no easy mark, as the young King's castle was well armed and well defended. Timor was a natural at strategy, a fact Timor's men quickly learned. As a result, they found it easy to obey and follow the young king. Godrin's men beset Timor's castle for three days with little effect. Godrin's men were tiring. On the fourth day Godrin left, and he left quite quickly. He was needed at home because the giant king Ohmthus and his horde had attacked his lands. Godrin was not sure he would be able defeat the giants as his men, now battle-weary and fewer in numbers, would have to rally themselves to fight. Godrin's men were strong and well trained, and he had faith in them, but they were already exhausted, and the long journey home would tax them further. Godrin knew he was in trouble.

Timor, seeing the haste in which Godrin had left wondered what had called his enemy away. He sent a scout to follow. The scout returned within a day. He had caught up with the retreating army, and masquerading as a farmer, spoke to one of the troops as they passed. "So," said Timor, "the giants attack Godrin. Call my war council, I would meet with them now."

Godrin was fighting for the life of his people and for his kingdom. If he hadn't been so greedy and sought to take Timor's kingdom for his own, his men would not be exhausted. His front lines would be holding, and the giants would be driven back. Godrin summoned the captain of his guard. "Sire, " said the guard. We need help. We cannot hold back Ohmthus. I do not wish to keep losing men. We must surrender."

Godrin heard truth in his Captain's voice. He could call for aid from one of the other kingdoms, but that would take time, time he did not have. "Bring my generals to me. Maybe there is some way out of this."

"But Sire," said the Captain.

"Bring them to me!" snapped Godrin. The Captain reluctantly left and returned with two of Godrin's four generals. "The others are dead Sire," said the Captain.

Godrin listened intently as his men laid out the situation. There was no way for him to win. In the few hours that he had wasted on trying to find a way out of this mess, he lost more men. Now he would have to live with that. He had no choice. "Send word to Ohmthus," said the King. "Ask him for his terms." The Kings head hung low as the soldiers silently saluted and left.

As Godrin returned to his castle, he wondered what Ohmthus would want. Most likely leave his brother Ningthus in charge. The king shuddered. His subjects would become slaves, toiling every day to feed the voracious appetites of the giants. He called his personal servant. "Remove my daughter from the castle. See to her safety." The servant bowed and left Godrin sitting in the dark on his throne alone.

The captain of Godrin's army made haste to the front lines. He hoped his men had held the giants long enough for him to arrive and represent the King's desire for surrender. But as he neared the front of the battle, he began to hear cheers from the men. Could they have turned this battle around? "What miracle could have saved us?" he thought. He could not believe his eyes. He dismounted his horse and walked over to King Timor as he pulled his sword from Ohmthus.

Timor's men were everywhere; the giants were scattering. The captain spoke to Timor. "My Lord, how is this possible...I mean no disrespect, but why? After...."

"Captain," said the young King. "I have my reasons. Take me to Godrin. I would speak with him."

Indeed, Timor did have his reasons. After Godrin's army departed and Timor had learned the nature of his situation, he met with his war council. He listened intently as his Captain and his chief officers made their case for counterattack and war. It would be easy to attack the rear flank and push through. With Godrin's army scattered, they would continue the surge and take out the giants as well. "No one would dare stand against us," said Irick, Timor's captain.

Timor listened intently, weighing all his options. After a few moments, he spoke. "Gentlemen, I am not convinced that attacking Godrin is our best option or in our best interest. Please hear me out."

The council listened intently to the young King as he laid out his plan-his vision. His ideas would effectively increase commerce between kingdoms, giving his kingdom the advantage without taking away any power from any of the other kings. It culminated with the death of Ohmthus which Timor insisted had to be at his hand. This alone would establish his credibility. His final act to seal the deal would be his betrothal to Godrin's daughter, Lorayne. When he had finished, the room was silent. "We leave in one hour. Prepare yourselves". Timor turned to leave. "Your Majesty," said Irick. Timor stopped to see his entire war council on their feet cheering him. "We follow you to the end." Timor held back his emotions. He turned and left to prepare himself for whatever fate the gods chose to be his.

The army was ready within the hour as he had commanded. Word of Timor's plan had spread through the troops, invigorating them, and filling them with the strength and power to follow their king. Timor said nothing as he rode to the front. He could not get a word in through the cheers hanging in the air. As he reached the front Irick yelled, "I hope stealth wasn't part of your plan, Sire. I'm sure the men can be heard all the way to Godrin's castle." Timor smiled. "My Lord Irick, I am counting on this momentum." Timor pulled his sword, pointed it forward, and started to ride. The final cheer felt like it shook the earth. Timor's army was on the move.

Battle March

King Godrin was a half day ahead of Timor's army, but Timor's men marched with deliberate purpose - refusing to stop. The King knew better and forced a two-hour rest - even though the men wanted to move, the horses needed the rest. Timor's army made up ground with their resolve and entered Godrin's Kingdom within twelve hours of starting their march, normally a day and a half journey. Timor figured another two hours at this pace, and they would be at the front battle lines... and then live or die, it was up to him.

Timor's army reached the back edge of the battle. The young King could see Omthus's strategy. Godrin's men had been forced into a gauntlet. The giants were systematically squeezing and destroying any chance that Godrin's men might have had to escape the trap.

Analyzing the situation quickly, Timor commanded Irick to send his men to the other side of the giants forcing them into a similar trap. The giants would have to fight on two fronts, giving Godrin's men critical time to regroup. Help had arrived. Timor's army split into three groups, two flanking either side and one with Timor proceeding right through the middle. The giants were taken aback by the maneuver, and though they were larger and stronger, they began to lose ground to the now reinforced troops.

When Timor reached the front line, the giants had been sufficiently pushed back for Timor to plainly see the giant's leader Ohmthus. Timor rode boldly forward and yelled "I am Timor, King of the Northern realm, I seek parlay with Ohmthus!"

Ohmthus heard the young King's demand. Surely this must be some sort of a joke, a ploy by Godrin to throw him and his men off balance. He chuckled to himself, that this was a truly futile gesture, a last desperate attempt to eke out a victory. Godrin had lost and if he had to slay one last victim so what, it was too late. "Ohmthus parlays with no one. Show me your blade and I will be swift. I mean to dine in Godrin's hall tonight."

Ohmthus strode forward slowly to meet the boy whom he would make his final kill to end this battle. Ohmthus stood thirteen feet tall, pear shaped as most giants. His arms were thick and muscular. His face bore a heavy beard and his nose was scarred from his many battles and fights. His gait was slow and deliberate as if he were prolonging the inevitable for spite.

Timor watched as the giant approached. He swallowed, drew his sword, and began to advance. "My Lord," said Irick, "Do not be daunted by his size he will be slow and cumbersome. The truth is you have the advantage. Use your speed and your mind. You will have seconds, but you can analyze his attack. I believe in you, Sire!"

Timor stared into the face of his Captain and smiled, "I must succeed. I cannot betray that kind of faith," he thought. They clasped hands and Timor continued forward. The air felt thick, and Timor could only hear himself breathe as fear, adrenalin, and determination moved him forward. In fact, the small skirmishes around had stopped, and all eyes were on the impending confrontation.

Timor carried his broadsword aloft. It seemed barely

capable of inflicting any damage or harm to Ohmthus at all. By comparison Ohmthus carried his crystalline sword which never chipped and was always razor sharp. Truly a formidable weapon. The two stopped some twenty feet from each other. While the distance seemed large it was merely a step and a half for the giant. An easy move to reach his mark. Even though it was less than ten seconds that they stared at each other it felt like an interminable amount of time for those looking on. Timor sat on his horse looking at his adversary, saying nothing. Ohmthus bellowed and without a word charged. The distance closed quickly. Timor did not move at the first footfall. He stood his ground. The giant's next step would close the gap and while his foot was in the air, Timor moved skirting the giant and moving behind him. Ohmthus's blade hit dirt. Timor's blade cut deep into Omthus's Achilles' tendon forcing the giant to his knee. Timor circled to face Ohmthus.

The surrounding armies remained silent afraid to make a sound. "So, the bee can sting," said Ohmthus. Timor just stared back at the giant silently, his sword in front of him. Ohmthus was hobbling but could still move. Without a sound he hurled his sword at Timor. Timor jumped from his horse to dodge the blade, but Ohmthus followed immediately with a boulder that he scooped up separating Timor from his horse further. The giant advanced. Timor seemed to be in trouble. The giant got to his sword and turned to face the small King and finish him. While his sword raised to deal the final blow, Timor ran forward sliding between the giant's legs and clipping his other Achilles' tendon. Ohmthus went to his knees. Timor let out a whistle and his horse ran up. The young king quickly mounted his steed and rode to face the giant. They faced each other for what seemed an eternity. Timor pulled a dagger from his boot and held his sword in one hand and the dagger in the other. Without a word Timor charged. The giant seemed ready, but Timor hurled his dagger to Ohmthus's head. The Giant raised his hands to block the blade. As he did Timor stood on his saddle and with the horse's momentum hurled himself forward raising his sword, he plunged it into Ohmthus's solar plexes, piercing the giants heart killing him instantly.

It was at this moment that Godrin's Captain arrived. He was in shock and could only comply with Timor's request to see his King. He rose to his feet and motioned Timor to follow.

Timor turned to Irick. "My Lord Irick you are with me. Place Darien and Kir in charge of the men. Have the men make camp. We will spend the night here and will begin our return in the morning. That is if good King Godrin has no objection to my army resting here for the night."

Godrin's Captain felt the weight of the young King's words. "No Sire," he said, "it would be our honor." Irick barked a command to his men and the three rode off to Godrin's castle.

Godrin sat on his throne silently thinking of his future

and what lay ahead for a dethroned monarch. He looked up as the doors to his great hall opened. He saw his Captain walking forward followed closely by two figures. He recognized Timor and he felt his insides tighten. "I have lost my throne and kingdom to a boy," he thought.

Timor stepped forward in front of the two Captains. "King Godrin, I seek audience with you."

King Godrin sprang to his feet and shouted, "Do you mock me boy!"

"No Sire," said Timor, "I did not come here to gloat or subjugate, I came as your equal with respect. I desire to establish an era of cooperation between you and I, and by our actions together with the other kingdoms."

Godrin fell back onto his throne. He couldn't believe what he had just heard. By right, Timor had won the kingdom and with that the authority to exile Godrin or run him through with his sword. Timor walked forward and explained his plan to establish trade routes throughout all the kingdoms. He further explained his idea of the kingdoms cooperating with each other against other seemingly stronger enemies. Godrin was amazed. The young King's plan was brilliant.

"And," Timor continued, "this will be sealed between us by the marriage of your daughter Lorayne to me." Timor stopped and waited for a reaction from Godrin. He just sat in silence for a few moments, pulling himself together, summoning his strength. "My daughter is your price?" he asked.

"Sire," said Timor, "It is necessary to ensure cooperation. Remember, you attacked me."

Timor's words stung Godrin; he felt the truth in them. "She is a strong-willed girl. She will not do this without protest."

"Do not worry Sire, I mean to win her heart. I leave Captain Irick here to finish the details. I will return in two weeks on my eighteenth birthday. I will meet your daughter then." Timor bowed and turned to leave. Godrin was barely able to utter, "I agree" as he watched his future son-in-law and peer leave the hall.

Timor spent the night with his troops going to each man and expressing his gratitude for a job well done. This sealed the bond with his men. They would follow him to the ends of the earth. He was truly their King.

Chapter 3

LORAYNE

Lorayne was the apple of her father's eye. Trapping his daughter in a loveless marriage was not the life he wished for her. It was too often that children's lives were sacrificed to the duties of state. But he was committed; he had no choice. What scared him more than the deal he made with Timor was having to tell his daughter. Taking a deep draught from his ale, he summoned her.

Lorayne wondered what had caused her father to make such an urgent call for her to come. It could not be good news. As she hastened through the castle halls, the streaking sunlight bounced from her hair, exposing its deep red features. Her eyes were piercing green and laid against her high cheeks and milky white skin. She was beautiful and many a young suitor was tongue-tied trying to talk to her. Her father had pressed her to find a suitable husband, but she rebuked most, saying she was not ready. They had started arriving since she was sixteen. She had felt she was too young. Soon she would be eighteen and she knew her father was going to have another talk soon. She hoped against hope this wasn't it.

As she entered the hall, she saw her father. He looked to be immersed in thought staring open-eyed, with an unseeing blank gaze seemingly looking at nothing. "Father," she said, "you sent for me?"

The King slowly turned toward his daughter, his unemotional eyes burning through her as though she wasn't there. "I .... I did," he said slowly as his countenance began to take on the familiarity of the man she knew and loved. "Lorayne, we need to talk," and as his eyes dropped, he began to speak laying out the contract he had made with King Timor. He didn't look up again until he had finished, knowing he would never have had the courage to tell of his shameful pact if he had seen her face, her eyes, her heart.

It was an eternity for Godrin and when his daughter finally spoke, he could feel her words pierce him like a sword right to his core. "Father, how could you? I WILL NOT be a bargaining chip for you or anyone. You cannot force me to do this." Lorayne abruptly turned to leave. The King spoke.

"Your feelings not-with-standing, you will marry King Timor," said Godrin. The young princess stopped mid-stride. "You cannot be serious," she said, "you know how I feel!"

"I do," said Godrin, "but I cannot let that affect my decision in this matter. I am responsible for all the subjects in my kingdom. They look to me to keep them safe, to protect them. I do not have the luxury of my personal feelings and quite frankly neither do you. Whatever unrequited love you may have laying in your past, or future plans, the kingdom must come first. Your birthright demands it."

The princess turned around and screamed, "I will renounce my birthright!"

"You can do that," said Godrin, "but I will have to relinquish my throne to Timor. We will both be outcasts. No one will take us in because we lost the Kingdom. We lost it to someone who proved he could protect them."

The silence was palpable. A wall of undetermined thickness, seemingly never to be breeched. "He's eighteen in two weeks," continued Godrin, "and he single-handedly defeated Ohmthus. My men and my subjects already look up to him. Go ahead - abdicate. We will lose everything."

Lorayne stopped and saw the truth in her father's face. The stress-worn features showing prominently on his brow as he admitted his failure to her. "I will do as you command my King," she said coldly. "I will never let him have access to me. I hope you won't mind not having an heir to your throne." The broken King buried his face in his hands and started sobbing uncontrollably. Lorayne stared at him for a few moments, turned and left. If she couldn't have the love she wanted, she would love no one. It was the choice for continuing to live as princess, and as queen. One tear fell from her eye as she walked silently from the hall.

Lorayne returned to her room. The confrontation with her father left her exhausted and she fell into bed falling into a deep sleep....and in her sleep she dreamed.

There was a young girl playing in a garden, a beautiful flower laden nursery, with fountains and trees. Birds sang continuously. Choruses floated through the air giving one the feeling of walking in Paradise. She felt exhilarated as she walked, ran, and played within the confines of her world.

She would laugh and talk aloud to the flowers, trees, and the birds. She took their gentle sway in the light breeze or their melodious chirps as responses to her queries. In this world she felt safe and content.

One morning as she was talking to the birds playing in one of the garden's many fountains, she heard a giggle from behind her. She spun around and found a young boy smiling at her from atop the garden wall.

""And who are you?" she asked. The boy just giggled. ""How did you get in here?" The boy pointed to a large oak whose branch straddled the wall from the outside. "So, you climbed the tree, did you?" Again, no answer. ""Do you have a name?" she pressed. Silence.

The young princess slightly turned away from her silent intruder and began focusing her attention on a flower in the garden next to her. She bent slightly to smell the bloom and plucked it. As she played with the petals she spoke into the flower. "I suppose your father is one of the kings or ambassadors here for the conference. If you tell me who you are, I might speak to my father about allowing you to come here through the castle, but I will have to give it some thought. After all this is MY private garden, and I don't allow just anyone in here. Tell me who you are, and I might consider it. "

Once more her comments were met with no response. She turned fully to face the boy and confront him as she was now irritated, but he had gone. Completely vexed, she huffed, turned, and stormed out of the garden to her room.

The next morning was just as beautiful as the morning before, except today, the young princess moved a little faster, ate her breakfast a little quicker, leaving some fruit still on the plate. "Are we in a hurry this morning princess? Asked the servant.

"Why do you ask that?" said Lorayne. She sounded a little irritated at the question.

"No reason your highness," said the servant, "you normally eat your whole breakfast, and don't eat as fast."

"I'm fine!" was the curt response. She wiped her hands on her napkin and headed to play.

When she entered the garden, her eyes went immediately to the large oak in the far corner that grew outside the wall. There was no one there. What did she expect? She basically told him she'd rather be alone. She must have scared him because he left so quickly. She

— 23 —

shrugged her shoulders and walked slowly into her garden, which for some reason today was far quieter, and seemed somewhat lonelier.

Still, she was happy to have her special place to escape to. As the morning passed, she forgot about her guest and began to enjoy her garden and her time alone. When the noon hour approached, Lorayne heard what she thought were stones hitting the garden wall. She walked over to the far corner where the towering oak and the wall met the outside world.

As she approached the oak, she could hear the tap, tap, tap, growing stronger. "I wonder who's doing that," she thought. ""Hello." No answer. "Hello, who's there?" Still no answer. Lorayne was becoming irritated. Not only did she not know who was rudely attacking her sanctuary, she could not see to the other side of the wall to get a glimpse of her assailant, that is until she heard a faint giggle. "Boy, is that you?" Another giggle. "You stop laughing, this instant, do you hear?"

Suddenly, there was silence. Lorayne ran to the tree. "Boy, can you hear me? You don't have to go." She waited a few minutes, listening but heard nothing. She shrugged her shoulders in disappointment and turned to walk back to the center of her garden, when she heard "Hey!" She spun around to see the young boy sitting in the tree above the wall. "There you are, said Lorayne. "Do you want to come down?"

"Sure." said the boy. "I'm just trying to make sure I have a way back up and out."

"How about the vines at the end of the wall?" said the princess.

"Great! And I can use them to get down too." said the boy.

The boy crawled along the top of the wall to the vines and climbed down into the garden.

When his feet touched the ground, he turned around and stood face-to-face with the Princess Lorayne. They stared at each other, not knowing what to say. Finally, the boy spoke, "Hi." The simple yet powerful statement unleashed a barrage of statements and questions.

"Who are you? Where are you from? Are you hungry? I'm Lorayne. Are you thirsty? How long will you be here? How did you get into the castle?" She seemed to do it all in one breath. She hesitated apparently to gasp for more air and the boy spoke.

"Hold on," he said. "One question at a time. My dad calls me Stick. Pleased to meet you, Lorayne." He bowed. The princess put her hand across her mouth and giggled. "Stick. What kind of name is that?"

"I don't know," said the boy, "but it's what my dad calls me."

"Stick it is then," she said.

For the next four days the two young friends played,

laughed, talked, and shared their inter-most thoughts and dreams.

Each morning Stick would arrive and climb down the vine along the west side of the garden and each afternoon, he climbed up the vine, crawled along the top of the fence to the great oak on the north side of the garden and leave. At the end of the fourth day Stick looked at Lorayne, sadness in his eyes and said, "We leave first thing tomorrow, I won't be coming."

"Ever again?" she said, but nothing could hide the sadness in her voice.

"I don't know," he said

Stick looked around on the ground bent over and picked up two, white pebbles. Both were so white as to look like they had never been touched by the soil. He slowly took one into his other hand and gave it to Lorayne. "This is my promise that I will come back", he said.

"I will wait for you even if it takes forever," she said. She threw her arms around him and hugged him tightly, let go, and ran off into the castle. She turned for one last look. Stick was already up on the wall and at the oak. They saw each other, stared for a moment and then he was gone. Lorayne felt her heart burst. "I will wait," she thought, "Forever."

Chapter 4

THE COURTSHIP

Lorayne awoke the next morning from a fitful sleep. Her emotions were a mix of anger and fear, coupled with depression for having to live with something out of her control. How could her father have done such a thing? She was nothing more to him than a piece of property. Tears streamed down her face as she fought to control herself. It was not an easy task.

She dressed and headed to the main hall for breakfast where she knew her father would be eating as well. It was their practice to sit with each other each morning (affairs of state permitting) and spend quality time together. She knew today would be strained. She was trapped. She either gave in or left altogether. She loved her father very much and she knew the latter would utterly destroy him. It would also leave the kingdom and its subjects to the unknown hands of King Timor.

She entered the hall and saw her father sitting alone at the table seemingly lost in his thoughts. "Good morning father," said the princess. Her voice sounded much colder than she intended. His gaze turned toward her. It was a troubled stare. He looked as though he bore the weight of the world. His mouth opened as if to speak, but no words were uttered. He just closed his mouth and looked down at his plate.

Before her sat not a king, but a man who had sacrificed the life and happiness of someone he loved for duty. It hurt her to see him this way. As tears began welling up in her eyes, she spoke softly. "Father, I will do as you ask...but do not ask me to find joy in this for I cannot."

He raised his head and met her tear-filled eyes with tears of his own. "I'm sorry," he said. "I have no words of comfort save that this young King has honor and I believe a good heart. I hope you can find something in him that will make this at least bearable for you."

The King rose slowly from his chair and as he did, Lorayne ran to her father and gave him a hug and she cried in his arms. Later that day the palace received word that King Timor would arrive by the end of the following week. A chill ran down her spine. She spoke aloud to no one in particular and said, "Give me strength!"

When Godrin received word of Timor's impending arrival, he dove deeply into planning a large gala. It was to be a combination birthday party and betrothal announcement. He brought in the best cooks, decorators, and party planners from throughout the kingdom. He tried to involve Lorayne, but she would have none of it. "Father, I am doing what you ask and am going to marry this king, please ask nothing more of me," she said.

For the next week Lorayne kept to herself, staying mostly in her room. She could hear the hustle and bustle outside her quarters as preparations were made for the big event. When word came of Timor's arrival, her heart sank, and the reality of the situation came to bear. She would have to do this. As she stood by the window lost in her thoughts, there was a knock on her door. "Who is it?" she said. "Your handmaid m'Lady, may I enter?"

The princess bade her to come in. The handmaid entered carrying one of the most beautiful gowns she had ever seen. "Your father sent this m'Lady. It belonged to your mother. He has requested that you wear this at the gala tomorrow."

Her first instinct was to refuse, but she did give her word to her father, and this dress belonged to her mother. Wearing it would be as if her mother were actually there with her. She would need such strength as her mother had. She held the dress close and inhaled the fabric. She could smell her mother. The knot in her stomach eased and she fell to her bed still holding the dress. She drifted off to sleep and didn't move again until morning.

Princess Lorayne rose and set about getting herself ready for the evening's coming festivities. She had made up her mind to give her mother's dress the respect it deserved, and she would wear it with pride, despite the fact that for her this was not a happy occasion. She would be a royal and with her mother's help accept her fate with dignity and aplomb. She would serve her father, her family, and her kingdom.

The evening approached quickly and soon it was time to make her entrance. She and her handmaids had labored all day to make sure every pleat in the gown was perfect, every curl was properly placed, and her jewel-studded tiara was placed on her head to enhance her features. At last, she was ready. She opened the door from her quarters looked at her handmaids with a sad smile and thanked them. Holding her head high she walked into the corridor and headed for the great hall. Two palace guards followed closely behind her each wishing they had the position and place to tell her how beautiful she looked. Unable to speak their thoughts, each guard walked taller on their march to the great hall, proudly bearing their charge to the King.

The great hall was alive with guests from all the kingdoms. Most came to get a glimpse of the boy-king. Word of his exploits and his battle with Omthus had circulated throughout the kingdoms, and everyone was interested to see him and speak with him.

There was quite a crowd around Timor when Lorayne arrived. As the herald announced the Princess all stopped. The room became silent as she entered. Her beauty silenced the room. Men bowed and women curtsied as she passed. She made her way to her father, who was speechless. He took a deep breath and said, "Lorayne, you are the incarnation of your mother. I never thought to see such beauty again in my life."

She smiled and curtsied. "I'm glad to have pleased you father."

She turned to face the crowd who had applauded her entrance and began to renew their conversations. She looked up only to be face-to-face with a very handsome young man. "Princess Lorayne, I am King Timor." The young king took a deep bow and presented the princess with a single, very beautiful red rose.

Lorayne curtsied and said, "Thank you, Sire."

"May I have this dance?" he asked.

She extended her hand and they moved to the center of the room. As they danced, she spoke again. "You are not wearing your crown."

"No," he said, "I am a guest in Godrin's kingdom. It is out of respect that I do not wear it."

"Was it out of respect for him that you forced this marriage to take place?" Her tone was no longer soft, but biting, as she continued. "Is this how the great King Timor gets things done, by kicking someone while they are down, or in a position to have to accept his terms?"

Timor stopped and stepped back. He was a little upset at her tone, but not totally surprised. "That is not my style." said Timor. "May I remind the princess that King Godrin and his army attacked my kingdom, not two weeks after my father died. And, despite that, we came to his aide to help him defeat Ohmthus. Had I defeated your father at my home I would have asked for the same and he would still have his Kingdom. Others would not have been as kind…and they would still have asked for your hand."

His tone was even, spoken with no anger. "I do not wish you and I to be enemies. I came in earnest and would like you to at least give me a chance."

Lorayne was doing everything in power to not create a scene. She was angry. She could not tell if he was being confident, arrogant, or condescending with his tone. He had made it sound as if he was noble in saving her from other much-less desirable options. "What conceit!" she thought.

She abruptly bowed to the young king and said, "Sire, please forgive me, I am not feeling well, I must excuse myself."

Timor seeing that she was making a hasty retreat reached out and touched her arm. She pulled her arm in hard and spun around. He spoke before she could. "Princess, I do not wish to cause you discomfort or angst. All I ask is you give me a chance. In fact, I will put a time limit to it. Give me a fortnight. If you still find me loathsome or have no feelings for me, I will leave. Your father's kingdom remains intact, our other agreements will stay in place, and you will be free, at least free of me."

Lorayne's anger subsided, "Why would you make such an offer? What else do you want?"

"Nothing," said Timor. "There are no other entanglements other than the agreements I have with King Godrin, those have nothing to do with you."

"Then why force me into marriage?" said the Princess.

"I will tell you at the end of the two weeks. Do you agree?" said Timor.

Lorayne gave a wary nod and said "Yes."

"Thank you," said Timor." Please do me the honor of riding with me in the morning."

"I will." said the Princess.

Timor smiled, turned, and walked away. He was immediately swallowed up by kings from the other realms wishing to speak with him.

Lorayne moved toward the door and was stopped by her father. "It is unseemly for the princess to leave her own betrothal party. Have you rebuked Timor already?"

Lorayne told her father of all that transpired and of her agreement with Timor. He listened attentively and was amazed at what he heard. The next two weeks would be very interesting. Lorayne kissed her father goodnight and went to her room.

The princess slept well. She awoke to a beautiful sun-filled day. She could hear the birds chirping and singing in her garden. She dressed and proceeded to the hall where she would have breakfast with her father, and then, as agreed she would go on a morning ride with King Timor.

She wasn't the least bit bothered as she knew all she had to do was wait out her two weeks and all, for her, would be back to normal. As she entered the hall, she saw her father, and seated with him was Timor. "How rude!" she thought. She was a bit annoyed as this was usually her time with her father. But in the spirit of her agreement, she put on her best smile and walked to the table.

King Timor immediately stood. "Good morning princess, I trust you slept well?"

"Well enough," she said. Her response was not as light and flippant as she had wished. "At least," she thought "he'll know this won't be easy."

Timor smiled. King Godrin looked up and welcomed his daughter. Timor excused himself telling the princess he would be in the courtyard awaiting her for their ride. He bowed, turned, and left. "You must have Timor explain his plans for us and the other kingdoms." said the elder king watching as Timor left. "His ideas for trade and commerce will be the best things to happen to all the realms in a very long time. It might make for good conversation on your ride this morning."

"How do you know he won't renege after our two-week courtship fails? Are you sure you can trust him?" said Lorayne.

"I'm certain I can," said the king, "he brought a trade

agreement for me and my counsel to review, and you are not mentioned at all. In fact, he explained his proposal concerning you to me this morning and asked me for the same two weeks. I do not know what he expects or what his plans are. He is a very complex young man. You, my daughter, have your work cut out for you."

"What!" shouted Lorayne. "I tell you he will not succeed."

Godrin looked at his daughter and gave a loving smile. "Lorayne, I do not know what holds your heart, but this young man has more character and strength than I ever had myself. Give him a chance. He did not ask me to speak for him, I am asking not as your king, but as your father."

"I...I can't," said Lorayne "He has given me a way out of this trap, and I mean to take it."

Lorayne, walked over to her father and gave him a hug and an affectionate kiss on the forehead and left for her ride with Timor.

When the princess entered the courtyard, she saw Timor speaking with her two guards, her horse and Timor's horse stood waiting.

"How many are there?" Said Timor

"It's hard to say Sire." Said the guard. "It looks like near a thousand."

"Can you get them to disburse?" asked the King.

"Disburse who?" chimed Lorayne from behind Timor.

The guard turned to face the Princess. "Your Majesty", he said, bowing to Lorayne. "There is a huge crowd lining the road. They are here to see King Timor. His exploits in the defeat of the giant Ohmthus have spread throughout the realm and many wish to at least catch a glimpse of him. He's become a hero."

"And what of my father-their King?" snapped Lorayne. "Does he not also warrant this adoration as well?" Lorayne was furious. "So, King Timor you would work to supplant my father? Has this been your plan all along?" Her gaze was burning a hole into Timor. As he opened his mouth to speak, the guard spoke again.

"My Lady", said the guard, "King Timor has asked if we could disperse the crowd. It is our opinion we cannot. There are just too many and it would not bode well for us to bring out a garrison to forcibly remove them. It is King Timor's suggestion that we send for King Godrin and have him join us on the ride as well. We have already sent word to your father and are awaiting a reply. See, we have prepared his horse." Lorayne turned her head to see another guard ride up with her father's horse.

"This is your doing." Said Lorayne as coldly as she could muster.

"I cannot deny this My Lady." Said Timor "But I may have a solution. I await your father."

A few moments later King Godrin appeared. He was

upset and it was apparent in his tone. What is the meaning of this?" he bellowed. You wish to set yourself above the King in his own realm?"

"No sire," said Timor, If I may speak to you privately, I believe I have the solution to this. I do not want the recognition and what's done is done. Now please if I may have your ear for a moment here is what I propose."

Timor spoke out of earshot to King Godrin. As he spoke the King's face could be seen to lighten up and calm down. When Timor finished, the two men returned to Lorayne and the horses.

"Captain," said Godrin, as he mounted his horse. "I want three guards in front and two in the rear. I would like the rear guards to try to move the people to our front so we may speak – We will address them a hundred yards from the drawbridge. I will be in the Center and my daughter will be at my right and King Timor at my left. Lorayne went to speak but was silenced by her father's open hand. "No one is to be harmed and all will be welcome to hear what we have to say. Now let us proceed."

The gate opened and the drawbridge lowered. A large crowd of the King's subjects lined both sides of the road. The crowd roared as the procession hit the road. Above the noise one name rang clear "Timor, Timor, Timor!" King Godrin smiled and waved as did Timor. After the entourage had gone about one hundred yards, King

Godrin stopped and turned his horse to face the crowd. Timor and Lorayne did likewise. As instructed, the guards slowly moved onlookers from behind the King Godrin to the front. All were anxious to hear.

'My loyal subjects," said Godrin. His voice was clear, crisp, and belied no signs of age or fear, only confidence. He paused a moment for the noise to die down. His presence alone began to hush the crowd. He began again.

"I see you have all come to see and thank King Timor for his bravery and courage as he helped us to defeat our shared enemy Ohmthus, and for this we are most grateful." The crowd erupted in thunderous applause. He continued. "I am so glad you have this opportunity to thank him in this way, and as it happens, he is here at my request. I have had an idea of how we could work together for the betterment of both our kingdoms and if successful we will begin to include the other realms as well. I believe that my plan and partnership with King Timor will bring more trade and revenue to all of us. Farmers, you will be able to grow and sell more of what you produce. Ranchers, you will need more cattle to be able to sell more beef. All business will profit from the trade we will establish. All subjects will be able to reap benefits." The King's voice remained strong and steady the crowd erupted in more cheers. "And because the kingdom as a whole will be earning more, you will be able to keep more. I will establish a flat tax that is lower than your current rates. I desire for you all to be able to be comfortable, safe, and secure." The crowd began slowly chanting "God-rin, God-rin, God-rin."

Godrin was in total control. The crowd was now his. "I leave you now, go to your homes, farms, and ranches. We plan to start very soon. PROSPERITY FOR ALL!" he yelled and turned his horse and together with Lorayne and Timor they rode off to continue their ride.

The crowd lingered long after they rode away. Word spread quickly throughout the kingdom of Godrin's plan. In a matter of minutes, he became the hero.

As they rode, Godrin glanced at Timor and said, "I must thank you again."

"No thanks are necessary." Said Timor. "We are partners and as such we look out for each other." Godrin smiled in agreement and began pointing the different sights of his realm.

Lorayne had dropped behind the two men as they talked. She was completely taken aback by what had happened this morning. She had been angry at the situation, because, as she saw it, her father's kingdom was in jeopardy. But in a completely selfless move Timor had steered the light away from him, and made it shine even more brightly on her father. She was beginning to realize it was going to be very difficult to not like this man.

The days that followed were filled with endless activities. Timor insisted Lorayne accompany him everywhere. He wanted to know all about her, her interests what she wanted to do when she became queen. The talked, and yes, they laughed. Lorayne could not deny the charms of her suitor.

During one of their many rides, they stopped for a picnic lunch which Timor had planned as a surprise. They stopped by a very beautiful scenic lake. Timor dismounted,

"Why are we stopping?" said Lorayne.

"I thought we'd have a quiet lunch," said Timor as he helped the Princess from her horse.

Before she could say anything, one of the guards produced a satchel with food, wine and ale and a blanket for them to spread on the ground to sit and relax.

"It seems you thought of everything", she said.

Timor smiled and took her arm and walked her closer to the lake. The Guards remained by the horses to give them privacy. The two found a nice spot, spread the blanket, pulled out the food and drink, sat down and started to eat. Timor was telling tales of when he was learning to ride. How he kept falling off and how hard the instructor laughed at him. Lorayne thought it was funny and she laughed as well. She told Timor she had never fallen from her horse. All-in-all it was a pleasant outing until Timor stopped talking and stood. "What is it?" said Lorayne. Timor spoke back in a low voice. "Don't move!"

Lorayne turned to see a large boar charging the two of them. Timor didn't have his sword, but he had his knife. He unsheathed it and ran directly at the boar.

"Timor...." screamed Lorayne followed by "Guards, guards!!"

The guards were about twenty-five yards away. The boar was closer. Timor and the boar closed the distance between them. Timor knew his timing would have to be perfect. A moment before he and the boar collided, Timor leaped into the air and flipped over the boar. The animal was momentarily stunned and stopped his charge. Timor landed on his feet not three feet from the big pig. He turned and threw himself onto the boar's back plunging his knife several times deep into the boar. The animal struggled and fought digging his tusk into Timor's arm. The young king did not relent and once again plunged his knife, this time hitting the boar's heart. The animal dropped.

Out of breath and a little dazed, Timor stood and began heading back to Lorayne. One guard was with her, and the other was running towards him. "Sire" said the guard, "you are hurt."

"I'm fine," said Timor. "Thank you for protecting the princess, I trust she is ok."

"Yes Sire, she is a bit shaken but okay," said the guard.

Timor and the guard walked up to Lorayne and the other guard. Before Timor could speak, "Timor you are wounded," said Lorayne. Her voice was shaky and uneven. She was upset and very concerned.

Timor said, "I will be fine. My physician will have to sew

me up a bit is all." He smiled and Lorayne smiled back. Timor turned to the guard next to him and said "Rin, I have some bandage cloth in my saddle bag. Please bring it to me so I can wrap this before we head back to the castle."

The guard ran to the horses to retrieve what his king had commanded. Lorayne took Timor's unhurt hand and led him to the lake so they could clean his wound. Timor tried to make light of the situation. "That wasn't how we rehearsed it. He was supposed to run in the other direction when I charged him."

"You shouldn't go to such lengths to impress me," joked Lorayne, "I was rooting for the pig."

They both laughed. Lorayne cleaned his wound and insisted on placing the bandage.

That night at the castle while Godrin's personal physician attended to Timor, Godrin said, "I appear to be once again in your debt Timor. You saved my daughter's life."

"Truthfully Sire," said Timor "I may have acted a little too hastily. It would have been better to just run into the lake, I doubt he would have followed, and I would have ten less stitches."

Godrin and Timor laughed. Timor would have his answer from Lorayne in two days, despite his injury, he felt she was responding to him. She laughed. She was appearing to act much more comfortable. He felt good.

The next day came, and Lorayne insisted due to Timor's injury, that they curtail any outside activities and stay close to the castle, so they settled in for a game of chess. It was Lorayne's suggestion and, truth be told, Timor was glad for a day of lighter events. They had a marvelous time and the hall where they played was full of laughter and friendly conversation.

Towards the end of the day, Timor ventured a question. "Will the princess have an answer for me tomorrow, as it will be the end of the two weeks?"

Suddenly the room became quiet. A chess piece falling from Lorayne's hand could be the only sound heard. As Timor looked into her eyes, he saw his answer. Lorayne's eyes began to tear up. She tried to talk but found it difficult.

"Sire, please excuse me," she said, and stood up and quickly left the room.

Timor sat alone staring at the chess board, cursing himself for mis-reading her behavior and for pushing her for an answer. He called in one of Godrin's servants. "Please fetch my Captain of the Guard."

The servant nodded and bowed. "Very good your Majesty."

Timor waited. A few moments later Irick, Timor's Captain appeared. "Yes Sire," he said.

"Ready the men, we leave at first light," said Timor.

"Very good Sire," said Irick, we will collect you in the morning."

"That will not be necessary," said the King. "Have my horse ready, I must first speak with Godrin. I will sleep in the camp tonight." Irick, nodded and left; Timor went to find Godrin.

Edgewise

The next morning when Lorayne came down from her room to eat breakfast, her father was sitting alone at the table.

"Where is King Timor?" she asked quietly.

Godrin's response was abrupt. "Gone!"

Lorayne felt a lump form in her throat. "Why father, did he say?"

"He was most apologetic," said Godrin. "He felt he upset you with his question and rather than put you through it again today, he decided it was in YOUR best interest he leave. He has strong feelings for you, and he feels you have some affection for him, but not enough to sway what lies deep in your heart. He wants you to be happy. That is his prime concern. He has left you a gift, why I cannot say, but he requested I give this to you."

Godrin reached into his robe and pulled out a small black ebony box. He pushed it over to his daughter. Lorayne stared at the box for a few minutes then slowly reached to take it. She lifted it and opened it. She gasped. Sitting in the box was a simple ring. A white gold band with a single stone, one white pebble.

"Stick!" said Lorayne, as more tears now fell down her face. Father, I have made a terrible mistake. Pease send your fastest rider and have King Timor return. Please father, immediately!"

"Why would I do that," said Godrin. "Hasn't he suffered enough humiliation?"

"Because," said Lorayne, now smiling through the tears. "We have a wedding to plan."

Chapter 5

THE WEDDING

King Godrin called his guard and told him to send his fastest rider after King Timor. Lorayne drafted a note to accompany the rider. Timor and his men had a five-hour head start.

"Please make all haste," said Lorayne to the rider as she handed him the note. The rider bowed and turned to leave. He was stopped by Godrin.

"Do not kill the horse. There are a few small villages along the way. Buy a new horse and tell them you will collect the one you leave behind on the way back." Godrin handed the rider a small pouch with gold coins. "It may cost you a little time, but in the long run fresh horses will get you there more quickly. Now make haste."

The rider bowed again and was off. It was late in the day when he caught up to Timor and his men. The messenger approached the king.

"You look exhausted man, what brings you here?" said Timor.

"Sire I bring you a message from the Princess Lorayne. I am to wait for a response." he said.

Timor took the note and read it. As he did a smile crept over his face. "Irick!" said Timor to his Captain. "See to this man's horse and see that he is fed. You and I will travel back with him tomorrow. I will answer this note in person."

"And the rest of the men Sire?" said Irick.

"Have them stay here. We will return in a day or two and finish our journey home. There will be no need for them to break camp," said Timor.

The three men left at sunrise. King Godrin's rider had made two stops on his quest to catch Timor and his entourage. He bought two horses and promised to fetch his original mounts on his way back. It was after the last town that the trio came across a very old man and a young boy of five or six (by Timor's estimate) slowly trying to make their way down the road. They looked to be having a very difficult time.

Timor stopped his horse next to the old man. "May we be of service?" he said.

The old man looked up and an expression of surprise crossed his face, but it was only for a moment, his recovery was quick and said, "Your Majesty!" He managed a very feeble bow, and he gently slapped the young boy across the head and growled "Bow!" out of the side of his mouth.

"You know who I am?' said a surprised Timor.

"Your acts of bravery and heroism have preceded you Sire. We are honored to meet you."

Timor smiled "I see you are in some discomfort. How may I help you?"

"Lord Timor," said the old man, "I am Peltor, the Wizard, and this young gentleman is Kordan, my apprentice," he continued. "We are heading to a small farm some miles from here. The cattle have become ill, and the farmer believes I can help. From what the man describes, I think his livestock has been poisoned, possibly by the giants. They are scattered and unorganized since your victory over Ohmthus and are likely hungry. They will eat meat poisoned or not. On the way this morning, I tripped, clumsy old fool that I am, and have sprained my ankle and alas it is difficult for me to move at any speed."

"Say no more," said the young King. "Can the boy ride?" The wizard nodded. "Good, we have two spare mounts. Please take them. They are yours. I hope this will help you get to your appointed task." Timor cast a glance back to Godrin's messanger. "And do not worry rider, I will reimburse King Godrin for his loss." Timor dismounted and helped the boy and the old wizard onto the horses.

"Good luck Peltor, and, young Kordan, take good care of your master." Timor smiled, wished them well, and mounted his horse to leave.

"Lord Timor." said Peltor. "I am in your debt. Should you ever need assistance from me or my apprentice, face into the wind and call my name three times. We will come." He gave Timor a nod and slowly rode away.

It was dusk when the three crossed the bridge into the castle. Lorayne was waiting in the courtyard. She walked up to Timor as he dismounted and looked at him.

"Come rider," said Irick, "Let us take these horses to the stable to be fed."

As they left, Lorayne said. "Stick, why didn't you tell me. I have been waiting for you since that day you left. Why didn't you tell me?"

Timor grabbed her hand, which now bore the ring he left and said, "Too many years had passed. I had heard about all the suitors that have been courting you since you turned sixteen. There is the competition and then of course duty. I wasn't sure you would remember me. I decided to try to win your heart. You had won mine a long time ago. I wanted to win your love anew. When you burst into tears the other night, I thought I could not hurt you if you truly loved another. I left the ring to show you I still love you. Hopefully, at least there would be fond memories."

"Foolish boy," said Lorayne. "I was torn in two. Your question made me realize I couldn't choose either since I had begun to love you." She threw her arms around Timor. "But that dilemma has been solved since I love you both. My Stick and my young King - you are the same person. "

More than anything Timor wished to stay to help his bride-to-be with the arrangements. The wedding would take place in Godrin's kingdom. Unfortunately, affairs of state do not wait. Lorayne knew this well, and she told

Timor to go. She would take care of the wedding plans. They settled on a date six weeks away on the Autumnal Equinox. Quick by most standards to be sure, but neither wanted to wait. Timor insisted on one item of formality before he left. He wanted to speak to her father.

Timor approached Godrin as he sat on his throne. "Sire," said Timor, "I respectfully request the hand of your daughter Lorayne, Princess of the Mid-Realm in marriage."

"And how does my daughter feel about this?" Said Godrin.

"I believe, Sire," replied Timor. "that we both wish this with all our hearts."

Godrin stood and spoke. His voice was even and strong. "King Timor, you have entered my kingdom, and while I thought it was your desire to supplant me, you did not. Even though I tried to do it to you. Your ideas and plans have begun to bring my kingdom and my subjects to new levels of prosperity and success. You seek to lay claim to the one thing I hold most precious in this world. You ask for permission for something that by all rights you have earned, in your deeds. You have been more generous to me than I have ever been to you. I stand here shamed by your humility. If my daughter truly loves you, then nothing I could say would stop her. So, I say to you, King Timor, that you may have my daughter's hand in marriage. From that day forward you will both be my children; I will proudly call you son, and both are heirs to my throne. Upon my death, our kingdoms will be one."

Timor rose to his feet. Lorayne walked up and stood by his side. "Father, I have no words." Her voice was shaky. A tear rolled down her face. Timor took one step forward and said, "and I will be proud to call you father!"

Godrin smiled and sat down, "Now plan your wedding!" The young couple smiled and left the hall.

Outside Timor kissed Lorayne and told her he would be back in four weeks. Lorayne went back into the hall where her father sat on his throne seemingly deep in thought. She walked up to him and put her arms around him. "Father, I love you with all my heart."

Godrin smiled and squeezed her, "I told you he was a good man." Lorayne smiled and nodded. She left the hall and set about handing out tasks to her handmaids to prepare for the wedding.

"Six weeks," she said to herself. "What was I thinking?"

The next four weeks went quickly. Each day was filled with endless hours and challenges. Invitations had to be sent. Riders were dispatched to all the kingdoms.

And, with her husband-to-be, there would be no refusals to attend. He was already a legend, and many would come just to catch a glimpse of him.

She was planning a wedding for thousands, it would seem. Word hit her ears of the throngs of townspeople, some already arriving, who were coming to see the marriage of Princess Lorayne to the most desirable young king in all the realms.

"How am I going to feed all these people?" she thought, "and where will I put them?"

As if as an answer to her innermost thoughts, her handmaid spoke, "m'Lady, there is a local farmer in the great hall, and he requests an audience with you."

"Did he say what this is regarding?" asked the princess

"Yes m'Lady," said the maid. "He said something about people camping on his land waiting for your wedding."

Lorayne rolled her eyes and gave a heavy sigh. "Very well", she said, "take me to him."

Lorayne entered the great hall to find three men waiting to see her, not one. As she approached, the one out in front spoke. "Your Highness, I am Philip Graywater and these gentlemen with me are Thomas Thornberry and Gaylord Garland. We are nearby farmers. In anticipation of the largest wedding many of us will ever see in our lifetimes, crowds of people are beginning to arrive and quite literally camping on our lands. We understand their desire to be a part of this great event, and so my friends and I have agreed to allow them access to our land for the duration. We realize this may become a large burden for you in your preparations. That being said, we would like to offer you some aid. The positive projections of King Godrin and King Timor's new economic policies will begin impacting us very soon. To further show our gratitude, we would like, in addition to opening our lands, on your wedding day to feed the guests on our properties. My friends and I each agree to donate the necessary cattle and produce to create a very tasty feast. We do, however have one request. We would like King Godrin to supply us with troops to help keep things in order. We would like to see that everyone leaves in an orderly fashion after the event and to ensure our guests make some attempt to clean up after themselves."

Lorayne was completely taken aback by the generosity of these three men and after a moment she spoke. "Gentlemen, your magnanimous offer humbles me. I accept. I will speak to my father about the troops, and I will send word to my Lord Timor to bring an extra garrison to help with the policing. King Timor will be here in two days. I would ask that you three and your wives dine with us the night he arrives. I want him to thank you personally. Until then gentlemen." Lorayne left the hall. She had never seen such a positive attitude toward the crown.

The Wedding plans were almost complete. Messengers were arriving daily with responses to the invitations. "I might actually sleep tonight," she thought. And sleep she did, with dreams of she and stick laughing and playing together. Now they would be together for the rest of their lives. It was the most wonderful sleep she had in weeks. King Timor arrived two days later. Lorayne could barely contain herself as she ran to meet him in the castle courtyard. He was as pleased to see her.

"My Lord," said Lorayne, "did my rider reach you?"

"Yes, he did," said Timor, "I sent instructions for the extra troops to come. They will be here before the wedding."

"Good!" said Lorayne, and she proceeded to tell Timor of the arrangement with the three farmers. "We will dine with them and their families tonight," she said.

"Let's meet with them ahead of the dinner," said Timor, "I don't want to talk business at dinner, I want them and their families to enjoy themselves. Please set up the meeting for an hour before." Timor went on to explain his plans to complement the generosity of the farmers. Lorayne could not have been more pleased. "Now I must speak with your father. I take your leave." He pulled Lorayne into his arms and kissed her deeply.

"Timor," she said in a familiar tone that was usually spoken when they were alone. "Not in front of the men." She blushed.

Timor laughed. "I don't care, let them see a King who is in love with his Queen." Then he stepped away, took her hand, bowed and kissed her hand formally, winked and walked into the castle.

That evening an hour before dinner, King Timor and Princess Lorayne entered the small antechamber to the dining hall where the three farmers stood waiting. As the Royal Couple entered, all three men bowed, "Your Majesties." They all spoke at once.

"Gentlemen," said Timor. I will make this quick as we have a temperamental cook and I do not wish to anger him." The men laughed; Timor continued. "The Princess Lorayne has told me of you plans and your generous offers. Please accept my humble thanks. The Princess and I are overwhelmed by such a gift. I have to respectfully request some changes which may add to your burden but be assured we will offer all the help we can to alleviate the impacts of my requests. I am going to ask that your three farms be the only places in the kingdom to house these extra people. I have heard that some other smaller farms have similar guests and I think it is in the best interest for all involved if we can consolidate and move these few to your farms. Yours are the closest to the castle and seem to be the ones drawing the most crowds. I will send riders from my garrison to the outlying areas and have those who wish to be part of the event move to your lands. I have spoken to King Godrin about this, and he is supportive and will help supply guards to ensure things stay safe and orderly. If this meets with your approval gentlemen, we will help further by giving you each one hundred gold sovereigns."

The men stood motionless and quiet. Philip Graywater spoke. "Sire, your request is far from unreasonable, a few more guests will be welcomed. We were trying to help and show you and Princess Lorayne how much we appreciate your policies and what you have done for all of us. I don't like to turn away money, but if you must give us money how about fifty gold sovereigns?"

Timor laughed, "No, one hundred and I insist. You will earn it. Trust me, you will thank me when this is all over. Even if people clean up after themselves, you all will still have a huge mess to deal with, and it will take days. Let me say, if you need fifty more sovereigns, I will give it to you. Just ask me. Also, we will visit your farms on the day after the actual wedding. There is no way we can break away from the palace and our obligations of that day to visit you all. So, we will start fresh the next day. Are we in agreement?"

The men each reached forward and shook the King's hand. "Now," said Timor, "before the cook poisons our food, let's eat."

The wedding took place two weeks later. Timor and Lorayne saw very little of each other during this time save for the few moments at dinner where they passed out while they were eating from exhaustion.

Timor's time was taken up with security and safety, which became an even bigger issue since the addition of three off-site locations and the overwhelming number of guests desiring to be part of the Royal Wedding. The three farmers were very supportive, but Timor couldn't help but feel their stress as hundreds invaded their lands to be a part of this event. In fact, Godrin's chief historian pointed out that this was the first wedding for as far back as records were kept where the Royal Couple were both Royals. It was to be a truly splendid event.

Lorayne's time was spent seeing to the actual wedding itself and well as the entertainment, food, and guest seating order at the Royal Reception. It was her job to make sure everyone was satisfied and that no one was snubbed. It was a difficult task as some were always over-enthused by their own stations. Still, everything proceeded smoothly and finally the big day arrived.

The Great Hall of King Godrin's castle was filled to capacity. Dignitaries were present from all the realms. When the bell in the castle tower rang to signify the wedding procession, the hall became silent as all eyes were focused on the door to catch a glimpse of Princess Lorayne and her Father King Godrin as they made their entrance. King Timor stood in the front of the hall next to the throne flanked by six of his private guards. His best friend and Captain of the Guard Irick stood by his side.

Princess Lorayne entered with her father; his left arm locked into hers. She was beautiful. She wore her late mother's gown. It was a long flowing dress of blue velvet with golden buttons lining the bodice and skirt. This magnificent garment trailed all the way to her ankles and featured fitted sleeves with buttons down the length. Underneath it all, she wore a chemise and breast band, as well as knee-length stockings. And, over their entire outfit, she wore a beautiful cloak with a long train. On her head she wore a crowned turret made of the finest silk. As she walked slowly forward through the crowd a stringed quartet could be heard playing beautifully in the background.

By contrast, King Timor wore loose-fitting linen breeches held up by a jeweled belt. Doublets featured elaborate buttons and terminated at his hips. Over the top of the whole, he wore a fur-lined tunic, that fell to his calves. On his head he wore his crown.

When King Godrin had presented his daughter to King Timor, he walked around to stand in front of them by his throne. He was going to officiate his daughter's wedding.

Godrin spoke. "I stand before you to bless the union of this young couple, my daughter Princess Lorayne, and King Timor of the Northern Realm. I am touched by your presence and by those of my subjects awaiting to see the future royal couple. None of this would be possible without the courage, bravery, and foresight of this young man, I should say King, who will this day become my son. Our kingdom owes him much - I owe him everything. I am proud and honored to introduce them. I believe they have written vows to each other which they will speak before you now."

Timor Spoke first. "Lorayne, I have wished for this moment most of my life. Few know our story and I hope that today will be proof that true love is the greatest thing life has to offer. Neither time, nor distance can stop it or change it. From the first day I saw you my heart was yours. Today, I offer you my hand. I will stand beside you through all that we will experience together, and as long as I live, I will love no other." Timor finished, took a deep breath, and waited for his bride to speak.

Lorayne smiled and began. "I have spent most of my life dreaming of when we met and wondering if what I felt was real or imagined. I became torn between the memory of who I loved and the reality of who I was falling in love with. You almost lost faith in yourself, which would have doomed us both to loneliness. The token you left me, the thing that held my heart was in your possession too. Upon revealing it to me a great load lifted because you were my past and my future. I could love you both one and the same, now and forever. I will never be parted from you again. We are one, my love. I am yours and you are mine always."

King Godrin was clearly holding back tears as his voice trembled when he spoke. "It is with the greatest pride and honor that I present to you King Timor and Queen Lorayne."

Wedding Song

Timor kissed his bride and the two turned to see the crowd standing on their feet screaming, "Long live King Timor and Queen Lorayne." The sound was deafening.

The next hours were spent speaking to friends and well-wishers, which later turned into a ball. The two were quite exhausted by days end, and tomorrow would be more of the same. "And to think," said Timor, we have to do this when we get back to my Kingdom."

"You go on without me," said Lorayne, "I am going to sleep for the next two days."

The next morning came quickly. The newlyweds skipped breakfast, and with a small complement of guards left the castle. Their first stop was the farm of Philip Graywater. He had fashioned a stage for the royal couple so they could say a few words to the guests. The crowd was remarkably well-behaved and bowed respectfully as the entourage passed.

"Mr. Graywater," said Timor, "I didn't expect to see this many people. Is this the same for the other two locations as well?"

"Yes Sire," said Graywater. "Ours is the largest. By my count we have close to three thousand guests, Thornberry and Garland have estimated each under two thousand. Not as many to be sure, but sizeable numbers none-the-less."

"Do you have enough help and food to feed all these people?" said Timor.

"I was concerned at first, Sire", said Graywater, "but many brought food with them and offered to help. We've divided the camps into 6 groups of five hundred and put someone in charge of each section. I have never seen such cooperation. This is all so they can just for a moment catch a glimpse of you and your Queen."

Timor was stunned. "Then we will give them more than a glimpse. We will speak to each section and thank them personally for making the journey to see us." Timor summoned his Captain of the Guard. "Irick send a rider to the other farms and tell them we will spend one day at each. I do not wish to disappoint King Godrin's subjects. Also tell them I will be adding another one hundred gold sovereigns to compensate for the extra food and supplies they will need."

Graywater stepped in. "Sire that is not necessary. When we saw the size of the crowds, we anticipated that you would need more time, so we planned for this. We are prepared and even have accommodations for you and the Queen, if that meets with your approval."

Timor smiled. "Good man Graywater. I will not forget this."

As Timor walked to his carriage, Lorayne grabbed his arm. "It seems they planned well. We are very fortunate to be taken care of by such wonderful people."

For the next three days, Lorayne and Timor talked, ate, and mingled with the people. It wasn't just Godrin's subjects, people had come from all the realms, to see the royal couple. No one was disappointed. Much to Irick's dismay both royals, while rarely leaving each other's side, were very interactive with the guests. Much too close for the captain's comfort, but everyone was courteous, respectful, and clearly in awe of Timor and Lorayne.

After saying their good-byes to the last of the three farms, the couple headed back to Godrin's palace. They rested there for two days and then began the ride back to Timor's kingdom. Upon their arrival, they witnessed something no one had seen before. The main road to the palace was lined with people for several miles all screaming "Hale to King Timor and Queen Lorayne."

To make it easier for people to see them, Timor and Lorayne moved to the top of their Royal Carriage and waved and greeted the people. When the onlookers saw them, their cheers grew even louder.

It was incredible. The people were not unruly; they stayed clear of the road and allowed the carriage to pass without incident. They policed themselves and kept their King and new Queen safe.

The procession made its way to the castle arriving late afternoon, where the celebration for the returning king and his new queen continued well into the next day.

Before he and Lorayne retired to get some rest, Timor told his guards to let the people know they would be holding court beginning in two days. The audiences would start mid-morning and continue until dusk for at least the next two weeks.

"Sire," said the guard, "those are very long days."

"I have a large kingdom," said Timor.

True to his word, the audiences began on the second day. The lines to see them extended further than the eye could see. When dusk arrived, many just stayed in their position in line and waited for the next day.

Timor and Lorayne were gracious hosts, with Lorayne often leaving her throne to accept gifts and personally thank the guests with a handshake, a hug, and to the children, a kiss on the forehead.

This was uncommon behavior for any Queen, and with her beauty and friendliness, she quickly became the darling of the realm as word spread quickly of her actions. After a week-and-a-half, the crowds began to dwindle and as the numbers became more manageable, both Timor and Lorayne were looking forward to a little time alone. In fact, when two weeks had ended, Timor told his guards there would be no court for two weeks and if any issues arose, Irick, his Captain would handle it.

After having rested, Timor and Lorayne began taking morning rides through different parts of the Kingdom. They often stopped and spoke to the townspeople and farmers, asking them how things were going, and listening intently to the replies.

There were even a few times when the King would send his accompanying guards to help farmers finish removing a tree stump or help pull a cow out of a mud pit.

Timor's subjects loved both he and Lorayne. And with his economic ideas and popular new Queen, peace and prosperity became part of everyday life in the Northern Realm.

More great news followed for after 6 months, it was made known that Queen Lorayne was with child. This was truly a joyous announcement and Timor gladly shared it with his subjects and future grandfather King Godrin.

The couple was very happy and began to create the nursery for the baby. Lorayne had already picked her nanny. She had known her since both were children.

Seriana was a commoner whose mother worked in the kitchen. She was often sent to bring the Princess her lunch. Lorayne would usually ask her to stay.

"What is your name?" Asked Lorayne.

"Seriana." Answered the girl.

"Seriana, then, please join me. I do not wish to eat alone, and the cook has made plenty," said Lorayne.

"Oh Princess," I am not allowed," said the girl.

"Who said this?" Asked a defiant Lorayne.

"My mother," said Seriana. "She works in the kitchen; she made your lunch."

"We'll see about that," said the Princess. "Come with me."

Lorayne found her way to the kitchen and spoke to Seriana, "Which is you mother?"

Seriana pointed to a thin woman working with pastry dough, preparing the King's dessert. Lorayne walked up to her as the other kitchen staff bowed in the presence of the Princess.

"Woman," said Lorayne.

The woman was taken aback as she did not see the princess enter. She immediately dropped to her knees. And spoke "Y y y yes your Highness."

"I wish your daughter to stay and have lunch with me, is this a problem?"

"N n n no your Highness," said Seriana's mother.

"Good," said Lorayne. "If I choose to have her stay with me for lunch you are to give her no problems, is that clear?"

"Y y y yes your Highness," said the woman, but what is your interest in her?"

"She is going to be my friend," said the princess. "Come Seriana."

The two girls left and friends they became. Lorayne confided in Seriana and Seriana did the same. Lorayne even spoke of Stick, the boy she met from the wall and showed Seriana the white pebble he gave her. "He will come back someday and marry me," said Lorayne.

The two laughed, played and stayed friends. When Seriana was old enough, she became one of Lorayne's handmaids. It was Serriana that Lorayne spoke to as the turmoil grew in her, as she realized she loved Timor and Stick and didn't know which to choose.

After the wedding, Seriana, moved with Queen Lorayne to be her Lady-in-Waiting. Now she was being asked to be nursemaid to the Queens child.

"My Queen," said Seriana. "It will be my honor."

"This is not a step down, this is important, my child will have two mothers: me and when I'm not here, you. You know me; how I think and feel. Timor will try, but as King his time will be limited. Raising a child will become secondary to his duties as head of state. Granted he will try harder than any King you may know to be a good father. His love and devotion are boundless. The three of us will be successful parents." Seriana smiled. Lorayne hugged her friend closely. "Thank you. This means the world to me. I can trust no other."

Seriana

The two friends continued with their preparations. The pregnancy seemed to be progressing well at least up until the last month. The pains were so bad, the Royal Physician ordered bedrest and around the clock care. Seriana, was always present and Timor rarely left her side. Lorayne appeared to be in good spirits, but all near her could see the pain was taking its toll and making her weak.

After several days, the Royal Physician approached the King. "My Lord," he said. "The baby is sideways in the womb and we cannot turn it. If I don't take the baby by cutting open the Queen, I will lose them both."

"What are the Queen's chances?" said Timor.

"Sire, I do not know she is weak, and the procedure will cause her to lose a lot of blood. She is already bleeding internally, and I don't know to what extent," said the physician.

"Do what you must," Said Timor, "but I will not leave, and I will tell her what you plan to do. Please do your best to save her." The Physician nodded and began preparing operate.

Timor knelt by the side of the bed and faced his wife. He tried to keep his voice strong and positive as he spoke, explaining to her what the Doctor was planning to do. Lorayne smiled and nodded that she understood.

"I am here," said Timor. "Grab my hand and squeeze as hard as you need, there will be pain."

Timor looked at the physician and nodded. The Doctor and his aide began.

Timor felt as if he were in a dream, a terrible nightmare that was searing his very soul. He felt something was being ripped from inside him as well. Then he heard the cry, a baby. Through teary eyes he looked over to the doctor, who said, "It's a girl."

Timor swallowed, fighting back his emotions, trying to keep his voice even as he spoke. "Did you hear that, we have a daughter."

Lorayne managed a small smile and tried to speak. Her voice so soft it was almost inaudible. Timor moved closer to hear. "Can we name her Alicanth? It was my mother's middle name."

"Of course," said Timor, "It's a beautiful name. Your Father will be proud."

"I love you Stick," said Lorayne. "Trust Seriana, she knows what to do."

Timor smiled and said, "As long as I live, I will love no other."

Lorayne smiled one last time to her husband as her last breath left her lips.

Timor wept. After a few moments he turned to see Alicanth being held, by Seriana. He motioned her to bring him the baby. As he took his daughter in his arms for the first time he said. "I will protect you with every fiber of my being, know that your mother and I will love you always."

He walked out of the room with Seriana in tow.

"Seriana, I will be appointing my two best and most loyal soldiers to guard you both. You will go nowhere without them."

Seriana remained silent and shook her head in acknowledgement of the King's order.

"Further," continued Timor, "whenever possible, I wish to eat my meals with her and to be there when she goes to bed at night. She will know me as a father before she knows me as a king."

The Kingdom was shocked at the death of their beloved Queen. Lorayne's body lay in-state for nearly a week as the palace main hall was left open day and night for those wishing to pay their respect. The line of mourners seemed endless. Lorayne's father, King Godrin wished to take her body back to her homeland for burial, but Timor insisted she be buried in his royal cemetery.

"She won the hearts of my subjects completely in her short time here. I believe people will come always to pay their respects to her, especially on the anniversary of her passing. She is your daughter, I understand, but she became more than that when she became my Queen and now, she belongs to them."

As Godrin looked at the seemingly unending line of mourners, he saw the truth in what his son-in-law said. He saw her legacy and saw it was larger than him. At that moment, he was filled with more pride than ever before in his life.

"Sire," said Timor to Godrin, "Alicanth needs to know her grandfather. I propose that around her fifth year she spend a week with you two to three times a year, more if she wants as she gets older, she does after all belong to two kingdoms and in reality, is heir to both."

Godrin looked at Timor through teary eyes, "And still you protect me...I would like that very much."

Timor was true to his word. He rarely ate a meal where his daughter was not present. He rarely missed tucking her into bed at night. Sometimes he had her present at his daily audiences, which as Alicanth approached her teen years, caused the King some embarrassment as she openly spoke her mind before the king had pronounced his judgement. He reprimanded her openly, but inwardly he saw her mother in her and was proud.

After Alicanth turned five, Timor sent her and Seriana to visit King Godrin. It didn't take Alicanth long to fall in love with her grandfather. She always enjoyed herself every time she went.

Things ran very smoothly during this time, and commerce was booming. All five kingdoms played off each other and the cooperation ensured everyone's success.

The giants seemed to have disappeared. Yes, there was a missing cow here and there, but nothing substantial. All seemed at peace.

Then shortly after Alicanth's eighteenth birthday word came to Timor of horrific attacks in the southern kingdoms.

Livestock and grain stolen, small villages incinerated, men, women and children driven from their homes, people killed.

Within a few weeks these attacks moved into his kingdom. Timor sent a garrison to help, but he lost five men. The Giants were attacking, and they had help. Ningthus was far more strategic than his brother Ohmthus, and he had a terrible weapon. Timor's men apparently were powerless to stop it.

Alicanth couldn't help but notice her father was distracted during their dinner. Something was weighing very heavily on him.

"Father, what bothers you?" said the princess.

Timor looked at his daughter and saw the concern in her eyes. He managed a small smile. "Nothing that you need to worry about at present. I'll get it figured out."

He rose from his seat and gave his daughter a deep kiss on her forehead and walked away.

Alicanth, while still worried, knew she needed to give her father time to think. He would tell her everything when he was ready.

Timor went to his quarters. He sat weighing his options. After some time had passed, he realized what he must do. He stood and walked to his west balcony. Once outside he felt the evening breeze on his face. "Perfect," he thought.

He took a deep breath and spoke deeply into the wind. "Peltor." He paused, looking side to side as if wondering if anyone had heard him. He took another breath and spoke, "Peltor." Again, he looked around, still nothing, just the night wind against his face. Another breath "Peltor." Another pause. "He did say three times," he thought. He waited another minute and turned to walk back into his quarters.

Suddenly a change. The wind began to blow harder. Timor turned to face the sky. Clouds formed and thunder rumbled in the distance and as it rolled it gained in volume and intensity. Lightning filled the sky, but not regular lightening, this was green in color as if there was some deep magic behind it. The weather phenomena lasted about 10 minutes and slowly died down.

Timor looked into the night; he wasn't sure what to expect. He had never witnessed that type of power before and he was visibly shaken by it. He slowly walked backward into his room sat down and waited. For what, he did not know.

Time seemed to pass slowly, and he drifted off into a fitful sleep as he sat in his chair. He woke suddenly as if startled and rose to splash some water on his face when he heard something in the distance. It took a couple of minutes before he recognized the sound. It was a crow. As he listened and waited the sound grew louder until it was almost on top of him. Then he saw it as it landed on his balcony – not a crow, a raven - a large, blue-black raven. Tied to its leg was a note. Timor slowly reached forward to retrieve it. He opened it. Scrawled on the paper were two words. "I'm coming."

Timor swallowed. "I hope you can forgive me. I am about to ask you to fight the fight of your life. You have to face a dragon!"

Chapter 6

THE COURT OF KING TIMOR

Kordan was weary from the long journey and from his encounter with Ningthus. While his incantation to turn the giant to stone was a simple spell, it was still a physical drain. The magic would have to remain strong for a fortnight while the spell worked its way inward to the giant's heart. As long as nothing happened to Kordan, the spell would remain intact and the giant would be vanquished.

Before he could rest however, he had to meet with King Timor. It was the King's summons that brought him here and he must honor the promise made by his departed master, Peltor. Kordan had sent out a murder of crows as reconnaissance to help him determine the nature of the King's need. The birds were not foolproof, but their report would act as an indicator of what Kordan was going to face.

The crows returned and spoke to him of giants marauding and burning whole farms, under the rule of Ningthus their Thane. So, upon his arrival he sought out and found the Giant and turned him to stone.

"Maybe I should have seen the King first," he thought, but he knew giants tend to scatter without their leader, and just maybe this early intervention would save, livestock, homes, and even lives. At any rate, he could undo any damage as the spell was still forming, and he would do whatever Lord Timor commanded.

He was nearing the castle quickly. After his encounter with the Princess Alicanth and even though he was tired, he realized he needed to make himself a little more presentable to the King's Court. Kordan took a small detour to the village near the castle to procure a room and freshen himself up before seeing the King.

Kordan stopped at an Inn on the main road. When he entered, he approached the Innkeeper to ask for a room. The proprietor was a tall slender man, who's soft countenance gave the appearance that his Inn was a friendly place.

"My heavens!" said the Innkeeper, "A Wizard, a least your staff would indicate so, and a young one too. I am Geoff, your servant, to what do we owe the honor of your presence?"

Kordan smiled, "I am here at the request of King Timor, and I require a room."

"Yes Sir," said the Innkeeper. "We haven't seen your kind here for many years, since before King Timor's father King Fadron. We had heard they were all gone."

"Mayhaps we are," said Kordan, "but one still walks

these lands and that is me."

Geoff let out a hearty laugh and said, "You are most welcome here my good sir, in fact it was told to me by my grandfather, that we let Wizards stay for free. It is a tradition, that I will uphold."

Kordan bowed to the Innkeeper and said, "Your generosity is greatly appreciated, but let me help pay my way by doing something to repay your generosity. Please come with me."

The Innkeeper came from around his counter and followed Kordan out through the front door. "Your sign is a bit dilapidated and in need of repair." Kordan raised his staff and said "Exsarcio!"

All was quiet for a few moments and then the sign began to shudder. It was barely hanging by a rope to one side. The rope was replaced with new chain on both sides. Splinters of wood smoothed out and the letters began to take on a more legible appearance and the Inn's name, "The Quiet Wife-Inn and Tavern," was now very prominent and easy to read.

Geoff stood in silence for a few minutes, and finally said, "My good sir, it is I who should be paying you. I have not had the time or money to fix it. Many travelers just pass us up looking for other accommodations. This will help me a lot."

Kordan spoke "I am glad to be of service, by the way, interesting name."

"Well," said the Innkeeper, "My Grandfather named the place. I asked him about it before he passed away. He told me that he felt if you put two words together that were the opposite of each other, it would make for a good name. People would remember it, and my grandmother was far from quiet."

Both men had a good laugh and went inside, the Innkeeper back to work, and Kordan to his room to prepare for his meeting.

Kordan cleaned up and was moving through the tavern towards the door to leave when Geoff called out to him, "Sir Wizard!" Kordan stopped, smiled, and turned to greet the friendly man as he made his way to him. "Yes," said Kordan politely.

"Sir," said the Innkeeper, "I hope I have not overstepped my bounds, but I have procured you a horse to use while you are here. I told the smithy that you might have need of one and he gladly loaned me this one for you."

"Not at all," said Kordan, "this will be most helpful, thank you." Kordan bowed and mounted the horse. He set his staff into a side holster that appeared to be designed expressly for a wizard's staff.

Kordan followed the road toward the castle. When he reached the gate, he dismounted, took his staff into his left hand and led the horse by the reins with his right. He asked a passer-by in the courtyard where he could leave his horse; he was directed to the castle livery. The stablemaster charged one shilling per day. Kordan paid the man and walked to the palace entrance. He walked up the steps to the great hall where he met a guard.

"What is your reason for requesting an audience with King Timor?" asked the guard.

"I am here at the King's request," said the Wizard.

"You will need to come back," said the guard. "Princess Alicanth is holding audience this morning in the King's absence. He will return later today."

Kordan opened his mouth to respond when another guard appeared from the great hall and whispered something into the entry guard's ear.

The Entry guard spoke, "Did you see the Princess earlier this morning on the road? I have been told a robed stranger, bearded, slight-of-build, bearing a staff is to be allowed entrance. Would that be you?"

Kordan heard the sarcasm in the guard's voice. "Yes, that is me. Please announce that Kordan has requested a Royal Audience. I bring news of the giant Ningthus."

The entry guard turned to the other guard who had not left yet and said, "Well you heard him, Kordan wishes to have an audience with the Princess. Let her know the gentleman in question is here. I will send him in forthwith."

The guard spent a few minutes looking into the doorway, then turned and began giving a long list of do's and don'ts for an appearance in front of the Princess.

"Bow from the waist and speak your name and the purpose of your visit clearly. When finished, stop talking and wait for the Princess to address or respond to your request. If she asks you a question, answer her slowly and clearly. Your voice can get lost in the great hall if you do not speak clearly. Whether the Princess grants you your request or denies it, when you are dismissed, bow and thank her for her time. Then turn and leave. You may collect your staff at that time." The guard held out his hand to take the wizard's staff. The wizard reluctantly complied.

Kordan stepped through the doorway into the Great Hall. The room was adorned with lavish paintings and tapestries hanging from ceilings twenty feet high. The hall was huge and by looks could accommodate close to one thousand people. It was lit by large windows and torches offset on the walls every ten feet.

Today the room appeared to be quite empty. Kordan counted approximately fifty people. Most were surrounding the Princess as she sat on the throne at the far end of the hall. He could see her speaking to what he assumed was an advisor and he could hear them speaking as he approached.

It took Kordan a few minutes to traverse from the doorway to the opposite end where the Princess sat. When he reached the throne, he bowed and spoke, "Your

Highness, I am Kordan the Wizard, and I seek audience with this court."

The Princess eyed the wizard carefully and spoke. "And to WHAT do we owe this visit wizard?"

Kordan could hear the edge in the Princess's voice. His response was clear and even, as he tried to sound calm and non-plussed.

"Your Highness, I believe the King summoned my Lord Peltor. Since he has passed, it has fallen to me to answer all requests for assistance." Kordan kept his voice calm. "If I just keep to the facts," he thought, "maybe I can turn this around." But to his dismay, the Princess would have none of it.

"Assistance!" she said with a cutting tone, "What assistance did YOU hope to provide?"

"Your Highness, many years ago your father performed a kindness to me and my Lord Peltor. To repay the favor, Peltor gave your father the means to summon him for any reason. That summons came upon the wind a few days ago. I am here to honor that promise." Kordan continued. "After King Timor conquered Omthus, the giants scattered and it took Ningthus many years, but he united most of the clans under his rule. I have heard that the giants have been more organized in their attacks, and they have been especially effective in your father's kingdom. The giants are difficult to stop, and their plan has been advancing through the rest of the Kingdoms. I felt the key was to destroy Ningthus then the giants would be without a leader and would scatter as they did before. When I arrived last night, I confronted Ningthus and turned him to stone."

When Kordan had finished, the Hall became very quiet. The Princess rose from the throne and slowly walked toward the wizard. "Who gave you permission to act without approval from this Court! You may have caused more harm than good. Our people can't be made to suffer from any retaliation by the giants due to your reckless act."

Kordan worked hard to not get defensive. "Princess," he said, "please hear what I am saying. My intervention has taken Ningthus out of the equation. He can no longer command his army. If the giants scatter, which is their history, then this is the beginning of your father's army getting the upper hand. Princess, I was only doing my best to help you end this scourge and help make safe your kingdom."

"No Wizard!" snapped the Princess. "We would be foolish to believe that. You yourself have pointed out that they are more organized. Plans may be in place that would not require a direct command from Ningthus. We must now prepare for more attacks and ready our troops for battle."

She continued, "And scatter or not, we are still at a tremendous disadvantage. You have left out the most dangerous piece of your solution. Ningthus may be gone, But What about the Dragon? Our troops are in far more danger from him."

Behest

Kordan felt like he had been hit with a cannonball. A dragon! How was it he did not hear about that. he stuttered, "Y.. y.. your H..Highness, I would have never..." Kordan never finished his sentence, from behind the throne he heard another voice.

"Yes, Sir Wizard, What about the Dragon?" King Timor appeared from behind his throne. "The giants may have no need to hear from Ningthus if Stelth is leading them. They have been following him on the raids and my men are helpless from his fiery attacks from the sky."

Kordan fell to one knee. "Sire, please let me know what I can do to correct this. The spell I placed on Ningthus can be reversed for a while longer. It will not become permanent for another few days. He is incapacitated and the transformation can be stopped. Before he regains consciousness, you can imprison him."

"Let's not be hasty Sir Wizard," said the King. "I think his silence might work to our advantage however, it will be more dangerous for you." The King paused for a moment, took a deep breath and said, "Defeating Stelth falls to you. I am sorry, but I can lose no more men; it is the true reason I summoned you."

Alicanth looked over to her father. "He came at your behest?"

"Yes daughter, he did. I have been listening to your heated words with him and while I agree he should have come here first, he acted to stop a threat to our people, and I cannot fault him for that."

Kordan saw a break in the conversation as Alicanth was taken aback by her father's words. "Your Majesties," he said as he rose to his feet, "I will take this challenge and do my best to defeat this dragon. I ask you to give me as much information as possible so I can understand the proper way to defeat him."

King Timor looked at the Wizard and said, "I did not make this choice lightly. This foe is beyond me, and I do not enjoy asking for aid especially when it may spell their doom. After all I just gave you and your Master horses to ride. This is hardly a fair trade."

"Unbeknownst to you Sire, those horses were life savers for us on many occasions and my Lord Peltor showered thanks and praise on you often. I do this with trepidation, but with a full heart. Now please point me to the person who has the most knowledge about this beast called Stelth."

King Timor cast a side glance to his daughter, and

Kordan knew immediately that his contact was the Princess Alicanth. Before anyone could say anything else Kordan shifted his body to face the Princess and spoke. "Princess, I fear our last two encounters have not been pleasant, and I accept full responsibility for that. Please let's go for a morning ride and you can educate me on what I need to know. I would be honored and forever grateful. I will need whatever you know if I am to be successful on this task." He finished and waited for an answer.

Alicanth managed a "Well I...." when King Timor boomed an answer

"It's settled then," said the King, "she will give you the information you need. My daughter likes to go on her morning rides early Wizard."

"Very good Sire," said Kordan. "Princess, I will meet you at the castle gates at sun-up."

Princess Alicanth silently nodded in agreement. "Until tomorrow," said Kordan, "Good day." He turned and walked out of the hall. He was eager to get his staff and get back to the Quiet Wife for an ale and a good night's rest. He was going to need it.

Chapter 7

STELTH

There are many different types of dragons. Some are solitary. Some are social. Some only mate every three years. Some mate for life. Stelth's parents were mated for life.

When Stelth was born, you could carry him in both of your hands, a little purple and black ball of scales and teeth. His breath was hot, but no flames. Those would come when he was older as his body matured and produced the volatile acids and gases that create the deadly dragon fire, generally at a time we know as puberty. His mother named him Stelth which in the Dragon tongue meant quiet and cunning.

Stelth's mother was a vixen called Vaneera. Stelth didn't get the chance to know his father for he was killed along with the wizard he battled shortly after Stelth was hatched. Since she was alone Vaneera had to leave Stelth for long stretches of time while she hunted for food. When she returned, she did her best to teach him as much as she could about their kind and their relationship with the world and other creatures in it.

The most complex relationship was with humans. It was a love-hate relationship, and not without reason. Some rogue dragons found humans to be tasty and a great food source. They also took delight in burning down whole villages. Some made pacts with local kingdoms and took human sacrifices to leave the villages alone. This behavior generated great fear among humans and is the main reason for all the attempts to eradicate dragons.

The other side of this coin was a very positive almost symbiotic relationship between dragon and human. An imprint occurs allowing seamless thought and communication with each other. This generally happens when the dragon is newly hatched either at the time of or just days after birth. (*Editor's note: There are no instances either recorded or spoken of this happening with a fully mature dragon.)*

Stelth would always listen intently. There was much for the young dragon to learn, but one day his mother left to hunt and never returned. Stelth was used to his mother going away for long periods, but after two weeks, his hunger grew to the point where he had to do something about it, so he ventured from the safety of his den to search for food.

He had never hunted before nor had he been taught, so his first attempts were dismal failures. He spent hours chasing a rabbit and for some reason was never quite able to catch it. It didn't help matters that he was still growing into his body and was gangly and uncoordinated.

He was angry at his failures and felt the forest was laughing at him. He tried different methods, like throwing rocks at his intended victims, which if he could have seen himself, he would have laughed at the sight.

Then one day after chasing a deer into an open field, he spread his wings and suddenly found himself off the ground and in the air. He was just a few feet up when the shock and fear, brought him crashing down on his face. "Hmmm," he thought "this might be very helpful". And so it happened, growling stomach and all, Stelth taught himself to fly.

He learned to control his movements in the air; closing his wings part way to dive and opening to slow down. This controlled his speed and gave him a huge advantage when hunting. He found his eyesight could spot the thermal signatures of his potential prey and in many instances, he could force them into the open where he would have a better chance at success. His first few attempts were unsuccessful, and he sprained his left talon when he misjudged and hit the ground. But he quickly understood where he made his mistakes and corrected them. When he caught his first rabbit, he put his head back and let out a large roar, which was substantial for his age and size (he stood about six feet on his haunches). He would never be hungry again.

Stelth kept to himself. He practiced his flying skills at

night when, due to his purple and black skin, he was virtually invisible against the night sky. He became quite an adept hunter and his skill in controlling himself when he flew was remarkable. He would frequently fly to a nearby mountain pass and navigate through the craggy rocks and outcroppings. Slowly at first then building speed as fast as his wings would take him. He got a little overconfident and thought he could do it with his eyes closed. He crashed into a rocky cliff face. It rendered him unconscious until morning. He found it difficult to fly as his head hurt and he was a bit dizzy. Still wobbling, he rose to the sky to fly home. He was hoping no one would see him, but that was not to be the case. Watching intently from the protection of the tall trees was Ningthus. He watched as Stelth slowly rose to the sky. He saw how shaky the young dragon appeared. He laughed and said to himself, "You're just what I'm looking for." Stelth's days of freedom were about to end.

Ningthus followed the young dragon as he flew back to his lair. He watched carefully as Stelth landed and slowly walked into his cave. In truth, Stelth was exhausted from his flight and his head pounded. Once inside, he found his favorite spot, laid down and fell fast asleep.

Ningthus waited for over an hour before approaching the opening to the cave. He peeked inside but could see nothing, He listened for any type of sound but heard nothing. "Good," thought the giant, "it's asleep."

Nignthus left and came back over the next few days, hoping to figure out the dragon's sleep patterns. It didn't take long. The beast hunted by night and slept during the day. The giant began to set his trap.

The plan was simple. Have two of his clan climb up to the cliff outcropping overlooking the dragon's cave. They would secure two ends of the net to the ground with a rock, just to hold it in place. Then they would each hold one of the other corners and wait. The net was made of a special metal material and was virtually impossible to break. When the dragon exited the cave, at the precise moment when his body had cleared the opening, and before he could fly off, they would throw the two ends out. The net would fall quickly due to the weight of the material. He most likely wouldn't see it coming since it would be night and the net itself black. When the first half of the net hit him, they would pull up the other two sides and drop them. Giants hiding below would catch and stretch the net tight forcing the beast to the ground. The giants would wait until their captive tired himself out trying to escape, then they would roll him up, bind him and carry him off to their stronghold.

The plan worked perfectly. Stelth was taken completely by surprise and was trapped. He struggled and roared at the top of his lungs; even managed a little smoke but no fire. In the end, he calmed down and allowed the capture to take place. They were large creatures and there were too many to fight. Instead of passing out from exhaustion, he sat up facing the one he guessed to be the leader and burned his yellow gaze into him. Ningthus walked over and stared back. "This one will be hard to break," he thought.

The giant had planned ahead and while he gathered information on Stelth's habits, he had a large iron cage built. It may not hold a full-grown dragon, but for a young one it would be a good temporary home until the beast was broken.

Stelth was silent and unaggressive as the giants tied him up in the net. In fact, he made no sounds or movements all the way back to the giant stronghold. Even when they put him in the cage and untied him, he did not move. The giants had left the net loose so he could crawl out from underneath easily. Stelth laid there unmoving and silent for three days refusing food and water lying still under the net.

On the fourth day, Ningthus entered the cage and slammed the door behind him. "I didn't bring you here to die," bellowed the giant. "You are here to do what I tell you to do, now get up!"

Stelth raised himself up, still under the net, refusing to shrug it off. He stared at Ningthus and said defiantly "I refuse."

Ningthus became enraged and stormed over to where Stelth was lying. He picked up the young dragon and threw him against the other side of the cage net and all. Stelth hit the metal wall and thudded to the ground. It hurt, but he still refused to move and laid still - unmoving and silent.

Ningthus stormed out of the cage. He was enraged at Stelth's strength of will and of his resolve. "He will just die," thought Ningthus, "unless I can give him a reason to live....and what better reason than revenge." He chuckled to himself and began to lay out a plan and a lie to sell to the young dragon.

A few months before one of Ningthus's men, Mok had returned from hunting with news that he had seen a dragon in the forest near the mountains.

The creature had just brought down a deer. It didn't stay down long and was back in the air quickly and out of sight. Ningthus was excited and told his man to take him to where he had spotted the beast.

The two giants did their best to stay hidden in the trees and waited quietly to hopefully see the dragon. The spot in the forest was near a small lake, mostly surrounded by trees. "This would be a good spot to hunt," thought Ningthus, "all creatures need water."

Ningthus knew this lake well. It was filled via an underground spring and was about fifty feet deep. From where they were, both giants had a good view of the entire lake. They wouldn't miss a thing.

They waited for most of the day and spotted nothing. Ningthus sent Mok back to bring food and blankets. They would stay here for a few days and wait to see if the dragon returned. While the Mok was gone, the dragon returned. It swooped down, landed, and bent its head down for a drink.

Ningthus could see, by the size and coloration, it was a she-dragon. He was excited and was glad he decided to stay for a few days. He would wait, hopefully be able to establish a pattern and then plan the best way to capture her.

The two giants waited and remained hidden with their view of the lake. Their patience was rewarded. At approximately the same time every day, the dragon appeared at the lake for water. And to further help to them, they saw that she drank consistently from the same spot. Ningthus was overjoyed. Now he could set his trap to capture her.

Ningthus sent Mok back to the Stronghold to bring back the largest net they had and four others to help with the capture.

"Bring everything here by tonight," said Ningthus. "We'll set it all up and bring her in tomorrow when she stops to drink." Mok nodded and was on his way.

Mok arrived shortly after sunset with the net and help in tow. Ningthus had his team lay the net out across the area where the dragon would stop to drink. It carried a good distance out into the lake. The net was carefully pulled back so as not to tangle and could be pulled forward in an instant. Then the giants took their positions behind rocks and trees. They were completely hidden, and each held onto their corners of the net which was camouflaged from view. Ningthus took a large tree branch to the ground and sand near the water to hide evidence of their tracks. All looked calm and peaceful. With luck, the dragon wouldn't suspect a thing.

"We'll spring the trap," said Ningthus, "when she bends her head down to drink. Timing and speed are everything. You have to get the net over her head before she raises her neck. If this works, she will fight and try to fly off. Try to keep her head down so you don't get burned by her flames. if we can keep her head in the water, she won't be able to use her fire. Hold the net tight. The struggle should tire her out. Then we can drag her to shore, tire her up and I can bind her mouth. It will be a long wait so be patient, and above all keep your mouths shut."

All the giants knew to mind Ningthus. His reputation did not tolerate disobedience. And so, they quietly waited. It was several hours before they heard the beat of dragon wings. They felt their bodies tense in anticipation. Through the cover of the trees and leaves, they saw the beast land. They saw her look around to make sure all was safe. She slowly approached the water and lowered her head and began to drink. "NOW!" screamed Ningthus in less than a second the attack launched. The giants were surprisingly agile and fast. They covered fifteen feet with every step forward thanks to their great height. Before the dragon could recover from being startled, in that split second the giants had covered enough ground to cover the dragon completely. They began to pull the net back toward the shore so they could hold her down on the edge of the lake.

Fire flew from her mouth, but thanks to the metallic construction of the net, its integrity held.

The plan looked like it was working, but Vaneera would have none of it. With all her strength she lifted her body and lunged forward trying to open her wings moving her to deeper water.

In the commotion three of the giants lost their grip on the net, and only Mok was able to hold on, because he weaved his arm between the spaces in the net. He desperately followed her along the bank trying to pull the net closer to him. But with all her movement she became more tangled and in the deeper water the heavy net took her down. The pull was too great and holding on the very end, Mok was dragged in with her. In their confusion, the other giants had hesitated before starting to rush to help Mok. It was a mere few seconds, but it was too late. Giants cannot swim and in this part of the deep lake, they could only watch as the water churned with the struggle below until finally the waters became still. It was over.

Ningthus brought two dead rabbits into the cage along with a chair. He tossed the rabbits over towards Stelth's head and said, "Where is your mother, dragon?"

Stelth did not move and continued his silence. Ningthus continued, "You know, I came upon King Timor and one of his regiments a few months back. I was alone, so I stayed hidden in the trees. He was near a lake, and he had managed to snare a dragon in one of his nets. I could tell it was a she-dragon from her color and smaller frame." He continued the entire story giving details of the dragon's fierce fight and her slow death by drowning replacing his men with Timor's.

He finished and stood up from his chair, turned to walk away, stopped and said, "There haven't been dragons in this area for many years. It stands to reason that when two suddenly show up, they must be related. If this was your mother, I felt I owed it to you to let you know. If you wish to continue to starve yourself, be my guest. King Timor killed my brother, and now it looks like he killed your mother. I am going to make him pay for my brother. Join me and together we can both achieve vengeance."

Ningthus waited a few moments for a response. Hearing none he slowly turned to leave. "Where is this King?" said Stelth as he slowly rose and worked his way out from under the net. Only six feet tall he was still dwarfed by the giant. That didn't matter he moved forward until he was a few feet from Ningthus, raised his head and stared into the giant's eyes with his deep yellow ones.

"Work with me, let me train you, together we can bring Timor to his knees. But you must be patient, and you must listen to me. Give me your allegiance and I promise you your revenge." Ningthus finished and waited.

"So be it," said Stelth. With that he turned and slowly made his way to the two rabbits Ningthus had brought and swallowed them whole.

Ningthus smiled and turned to leave. "Thou need not lock me in," said Stelth, "I will not leave." Ningthus nodded and walked out of the cage, leaving the door wide open.

After he had walked some distance, he pulled one of his guards over and said, "Don't let him see you watching him. If he leaves, kill him if you can."

The pact that was laid down between the giant and the dragon was new and fragile. Ningthus was not taking any chances. His gamble and lie had worked. Stelth would only see the truth as the giant saw it. Even his freedom would be a lie. Still, it was very dangerous and difficult to control a dragon. If Stelth rebelled, the window to destroy him was closing. As the dragon grew and his skin hardened, he would be near impossible to kill. Ningthus knew he would have to seed the beast's lust for vengeance every day.

Ningthus allowed a few days to go to let Stelth regain his strength. The Giants fed him twice daily and they were amazed how quickly Stelth grew as a result. Ningthus began his training and instead of looking down at Stelth he was greeted face-to-face.

Ningthus tested Stelth's abilities, He watched him fly, and was amazed at how well the dragon had trained himself. Ningthus wondered when Stelth would be able to breathe fire. His answer came one day when after a big meal Stelth burped and set a nearby tree on fire. Once fire became a usable weapon, the training intensified.

Stelth had to learn to control the fire, when to release

and when not. The physiology of the fire required Stelth to expel the gases that created his fire. He found he could expel just the gas without fire or with a click of a bone in his throat he could ignite the flame. The flame itself was a deadly mixture of gas and acid and was quite destructive and very difficult to extinguish.

Ningthus set up targets for Stelth to ignite and slowly he helped the dragon attain accuracy and distance. He was also taught to carry large, boulder-size rocks aloft, breathe his fire on them and drop on specified targets. And as the days and weeks passed, Stelth grew in size and strength. He was probably the most formidable creature alive. Most of the giants were wary and fearful of what Ningthus had created and were glad he was able to exert his control.

In this short span of time Stelth had grown to nearly twenty feet in height, his armor was nearly impenetrable, and he developed a keen ability to read the giants and he questioned his place among them.

One evening, Stelth asked Ningthus, "When do we attack this king?"

"I have a plan," said the giant, "but first we divide his troops and busy them elsewhere throughout his kingdom. Then when he is least protected, we will strike." He continued, "All of our attacks will come at night, the same way you hunted. He will not be aware of you until it is too late, and then we will both have our revenge."

Stelth looked at Ningthus as if he was studying him. "Thou hast told me everything?" he asked. Ningthus replied in a strong even voice. "Of course."

"Hmmmm," replied Stelth. "Then I will abide by thy plan." Stelth then leapt up into the sky and went hunting.

Stelth preferred his solitude when eating and he was glad of the time alone. He could feel the uneasiness of the giants when he was around. They had nothing to fear from him. He would fully honor his promise to Ningthus; he would be true to his word. To not cause tension, Stelth would rest during the day in one of the caves above the Stronghold, and only come when he was summoned. Ningthus had a large horn which hung in the center of the stronghold courtyard. Stelth agreed to come when the horn was blown.

One Morning Stelth heard the horn. He answered the call, flying to the inner wall of the stronghold. There he found Ningthus and his three generals, Thembos, Klamdous and Cilios. Stelth landed and Ningthus spoke. "The time to unfold our plan has come," he said.

He began to elaborate in precise detail how they would execute their attacks. All would happen at night and during the new moon phase. "Won't it be difficult for us to see?" asked Klamdous.

"We won't attack until we can see." said Ningthus. His three generals looked confused. He continued, "Our attack starts after Stelth rains fire down from the sky. The reason I've chosen this time of night and month is because Stelth will be invisible against the sky. It will be a complete surprise. No one will be able to stop us. We will start with some small farms and a small village in Godrin's Kingdom, then we will swing back and start here in Timor's kingdom. This will draw him out. This will spell his doom. Once we control the Northern Realm, none will be able to stand against us. We have our secret weapon: Stelth."

Ningthus finished and looked at everyone as if waiting for questions. He finished with "We leave in two days; our first raid will be the night we arrive.' He paused and looked at the dragon. "Stelth, you will leave at night I don't want you seen."

Stelth slowly turned and spoke. "Tell me thy location. I will meet thee there the night of thy raid. None shall see me." Finishing, he spread his wings and flew up to his cave above the stronghold.

Two days later at dawn, Stelth heard the horn. He flew down and saw Ningthus with six others. When he had landed the giant walked up to him and spoke. "Follow the river until you reach the fork and turn in towards the fields. Send a fire rock in next to the structure there. That will be the signal you are there. Then destroy all the crops. Leave the livestock we will take care of those. When you've done hide until the next night, we will attack the nearby village. When completely dark send in another fire rock into the center of town. Lay a ring of fire around half the town. Then come back here. Then we will start with Timor's Kingdom at the next new moon."

"I know this place; I will see thee tonight," said the dragon. And he flew back to his lair.

The location of the first raid was some fifty miles from where they started, and while it would take a garrison of soldiers if they moved non-stop approximately seventeen hours for the journey, the giants could move faster and make the trip in seven hours. This would give them ample time to rest until Stelth arrived.

The giants waited patiently. Then when the sun had set and the night closed in, a burning boulder fell from the sky and landed between the farmhouse and the barn. It lit the area up enough for the giants to spring into action. They ran to the burning rock and four lit their torches, and two ran and started scooping livestock into large nets and carried away as many as they could on their shoulders. Stelth began burning all the fields while the others began lighting the structures on fire.

The residents fled screaming. Those that escaped could, those that didn't were consumed in the infernos that used to be their homes. The giants didn't much care what happened.

Most ran away from the carnage. Any who stood to defend their homes and fight the giants were cut down and left for all to see. The destruction was complete. And no one saw Stelth. When the giants had finished Ningthus sounded his horn and the giants retreated into the forest leaving the sky ablaze.

The giants traveled back to their stronghold. They arrived just before dawn. Stelth had landed and took the nets with the livestock and carried them back in his large talons. He arrived much sooner and retreated to his lair and waited for the others to return.

Ningthus was pleased. His plan had worked. In order to not leave a large trail for soldiers to follow, the giants had walked in the river. It wasn't very deep and so they could wade for most of the way. No one would know which way they had gone. They would rest a day and return to the town near to their first raid to instill fear and show the townspeople their strength.

The raids continued, and still no one saw Stelth. Then one night during one of the attacks in King Timor's kingdom, a garrison of soldiers happened by and ran in to help the farmers. Stelth saw them and moved in for a better look. The soldiers began firing arrows at the flames and spears in the direction of the fire. The arrows were incinerated in the flames and the spears hit the dragon's impenetrable skin and fell to the ground. The guards may or may not have been able to see him because of the flames and the blackness of the night. Ningthus yelled "Stelth!" the dragon roared and moved away.

The giants picked up the burning rocks with what looked like shovels and threw them at the soldiers several caught fire from the rocks hitting them and were lost to the flames.

In the ensuing chaos, the giants retreated and fled to their stronghold. The next day, Ningthus summoned Stelth and yelled, "What were you thinking? I never told you to come in we had the whole thing under control."

"Thou didst draw out the King's men as thou hath predicted," said Stelth. "I wished to see if the King was amongst them."

Ningthus looked at the dragon and said, "Unless I call you, do not come in. Is that clear?"

Stelth looked at Ningthus and lowered his neck so they were at eye level. "I will be called if this King comes, if not I will still come. This King is mine,"

The dragon lifted his neck, turned his body, and flew up to his cave. As he left Ningthus thought to himself, "He is getting harder to control. I have to find a way to kill him."

Two days later Ningthus and his general Thembos were scouting the area for the next farm to raid when Ningthus was confronted by a wizard. The sky had turned stormy and there was a greenish haze to the clouds. Green lightening emanated from them. The sorcerer tapped his staff to the ground and spoke "VENIRE!. Ningthus jerked as if fighting some unknown force and was pulled from the trees. "Who calls me?" he said as he stood face-to-face with the small-framed adversary. Thembos stayed behind frozen with fear at this kind of power. He watched as the small man stood defiantly while Ningthus charged with his knife drawn. He trembled as the wizard spoke his incantation and stood in horror as he witnessed his Thane turn to stone and fall to the ground.

After the Wizard left, Thembos stood alone for what seemed like an eternity. When he finally worked up the courage, he walked over to where Ningthus laid. He bent over and touched his skin and recoiled. It was eerie how cold it felt. He turned and ran back to the stronghold blowing his horn as he entered the courtyard. The dragon answered the call immediately.

Stelth saw Thembos holding the horn and shaking. "Where is Ningthus?" asked the dragon. By now others had gathered and were echoing the dragon's question. Thembos composed himself still shaking he answered. "A wizard has turned him to stone."

The crowd of giants began to clamor loudly with disbelief and anger. Some drew their swords and yelled "Death to the wizard!" The crowd seemed to agree with louder shouts joining the chant to kill the wizard.

Stelth let out a large roar. The crowd suddenly went silent and took a step back from the dragon. "This vengeance is mine. I will speak with this wizard and then destroy him. Thembos go with Cilios and find out information on where I might find him. DO NOTHING and report back to me."

The two giants nodded in response. Stelth flew to his

cave. After the dragon had left, Thembos turned to two older giants to his left and said, "How goes the weapon."

Grimp the taller of the two answered. "It is finished general. It is harder than any weapon we have ever forged. It can slice stone. It will stop Stelth."

"Excellent," said Thembos. All three generals knew that without Ningthus, Stelth posed a large danger and would need to be destroyed. "We will let him kill the wizard," thought Thembos. Then when he returns, we will kill him." Cilios joined him and they left to find out the information that Stelth had asked for.

The two giants returned and summoned Stelth. They told the dragon that through their informants they found out the wizard would be on a morning ride tomorrow with the Princess Alicanth. "The Princess rides daily and generally stays to the main road; her two guards never leave her side."

"I thank thee for thy help," said the dragon. "I will find him."

"And kill him!" said Cilios.

"If need be." replied Stelth stoically and flew away.

The two giants turned and stared at each other. "What did he mean by that?" said Thembos. Cilios shrugged his shoulders and stood there just shaking his head. Both felt it was a foregone conclusion that the wizard must die. Stelth thought differently. If the wizard was brought in by

King Timor, then yes, he would kill him, but if by chance the wizard was here because Ningthus had other enemies, then that had nothing to do with him. His pact with Ningthus was solely dealing with King Timor. Anything else was none of his concern. The evidence seemed clear however that the wizard was here at King Timor's bidding. Why else would the wizard be riding with the princess. He would have his answer soon.

Chapter 8

THE ENCOUNTER

I t was a beautiful morning. The air was not too crisp, the sun was just rising, and the sky was blue as far as the eye could see. The landscape looked lush and green. The land could be seen dotted with people starting their day.

Kordan was looking forward to riding with the Princess. He was very interested in learning everything he could about this dragon, and he was hoping to understand her better as well. He could hardly stop thinking about her. He couldn't remember ever seeing someone so beautiful. Her piercing green eyes, her flowing red hair. He had to stop himself and remember he was here to subdue and defeat this dragon. Still, he really hoped he could find a way to establish a much more friendly tone with Alicanth. "It may be easier to deal with the dragon," he thought, but the day was so beautiful. It all seemed perfect. He would put his best foot forward and hope for positive results.

Kordan arrived at the castle gate just as Alicanth rode out with her two guards.

"Well, Sir Wizard," said the Princess, "perfect timing, shall we go?"

"Yes, let's," said Kordan, "and If it please the Princess, would you call me by my name, it is Kordan." The Wizard smiled and to his surprise, the Princess smiled back. Her features were made even prettier by the rays of the rising sun and her beautiful smile.

"I would like that," said the Princess, "and please call me Alicanth, you have found favor with my father, and I wish us to be friends. After much thought, it is a brave thing you do to remain here knowing that you must do battle with a terrible beast. Nothing holds you here except an old promise. You honor your Master by staying."

Kordan thanked her. "I have studied dragons over the years," said Kordan. "They are very interesting creatures, mostly solitary and some were bound to humans through a type of psychic connection. He continued, "I have heard of some wizards who worked with dragons. They kept their relationship and how it was maintained a secret. Dragons as a rule were destructive. Most beasts were less than friendly to farms, livestock, and people. In fact, a whole career was created and would be dragon slayers roamed from town-to town charging large sums to destroy the beasts. Most were charlatans and left fleecing the townspeople, farmers, and ranchers of their money. Some were caught and hanged, most got away. The deed then fell to any available wizard who was willing to do battle with said beast. The result has been the disappearance of both dragon and wizard. I'm not sure the outcomes are related, but I've not seen or heard of dragons in my lifetime until now. Peltor said he was the last of his order. As far as I know, now I am the last of his order. This dragon of yours, Stelth, may be the last of his kind as well. I would like to understand his relationship with Ningthus and the other giants. It may be unique and worth studying. Although based on just a few of the things you have said that may not be possible."

Alicanth listened intently as they rode side-by-side. "Well," she said, "and I thought I was going to teach you about dragons. Your studies have been quite extensive. I'm impressed!"

Kordan smiled and placed his hand over his stomach and bent over as if to bow. The princess let out a soft laugh and nodded to acknowledge his gesture. They both laughed and as they did their eyes met. Kordan could see nothing but her and she blushed at his stare. The two guards looked at each other and smiled. The ride continued.

When Kordan's eyes met the Princess's he felt his heart beat faster, and when he saw her blush, he lowered his head, cleared his throat and nervously said, "So Alicanth, what can you tell me about Stelth?"

The Princess was relieved for the question. She had been hasty in her assumptions about Kordan and was taken aback by his sincerity and charm. With his hood pulled back she could see his face and she found him quite handsome.

"We really don't know that much about him," said the Princess. "We found out his name from one of the farm owners whose lands were attacked. He heard a giant's voice we believe to be Ningthus call out his name. We don't know what he looks like as the attacks have been at night. From what we have been told, and mind you this is second-hand, Stelth towers over the giants. We have heard he is at least twenty feet tall."

Kordan's eyes widened. "That indeed is big. This may take every skill I have. I still can't understand why I have not heard anything from the other Kingdoms about this. I would think news would pass through Godrin's realm where Peltor's temple is located."

"My grandfather's Kingdom is next to my father's," said Alicanth, "and he is unaware of the dragon. He knows about the attacks as those were mentioned when riders came through on their way to see my father. No one spoke of the dragon because no one really saw him. Most felt the Giants were setting the fires and using catapults to throw fiery rocks. All the realms knew that my father killed Ohmthus and that most likely Ningthus would be attacking him in revenge for his brother's death. By the time word of the other attacks came to my father, several had already occurred in our Kingdom. He sent out a garrison of soldiers to patrol, and they were unfortunate to come across an attack as it was happening. The men did their best to protect the people and the livestock but had little success. My father lost five men that night. The report that came back to my father gave a clearer indication of the real threat. The men said they saw streams of fire coming from the sky. They shot arrows and threw spears towards the source of the fire. The arrows were incinerated by the flames, and it appeared some of the spears hit something but just fell back to the ground. The most important clue to the culprit was the roar of some kind of beast as the carnage took place. When my father heard that, his suspicions were proven. The attacks were aided by a dragon. He sent men to investigate those who had been attacked and gather information. The aftermath was terrible; the houses and land were devastated. My Father sent supplies and men to help his subjects rebuild. He has no idea how to stop this threat, so you were summoned. I had no idea he had sent for you until yesterday. He had asked me if I could find anything in our libraries about dragons when he told me about what he believed was causing the attacks. This is all I know."

Kordan listened intently to everything the Princess said. This was a lot to process, and he needed time to prepare himself for the confrontation that would inevitably occur. Also evident was the fact that he had turned Ningthus to stone and that Stelth would soon get word. The giants would know that only a wizard could have done this, which could mean only one thing. Time was shorter than he thought; he was putting the Princess in danger.

"Alicanth," said Kordan urgently. "You must get back to the castle immediately!"

Before the Wizard could say another word, a large shadow passed over them momentarily blotting out the sun. They could hear what sounded like the beating of large wings followed by a beastly roar. The horses were spooked and were difficult to control. While all were focused on their mounts a tremor was felt on the ground before them. When Kordan and company looked to the sound, they saw both an impressive and terrible sight. Stelth had found them.

The dragon stood before them on his haunches; he was over twenty feet tall. His wings outstretched were over fifty feet. He was deep purple with black undertones which glistened like jewels in the sunlight. He had horns above his brow and his deep-set eyes glowed yellow against the day. He was magnificent.

Kordan calmed the horses saying "tranquilum." He then looked at the guards and said, "Get the Princess to safety."

The two guards acted immediately flanking the Princess and trying to force her to move back to the castle. "No!" she said, "I'm staying. Kordan will protect me."

Kordan was fearful and said, "Alicanth, please go. I can protect you and the others best if I am not distracted and worried about your safety."

She heard the truth in his voice and turned to leave when the air was pierced with a deep, low guttural voice that chilled them all to their bones.

"Wizard, I would speak with thee!"

All stopped. Alicanth turned her horse to face the dragon and Kordan dismounted took his staff from its sheath and walked toward Stelth.

"I am here, what do you want?

Stelth spoke. "Was it thee that turned Ningthus to stone."

"Yes." Replied Kordan firmly and without hesitation. There was no fear in his tone.

There was a moment of silence and Stelth settled on all four feet and pulled in his wings. "Why?"

"Ningthus and his hoards were destroying farms, livestock, and villages, with your help. Innocent people were dying," said the wizard. "He had to be stopped and so must you. King Timor wasn't able to protect his people, and I am here for that reason."

"Then we are enemies," said the dragon. "I must honor my pledge and kill thee."

Kordan heard Alicanth scream "Kordan!" The guards could not force her to leave. As the dragon inhaled Kordan spoke "Custodire saeptum omnae mihi." As the Dragon exhaled his fiery breath a shield appeared protecting

Kordan and all behind him.

But something was different. The force of the flames began pushing Kordan back. He could feel the heat through the barrier. He thought, "How is this happening?"

Suddenly the flames stopped. Stelth's mind reached out to the wizard, "I hear thy thoughts."

"What?" thought Kordan, "You heard me? I never said a word."

"I was told when I was young that I could find a being with whom I might bond with. That person would hear my thoughts as I would hear theirs," said Stelth, "as I hear thee."

Kordan did hear Stelth as thoughts not as words. Kordan's mind was searching, trying to remember from his studies if he had been told or read anything about this.

"I need time to process this," thought Kordan. "You and I need to understand what this means to us both."

Stelth stared for a moment at Kordan, then spoke aloud. "I too must think on this, I will see thee again."

Stelth spread his massive wings and leapt into the air. In a few moments he was gone.

Stelth did not want to be near or with the giants right now, so he flew back to the cave where he was born and withdrew into the dark recesses of his former den. Something was different. He could feel the wizard. He knew his name – Kordan. And while Stelth contemplated his situation and future, he wondered about everything Ningthus had told him. He wondered if he would have to break his oath. Sooner or later, he would have to choose.

Stelth

Kordan's immediate attention went to the Princess. "Alicanth, are you alright?"

"Yes, you had some kind of barrier all around us. I've never seen anything like it. You saved us," she said, as she jumped off her horse ran to Kordan and threw her arms around him.

"Alicanth you should have left, the larger the spell, the less chance of it holding, you could have been injured or killed," said Kordan.

"I couldn't leave you," said the Princess. "I...I couldn't. I heard Stelth and you speak and then you and the dragon just stared at each other as if you were talking. He spoke and flew away."

Kordan took her hand. It was trembling. He looked at the guards and said, "Please escort the Princess back to the castle. There are a few things I must look into."

Alicanth started to protest, and Kordan interrupted. "No Princess, you must return where you are safe. I must try to find answers to what happened. I need to understand why Stelth stopped his attack and did not kill us. I will see you in the morning."

That night back in his room, Kordan prepared to perform a ritual which would allow him to project his spirit form back to Peltor's Temple and library. He needed to research and understand what had happened between him and Stelth.

Sitting in a chair, he found it difficult to clear his mind. All his thoughts were of Alicanth. Her face, the wind in her hair, the tone of her voice. How his incantation weakened. If that had failed, she would have been injured or killed. The thought made him wince painfully.

Slowly he cleared his mind and started reciting the incantation "a corpore io animum ad spiritum" over and over. Kordan began to feel his spirit traveling and in a matter of seconds he was inside the library of Peltor's Temple. Something didn't feel right, he felt thin and kept fading in and out. He tried concentrating harder to hold his spirit in place. The spell was taxing him. It took all his energy to hold himself in place. He moved quickly before he lost his connection altogether. He located the book he was looking for and levitated it over to a table. Once there he used his mind to open the book and turn the pages. Every time he used more power he would blink in and out. He could feel himself slipping back. He read the pages and understood now what had taken place between he and Stelth and what it implied. He also now understood why there were so few dragons and wizards. "We are dying," he thought.

He had finished and none too soon. He faded out of the Temple Library and woke up in his room. He was drenched in sweat and exhausted. He got up from his chair and staggered over to his bed and collapsed. "I'm falling in love with Alicanth, and I'm losing my powers." Those were his last thoughts before he passed out.

Deep in the forest, laying among the fallen leaves, a stone figure began to glow. Pieces of stone began to dissolve into skin. The spell on Ningthus was breaking.

Chapter 9

THE RESURRECTION OF NINGTHUS

Ningthus had never known such pain. As the spell wore off and his mind cleared, he became more aware; he could feel his cells screaming for oxygen. His breathing was labored, and he could barely move. He laid there for a full day. As the spell waned, he could slowly feel sensation coming back to his hands, feet, and limbs. On the second day he managed to sit up. He wanted to move, and he was thirsty and hungry, but after a few minutes he laid down and fell asleep exhausted from the effort. On the third day, he could fully feel his hands and feet. He managed to roll over and was able to get himself into a crawling position and began his long way back to the giant stronghold.

By day five, he had managed to get to his feet. He was famished and thirsty. He found some berries to eat and ate all he could get his hands on. They helped, but it was his anger that drove him. It kept him moving and focused. And on day five late in the afternoon, Ningthus arrived at the stronghold. He stood tall and silent, unable to speak. Three of his soldiers spotted him. Two ran to help him and the third ran to inform the generals. Ningthus had returned from the dead.

The next two days were spent resting and regaining his strength. He was able to move around fairly well, although his joints creaked and popped a lot. As he made his way around the compound, he grabbed one of his soldiers and said, "Bring my Generals to me." The soldier nodded and ran off. A few minutes later, the three generals appeared, and with them was Grimp. In Grimp's hand was a spear with a black point. Ningthus had never seen anything like it before. "What do you bring me master forger?" asked the giant.

"A new weapon my Thane," said Grimp. As he spoke, he turned and hurled the spear at a boulder ten feet to the left of Ningthus. Instead of glancing off the stone the tip buried itself deep into the rock.

Ningthus was amazed. He clapped his hands together and yelled "Well done forger. Well done!" He hobbled over to the boulder and pulled the spear from the rock. He examined it closely, slowly moved away from the stone and hurled the spear again. It stuck. "Excellent! How many do we have?" he asked.

"At this time, we have ten and I am creating a mixture for ten more," said Grimp. Ningthus paused a moment then looked up and said, "Master Forger, how does this material stand up against dragon fire?"

Grimp thought a moment and said, "It should stand

very well, my lord. Even better than just stone. The crystal qualities embedded with the stone may help make the dragon fire cooler, I'm not totally sure I would need to ask Stelth to help me test that."

Ningthus spun around and looked at Grimp. "Tell Stelth nothing of this, do you understand?" Grimp nodded. "Stop making the spears," said Ningthus, "instead forge me a shield."

Grimp looked at Ningthus. "It can be done my lord, but it will take time."

"I need this in two days," said Ningthus. "I don't care how you do it, but get it done."

Grimp was barely able to speak but managed, "I'll do my best my lord." He turned to hurry back to his forge. His Thane did not tolerate failure. This shield had better be ready within one day.

After the Master Forger had left, Ningthus turned his attention to his three generals. He walked up to Thembos and said, "Give me your sword!" Thembos, was stunned at the request and slowly and shakily withdrew his sword. He bowed his head and handed the sword hilt-first to his Thane. Ningthus took the blade and turned his back to Thembos. He swung the weapon a few times, nodding and saying, "This has a good feel and balance." He turned to face his general and without a word ran the blade through Thembos. The giant fell to the ground sputtering for air. As Ningthus pulled the sword out he said, "That's for leaving me to die." The downed soldier could not speak. A look of horror was on his face. As blood filled his throat, he coughed, and died.

Ningthus

"Now," said Ningthus to his other two generals, "we have much to plan for. Listen well, I want no more mistakes. This is what we will do..." And so Ningthus laid out his plans. Most interesting to both the generals was the omission of any involvement from Stelth. When Ningthus had finished, Klamdous asked, "What of Stelth?"

Ningthus looked at his general and took a few moments to carefully frame his words. "Stelth has served his usefulness. I'm told that both wizard and dragon met and that Stelth attacked the wizard, but then stopped short of killing him. Our dragon then flew off and hasn't been seen since. We've tried to summon him but there has been no response. I sent one of my guards up to the caves above the stronghold, and Stelth is not there. I cannot afford to worry about his dragon sensibilities, or his agenda. If he returns and joins us in this fight, he will be welcome, I need him with me not against me. If not, we have the means to destroy him, and we will do so."

The Two generals saluted and left. Ningthus returned

to his room to rest. He wished he knew what had occurred with Stelth. "That dragon is too smart for his own good," he thought. "What a waste, what a waste."

Chapter 10

THE BETRAYAL

K ordan had a fitful sleep. He had never been so anxious or worried in his life. His powers were quickly waning, his spell on Ningthus was almost certainly reversing, how could he tell the princess how he feels, how could he protect her. And Stelth, the imprint, the connection, it changed the whole dynamic. Would he have to fight the dragon, or would he become an ally.

The wizard rose from his bed and hurried about getting ready to go to the palace. He had left Alicanth rather abruptly and was concerned he may have been off-putting. She was foremost in his thoughts. His feelings for her could have caused her harm. He may have not been able to protect her. What if the shield had collapsed, what if Stelth had pushed further, they would have all perished.

Kordan shook off his doubts. Powers or not, he was in for the battle of his life. The Innkeeper brought his horse around to the front of the inn. As Kordan mounted his horse, he saw a small squad of soldiers approaching. Kordan recognized the leader of the group.

"Darien, is it?" asked the Wizard.

"Yes, my lord it is," said the guard. "The King has sent us to escort you to the castle. He is anxious to speak with you."

Kordan rode next to Darien. "Is the Princess doing well today?" asked the wizard. "Yesterday was a pretty harrowing experience."

"She is fine, my lord," responded the guard, smiling as he said it. "In fact, she wanted to join us as we fetched you, but the King bade her to wait."

"Oh," said Kordan keeping his head down to avoid eye contact with the guard. He could feel his face turning red.

When the entourage entered the castle courtyard another group of guards were waiting to escort Kordan into the great hall. Darien followed quietly behind. Upon entering the hall, the head guard of the group announced loudly, "Your Majesties, the wizard has been brought to you per your instructions." Having spoken, he bowed turned and walked away, in fact all did, leaving Kordan alone, with Darien, quietly behind him.

Kordan glanced over to Alicanth and smiled briefly and bowed to Timor. "Sire, you sent for me."

"Yes, I did," said Timor. "First and foremost, you have the gratitude of this Court and this father for saving the life of Princess Alicanth yesterday. "Although," he continued with a parental glance over to his daughter, "it might not have been necessary if she had listened to her guards, who were trying to comply with your instructions to leave."

A smile appeared on Kordan's face as he spoke, "Don't be to cross with her Sire, Stelth's presence is quite captivating, and his voice almost hypnotic. I would have been hard pressed to leave even as he asked to speak to me."

"He asked to speak to you?" asked the King.

"Yes Sire," said the wizard. "He attacked only after I told him that you had summoned me, at which point he declared us enemies."

Kordan related the rest of encounter to Timor even mentioning that he felt the heat of Stelth's flame and that his barrier was beginning to waver.

Kordan continued, "I could not understand why the magic was weakening and I thought, 'How is this happening?' when suddenly the attacked stopped. The dragon heard my thoughts. When the Princess saw the two of us looking at each other, we were actually having a conversation. I could feel him, and he could feel me. Stelth was confused by the event and left to try and understand it. I agreed with him, as I needed to do the same."

"Interesting," said the King, do you think Stelth is against us still?"

Kordan thought for a moment and answered. "Several things are at play here. First, I question how strong Stelth's loyalty is to Ningthus. He asked me if it was you who summoned me here. I told him yes. It seems to me that if you had not brought me here, he would have assumed I was here from another enemy of Ningthus. Why even ask me that question unless it made a difference? I feel he would have left and never tried to kill us. I know why Ningthus hates you, you killed his brother, I don't know the connection that causes Stelth to consider you an enemy. I hope to understand that soon."

Second, since my spell of protection began to falter, I must consider that the spell I used to turn Ningthus to stone has also unraveled and the giant has returned to his normal self. I fear our position is compromised and a battle with the giants is inevitable. I believe I can prevent a war between you and the giants, by facing Ningthus and defeating him once and for all."

"No, you can't!" Alicanth jumped up from her throne. "If what you say about your power to weave your spells is true, you'll be killed."

"Princess," said Kordan, "this is the only way to ensure the least casualties. We must assume Stelth is still with the giants, we have not been told differently. I am sure your father would rather not send his men to horrible deaths."

"That is all very true," said the King, "but I do not want you to come to harm either. You have saved my daughter's life and I am not pleased this is the only option."

Kordan stopped the King. "Sire, this IS the only way. My powers have weakened, but I am not helpless.

Ningthus's plans have all been designed to draw you out and expose you to Stelth. He did not attack your castle. You have better weapons and protection, not to mention your numbers are far greater. You can't attack the giant stronghold because there is only one way in and with Stelth, your escape would be blocked. The walls are thirty feet tall in front the 100 feet on the sides. They are solid granite and three feet thick, and the back is butted up to a mountain. Scaling them is near impossible and risky. He planned his attacks strategically, and he kept Stelth hidden. You foiled them a bit with the troops you sent on patrol; they inadvertently discovered the dragon. Ningthus must rethink his schemes. My guess is he has two plans, one with and one without Stelth. He may even have the means to destroy Stelth. In this I am guessing. But he needs to be met head on. You are too valuable to the five realms, so it still falls to me. You need to establish two plans as well. One if Ningthus defeats me and one to deal with the giants when they have no leader."

Timor rose from his throne. He glanced over at Alicanth who was sitting rigidly in her seat. "Kordan, your plan seems well thought out, but I can't help feeling that we are sending you to your death. This makes me uncomfortable and a bit helpless. It is a position I am not used to."

Kordan smiled. "Thank you Sire, please understand, I don't view this as a suicide mission. I am trained in many different forms of self-defense, and with Ningthus, I may have to use them all. My powers may be waning, but I do not fear facing my foe. The wild card in this whole thing is Stelth. I just wish I knew what part he will play."

"I see I can't talk you out of this," said Timor. "How will you draw him out?"

"I have selected the place of our first meeting in the forest," said the wizard. "I will dispatch a raven and I will insist we meet alone at the appointed place. I doubt he will comply, but his soldiers are already wary of me and will stay clear. I'm sure I can goad him to talk and finally attack. From that point, I must rely on cunning and speed." He looked over at Alicanth, smiled and said, "I'll be fine. Now if you will excuse me, I must leave. It will take me several days to prepare."

Kordan bowed to both King and Princess and turned to leave. The great hall was eerily quiet save for the tapping of the wizards' staff as he walked to the exit.

After Kordan had left, Alicanth jumped up from her seat, "Father, you must stop him!" She was near tears as she spoke.

"Alicanth," said the King in a calm, even voice, "I cannot. He is right in everything he said. He is the only choice to keep this from escalating. I am torn as much as you. I have to prepare my men to fight in case Kordan fails. We can handle the giants they can be stopped, but I have no defense against Stelth. It is not what I wish to do. I feel guilt for summoning him here. And...I see, you have feelings for him. I only pray you can forgive me on all accounts."

Alicanth ran to her father and hugged him. As tears flowed down her cheeks she said, "All we can do is hope, pray, and wait."

Kordan spent the next five days doing his best to prepare himself for battle. He started by gathering materials that would augment and weaponize the items in his wizard's pouch. The process was tedious and time-consuming. He was thankful he had studied and read the books Peltor had given him.

On the sixth day he rode his horse into the forest where he had first encountered Ningthus. It was an area with a small clearing that was heavily surrounded by trees. It was known as "Root Glade" and aptly so. The ground was uneven as it was littered with vines and stones of all sizes. "Weapons that can be used against me," he thought. He studied the area carefully, looking for any strategic advantage. There were few. This area favored the giant. Kordan felt his best hope would be darting in and out of the trees, but that would only happen if he could keep the giant distracted and how quickly he could maneuver to get behind him. "This will be very tricky," he thought. "I have no room for error."

He practiced for several hours running a few scenarios in his mind and moving through the steps. He would use sulfurous ash to create smoke screens to buy him time to get to the tree line. Maneuvering through the trees was difficult as the forest was dense. Getting behind the giant may not be doable, but Ningthus would have the same problem trying to flush out the wizard. "This is hit or miss," he thought.

He tried a few spells. He managed to get a rock to roll over. "it's almost better to not use any spells at all," he thought. "If Ningthus knows my magic is gone, I will have no chance."

When Kordan returned to the inn, it was already dusk. He was exhausted and a bit depressed. He stabled his horse and walked to the door at the front of the inn. As he entered, he heard the Innkeeper shout," Sir Wizard, you have come back at last!" The Innkeeper rushed up to Kordan carrying a large, shielded broadsword. "King Timor's personal guard left this as a gift for you. There is a note attached."

Kordan couldn't believe the gift. It was one of the most beautiful swords he had ever seen. He unsheathed it and felt it's weight and balance. He re-sheathed the sword and read the note attached.

Kordan,

I have no solace to give. Maybe this sword will bring you luck. It is the one I used to slay Ohmthus, Ningthus's brother.

May it swing true for you as it did for me.

Timor

Kordan felt humbled by the gift. He felt sure it would be useful not only as a physical weapon, but a psychological one too. Now there was one final thing to do. Invite Ningthus.

The wizard went out to the back of the inn near the stables. There he found a small open area. In his one hand was a prepared note addressed to Ningthus. In his other his staff. He raised his staff and spoke his enchantment, "Venire Caeruleus." Several minutes passed and still there was no response. He raised his staff again and spoke the charm once more, slower and louder, "Ven-ire Cae-ru-le-us." Again, he waited, and again no response. He closed his eyes and breathed deeply, this time banging his staff into the ground, and in his deepest clearest voice said "Ven-ire Cae-ru-le-us." This time he felt his staff tingle in his hand. He raised his right arm and from the sky a dark blue/black raven appeared and landed on the wizard's outstretched limb. The bird cawed as if saying, "Yes Master."

Kordan walked over to a nearby fence and rested his staff against it. He then moved the raven over to a crossbeam on the fence and tied his note to the raven's leg.

"Caeruleus my friend, take this to the giant stronghold." Kordan pointed the direction to the bird. "It is a few miles to the north; you can't miss it. Wait for his response." The raven cawed two more times and was off.

Kordan grabbed his staff and headed back to the inn. When he entered, he noticed it was empty. As he turned to the front door he saw why. Waiting for him was Alicanth and her two guards. They had cleared the room. The wizard approached her, "Alicanth, why have you come?"

"Is there no other way?" she said. "This is madness. I watched you out back as you tried to summon your raven. It almost didn't work. How can you face Ningthus?"

Kordan looked around at the empty room and then spoke to the guards. "Darien could you and Kir give us a moment alone?" Both men nodded Darien took guard outside the front door and Kir out the back. Kordan motioned to a nearby table and he and the Princess sat down.

Kordan had his head down for a minute, then looked up into Alicanth's eyes. "Alicanth, I laid out everything for you and your father earlier. There is no other way, at least not without putting innocents, the troops, and your father in danger. I cannot allow that to happen. I cannot allow you to be in any more danger than you were the other day. I could never forgive myself should anything happen to you. I must do this"

Alicanth reached over and took Kordan's hand. "I know what you must do," she said. "The problem is I don't want you to. I just found you and now I may never see you again."

"Princess…." began Kordan; she interrupted "And besides you forgot about a third scenario." Kordan's eyes widened. "What if Stelth has gone and won't return?" she said. "If he is gone, my father can stop the giants…"

Kordan squeezed her hand and said softly. "He is not gone. I can feel him, I don't have enough of a connection yet to know what he intends to do. He must remain our enemy and I must face Ningthus."

Alicanth squeezed back. She bowed her head and glanced down. She saw the scabbard at Kordan's side. "I see my father sent you his sword. Please return it to him when you're done. Bring it back when you return to me." She leaned forward and gave Kordan a kiss. When she finished and pulled back. Kordan could see the tears in her eyes and her voice wavered as she spoke." Remember, return to me."

Alicanth turned quickly and ran out the front door. Darien stuck his head in and yelled "Kir!" The guard at the back door entered and began moving quickly to the front. When he reached Kordan, he stopped for a moment and said "Sir Wizard, I wish you success, all our hopes are with you." He saluted Kordan and left.

Kordan sat quietly for a moment and slowly put his hand to his lips where the Princess had kissed him. He felt a lump in his throat and could barely swallow. He hoped he had made the right choices, because for the first time in his life he was afraid.

Caeruleus circled the stronghold several times, swooped down and landed on a rock near where several giants were having a conversation. Once he was secure where he was, he cawed at those in front of him. One giant went to shoo the raven away when the other stopped him.

"He bears a note." Slowly the giant walked over and carefully took the note from the raven's leg. The raven remained on the rock. The giant opened the note and read it. He looked up at the other two with him and said, "Take this to Ningthus immediately."

A few minutes later Ningthus appeared along with his Master Forger, Grimp. On Ningthus's left arm was the new shield Grimp had created for him, in his right hand was the note brought by the raven.

"Does this wizard think me a fool?" said Ningthus. "I will meet him, but not alone. That forest can hide at least two men from his view. I will bring Klamdous and Cilios with me. If things begin to go amiss, they can circle through the dense trees and attack him from behind. He'll suspect nothing."

Ningthus walked over to the Raven. "Can you understand me bird?" Caeruleus cawed in answer. "Then tell your master I accept." Caeruleus flew away. He circled the giants cawing three times and headed back to Kordan. He was glad to be leaving them behind.

Kordan was outside by the stable grooming his horse, trying to get his mind off his upcoming confrontation when the raven landed on a nearby post. "So," said Kordan, he is coming." Caeruleus cawed once. Then the black bird began making sounds-a series of clicks in his throat. Kordan stopped what he was doing and listened intently. "Not coming alone," said the wizard. "Thanks for the warning. I will be aware of what is behind me." Having finished, the raven flew away. "Great," thought Kordan, "Now I have to worry about three of them."

That night Kordan took inventory of his supplies and his magical accessories and what he'd use them for:

Sulferous ash – Creates a blinding light and smoke. Good as a distraction and to cover quick movements

Pepper Vials – Small Vials of pepper and water and an agent that causes the water to expand exploding the vial. The agent is separated from the pepper and water by a small barrier that is moved by pulling a string at the top of the vial. When the two meet, the vial will explode in about 6 seconds. Good for stinging the eyes. And temporarily blinding an opponent.

Rope – with a lasso may be good for pulling vines and branches in the way of an opponent's feet causing them to trip.

Not much, but then he never needed much. He always counted on his spells to confront any foe. Most of the time the other backed down and he rarely had to show his strength. This was going to be different. He would have very little magic to help. What he may be able to conjure would also tax his strength. And from what he could tell, he was going to need all of it.

Kordan had a fitful night's sleep. He was plagued with dreams of his confrontation and failed magic spells. He would have to rely on his speed and his wits. He was just six feet tall, and his opponent was over twelve feet. His plan was to stick to the most uneven areas of the glade. This would make it difficult for Ningthus to charge him. But it would be more difficult for him to maneuver too. "Don't over think this." He thought. "Keep your mind clear and focus on your opponent. See how he moves; watch his eyes. Look to see which leg his weight shifts to. Be ready to move. Be alert, and above all don't panic. Remain calm."

It was dawn and Kordan made his way from his room. He saw the innkeeper preparing for the day. "Geoff," said the wizard. "I require some time alone. I will be in the back beyond the stables. Can you see I am not disturbed?" The innkeeper shook his head yes in answer to the request. "One more request," said Kordan. "Can you please have my horse saddled and ready by late afternoon, before dusk?"

The Innkeeper smiled and said, "As you wish."

Kordan left the inn and walked facing the sun, feeling its warmth as he walked. He couldn't help but think of Alicanth and the kiss she gave him; her parting words "return to me." He hoped with all his heart this would happen, but he had doubts. He found an area of soft grass. He sat cross-legged on the ground and cleared his mind and relaxed his body and spirit. This was his last step in preparation for his upcoming battle. There he waited until it was time to leave. His horse was saddled and waiting. He mounted his steed, placed his staff in its holder, patted the sword at his side and checked his pouch to make sure the sulfurous ash and pepper water were there. The rope was tied loosely to the saddle. He had everything he needed. Kordan took a deep breath, kicked the sides of the horse, and galloped off with the setting sun behind him.

When Kordan arrived at the glade no one else was there. He dismounted his horse and removed his staff and the rope from their holders on the saddle. He walked over to the front of the horse and stroked the mane and horse's snout and spoke softly to the animal. "Thank you for bearing me here. It is time for you to go home; return to your safe stable. There is only danger, pain, and death for you here." The horse snorted and shook his head. He nuzzled Kordan for a moment, turned, and galloped off towards his home.

Kordan did not know how much longer he would be alone, so he took a few moments to set a small trap. He didn't even know if he would be able to use it. But he was counting on the fading light to work in his favor. He found a protruding vine on the floor of the glade and tied his rope to it. Then he hid the rest of the rope along some exposed tree roots to hide it, found a smooth area for himself to stand in and laid the rope by his foot. "If I can get the right angle," he thought, "maybe I can trip the giant and cause him to fall." He then found another smooth area and brought wood to build a fire. If it became too dark neither would see each other. This would at least give them both a chance to keep each other in view. There was a very small chance that Ningthus would want to discuss matters and come to a more peaceful settlement, especially with Stelth's involvement in question. But he knew that was wishful thinking.

There was still a little light, just before the full sunset when Kordan heard noise in the trees. He moved away from the sound closer to where his rope lay hidden, directly across from the rustling. A few moments later Ningthus slowly appeared. The closing night had already made the forest impossible to see into. There was no way he could see the other two giants hidden among the branches. "They might already be behind me," he thought.

Both were eying each other carefully, judging the distance and the terrain. Ningthus broke the silence. "Where's Stelth?"

"How should I know," said Kordan. "You control him, not me."

"He's missing at the moment," said the giant. "I thought you put some sort of spell on him to turn against me. I was preparing to fight you both."

Ningthus slowly paced left and right. Kordan could see

he held a spear in one hand and a large stone shield slid over his arm and hand. Kordan matched his pace moving the opposite direction of the giant.

Kordan laughed, "Dragons are creatures of magic. Most spells do not work on them."

"Where is your magic now wizard." Said Ningthus. "Your spell didn't work completely on me, maybe I'm magic too." He let out a loud deafening laugh and slowly inched forward.

Kordan ignored the question, and took a deep breath, tapping the ground heavily with his staff. Summoning all his concentration he said, "Pone Super Igne." He stood perfectly still and waited. It was just a few seconds, but it felt like hours. Kordan felt a slight tingle in his staff. Smoke rose from the pile of wood and then flames erupted. Ningthus stopped moving. Kordan thought he saw concern in the giant's eyes, but the look vanished quickly.

Kordan continued. "So, how exactly do you control Stelth. I'm curious."

"Why should I tell you anything," said the giant. "After tonight you will no longer be a problem."

Kordan continued to goad the giant. "Nothing makes sense, you have the dragon, why not attack Timor directly. There is no defense against him. You could have destroyed the castle and Timor."

Ningthus laughed again. "Fool, Timor's death serves only one purpose, and that is to avenge my brother's death. But I want Timor's kingdom and eventually all five realms. Destroying the castle will not make it easy for me to rule you puny men. The castle, in fact all the castles are the symbols of ruling, my stronghold is not. I need the castles intact. Timor is the most powerful of all the Kings. His capture and eventual death will ensure my revenge and power throughout the realms. I was using Stelth to help draw him out, this would prevent the castle's destruction, and facilitate his capture. It may take weeks if the King is defending his castle. In the open it's a matter of minutes."

"Interesting plan," said Kordan, "but what's Stelth's motivation for the attacks other than helping you.?"

"Don't you know," said Ningthus, "good King Timor killed Stelth's mother, and he too wants his revenge."

"I don't think that's true," said the wizard pushing the giant further. "No one here even knew dragons existed until Stelth was accidentally discovered when he killed five of the king's men on one of your raids. Dragons were a myth to them. How could Timor have killed something he didn't even knew existed?"

"Well," replied the giant, "he actually didn't kill her. I convinced him that it was Timor's fault. Vengeance makes a powerful ally."

"I see," said Kordan pressing further. "I'm guessing it was you who killed his mother and put the blame on King

Timor. What's Stelth going to do to you when he finds out you lied to him?"

"Enough!" screamed Ningthus. Enraged at Kordan's goading, the giant hurled his spear at the wizard. Kordan saw the giant's arm cock back to hurl the weapon and dove to the ground. The projectile missed him but when Kordan looked up, he saw the spear embedded in the rock behind him. "They have the means to destroy Stelth." he thought.

Angered further, Ningthus went to charge, but the uneven ground, rocks and vines kept him from gaining any traction. Kordan, seeing his opportunity, laid down his staff, picked up the end of the rope, reached into his pouch and threw down a handful of the sulfurous ash. The ensuing bright flash and smoke caused enough confusion to allow Kordan to maneuver around the giant with the rope. When Ningthus tried to move, Kordan pulled the rope tight at the giant's ankles causing him to fall forward to the ground. Kordan wasted no time and was able to get close enough to run Timor's sword into the giant's thigh. Ningthus bellowed at the pain and as Kordan pulled the blade and raised to strike again, Ningthus rolled over and hit the wizard full on with his shield. Kordan flew back at least twenty feet hitting the rocks and vines on the ground hard. He felt his ribs crack and was engulfed in terrible pain. He had dropped the sword from the impact, but his body had hit the ground first, protecting his pouch.

He reached in and pulled out a pepper vial. He could see Ningthus was on his knees slowly standing up. He pulled the string, releasing the activating agent into the water. Through the searing pain, he threw the vial. He threw high and waited. He heard the vial pop and heard Ningthus again cry in pain as his face was covered with pepper water and small chards of glass. He could barely move, but he was on his feet. He was coughing up blood and it was difficult to see through the pain. It felt like an eternity, but he managed to reach his staff. Ningthus hadn't moved as he was trying to clear his eyes, but he had enough presence of mind to grab a large rock and throw it in Kordan's direction. The rock missed but it was followed by a larger boulder. The wizard knew he could not dodge this one so grasping his staff and summoning what strength he had left he shouted through the blood "custodire." He felt his staff tingle slightly and a weak shield appeared just as the boulder hit. Kordan was knocked down again. As he fell back, the boulder rocked forward and broke his leg as it rolled off his body.

Kordan could barely move. He couldn't think through the pain. He definitely couldn't stand up. He looked over and saw his staff, which he dropped when the boulder hit. He was desperately trying to reach it. He heard Ningthus chuckling. "I see you stuck me with King Timor's sword. How ironic, I will use the sword that killed my brother to kill you."

As the giant limped on the uneven ground toward

Kordan, a faint sound could be heard, a sound that grew steadily louder. It sounded like a heartbeat in the air. It was followed by the deafening roar of an approaching storm. That storm was Stelth. Ningthus stopped as Stelth landed near the wizard his front claw was mere inches away. "Stelth," said Ningthus, "Finish him; he's beaten. Crush him with your claw."

With all his strength, Kordan moved his body a few inches coughing blood and trying to stay conscious. He was able to touch Stelth's talon. As he did, Stelth's neck stood straight up as his mind and Kordan's met. The wizard's memory replayed his entire conversation with Ningthus.

As the dragon absorbed all that Kordan gave him, Ningthus kept yelling. "Finish him Stelth. Timor hired him to kill us both. You can't let him live. We're together on this."

When the memory had played out, Kordan passed out and his body went limp. The dragon moved his claw carefully away from the unconscious body. His neck came down even with the giant. "I see thy lies."

Ningthus pulled his shield around just as Stelth let loose a stream of fire at the giant. The shield held. The dragon stopped his onslaught and quickly looked around. His vision was able to see the heat of the bodies hidden in the forest as they slowly moved to maneuver behind him. He also saw the spear sticking out of the stone and realized more weapons like that could be used against him. To protect himself and Kordan, He laid a stream of fire between him and Ningthus, then turning around he laid another line between him and the forest. The forest was too dense to allow the other giants to accurately throw their spears. The line of fire kept them from entering the clearing.

Ningthus kept talking over the fire that separated him from his victory over the wizard. "Stelth, we can talk. What do you know? Let me explain."

Stelth ignored the giant and carefully put Kordan and his staff in his claw. Holding the downed wizard close, he rose to the sky and could hear Ningthus screaming, "Stelth, we have a deal. You owe me - S-T-E-L-T-H!!!!!!"

Stelth flew to King Timor's castle and landed in the courtyard. He held the crumpled body of Kordan close to his chest, shielding him with his wings. The castle guards threw spears and shot arrows, which fell uselessly to the ground. As the main battery set themselves to attack the dragon again, a voice could be heard yelling from a window in the tower.

"Cease fire, Cease fire." The men stopped and turned to see King Timor shouting to them. The men did as they were told. A moment later King Timor walked out of the Great Hall into the courtyard with Irick, the Captain of the Guard. The two men seemed to be having a disagreement which Irick apparently lost because he stood alone as

Timor walked forward to address Stelth. "You could have destroyed my men but did not. I can only assume you wish to talk. What is it you want?"

Stelth pulled his wings back and laid Kordan's beaten body at the feet of the King. Timor was shocked, he turned to Irick. "Fetch Alicanth and bring a healer and a stretcher."

"He is badly wounded," said Stelth. "He used what strength he had left to allow me to see the truth. Thou art not my enemy King."

As King and dragon stared at each other for a moment searching for words, Alicanth arrived accompanied by the palace physician. "Doctor, please save him," said the Princess.

The doctor looked over to King Timor and shrugged his shoulders. "I will do my best Your Majesty."

Stelth watched quietly as they took Kordan away. When the wizard was out of sight, Stelth looked at King Timor. "I will be close by. No harm will come to thee. The wizard and this castle are now under my protection."

Stelth opened his wings and leapt into the air. He would do nothing more until he knew Kordan was going to live.

Chapter 11

THE EXCLUSION OF ALL ELSE

A licanth rarely left Kordan's side. The physician shook his head. "His internal injuries appear extensive. His body must have taken quite a beating. I've set his leg and bandaged his ribs. His breathing is shallow. I can barely detect it. I've done all I can." The healer bowed to the Princess and turned to leave. He paused for a moment and said, "Send for me if there is any change," and left. The doctor had seen men with fewer injuries not survive. He didn't hold out much hope for the wizard. He wished he could give Alicanth better news. He could tell she cared for the young man. "All we can do now is wait," he thought.

Kordan felt as though he was spinning. There were what looked like clouds all around him and as he turned, he passed through them. It felt like it would never end. Then abruptly, he stopped and came to rest on what appeared to be a floor of soft green grass. He could smell its freshness in the air; feel its texture in his hands.

He had landed on his back. When he rolled over and pushed himself up, he saw a field of lush green with a road leading to a tall mountain. He saw trees waving in the breeze and he could hear the leaves rustling softly. He thought he heard them calling his name, but he couldn't quite make it out.

He was amazed. He could feel no pain and he was able to breathe deeply without coughing up blood. As he climbed to his feet he wondered, "Have I died?" He had a strong compulsion to get to the road ahead and start following it to the mountain. He tried to determine the time of day, and though it was light and the landscape sunlit, he could not see the sun or which direction the light emanated from. "If I'm not dead," he thought, "I must be dreaming." But he had never had a dream as real or beautiful as this.

He reached the path quickly and began walking toward the mountain. He didn't think he was in a hurry, but he noticed he was walking at quite a brisk clip. As he walked, he noticed the different wildlife - deer, rabbits, bears, raccoons. All were busy eating or drinking water from the small creek that ran alongside the road. All seemed content and appeared to be in harmony with themselves and nature. "What is this place?" wondered Kordan. If this was all normal, he would have stopped and observed events as they unfolded in front of him. But regardless of his thoughts, something compelled him to keep moving.

It wasn't long before he reached the base of the mountain. He forced himself to stop. He took a moment before beginning his long climb to look up at the majestic peak that lay before him.

"I have to climb this?" he thought.

Once again, he started moving quickly up the path into the mountain. He had no idea of where he was going or why, only that he had to keep moving. As Kordan rushed along, he began to wonder, "Why am I not hungry, thirsty, or tired? I have not stopped to rest."

He had no concept of how much time it was taking him. It could have been hours or days. He didn't stop for any reason, and he could see by looking below, he was now pretty far up the mountain. "I wonder how much further?" he thought. He couldn't explain it, but he had no feeling of fear or dread. He just felt compelled to reach the top.

He passed what would be called the timber line and could see snow all around. Oddly, there was no snow or ice on the road he was traveling. He came to a steeper section with a sharp turn, and when he came around the bend, he saw a large cave. The path led directly into it. As he got closer, he could see a bright light emanating from the opening. Upon reaching the mouth of the cave, he felt he regained control of his body and no longer felt the need to rush. Looking around, he instinctively grabbed for his staff. It wasn't there. He slowly entered and walked forward cautiously.

All the light seemed to come from the front. It was magnified by the very walls of the huge cavern he now appeared to be in. The rocks reflected brilliant colors and patterns. It was one of the most beautiful things he had ever seen. Blues, greens, golds, reds, all entwined together. It left him speechless.

He wanted to stop and touch the walls, but then he felt the compulsion return to move forward. As he neared the front, he saw something he did not expect. The most beautiful golden dragon. He was larger and broader than Stelth. He was covered in glistening gold scales and his muscles seemed to ripple as he moved. He sat on a large red velvet pillow. There were smokeless candles all around that were the source of the cavern's light. Kordan stood motionless in front of the creature not knowing what to do or say.

As if on cue, the beast drew himself up and spoke. "I have been waiting for thee. I am sorry to have hurried thee, but there is much to say, and time is short."

Kordan was amazed. "Who are you and why am I here?" he asked.

The dragon responded, "I am Aureas. I am the first dragon. It was I who worked with the first Wizard Theros, to create the charm of connection that runs through the bloodline of all who are touched by magic. It was we who started the schools to train future wizards. I worked to ensure that new dragon eggs were infused with the magic so the connection between wizard and newly hatched eggs would imprint immediately. They became bound for life. It was a great symbiosis. We complimented and fed each other. Our strength was unparalleled. It existed this way for hundreds of years. Wizard families would merge with dragon families sometimes for generations making the bond even stronger. We worked together for the betterment of humankind and balance in the universe.

At this point it is unclear where things changed. Wizards began to break off into their own groups caring nothing for the world except for the power they possessed and coveted. They studied and became withdrawn forsaking all else except their own need to acquire more power. Many became disenchanted and left, going back into the world, living normal lives. They never used their powers again and forgot how to call on their magic. To them it was physically lost, though it was now infused in their bloodlines. Some thought the dark arts were more powerful and chose to study them. They held sway over the abominations of the night. Others who stayed and studied plateaued. They thought they had attained all they could, but they were wrong; something was missing. They did their best to help humanity by doing good when they could, but mostly found themselves fighting the dark practitioners, who thought power was best defined as domination."

During this time many dragons went rogue and became wanton and destructive. Some made pacts with kingdoms to leave the lands alone if they were given sacrifices of food and human flesh. Others somehow inadvertently met when a young man or woman found a dragon egg. When the egg hatched if there was any magic blood in the humans that found the eggs imprints occurred. These people became dragon riders and formed an elite group that helped fight off the evil wizards and their minions. Because the riders were of magical heritage the dragon and rider could share small amounts of magic together. But this was short-lived. The rogue dragons and evil wizards had made bad reputations for all. People were angry and wanted them out of their lives. Kings entreated any good wizard they could find to help destroy the evils that plagued humanity. Many great wars were fought. Ironically wizard and dragon ended up killing each other to the verge of extinction."

After a few hundred years there were only a handful of each group left. And now we are down to two. Stelth and thee."

Kordan stared at Aureas for a moment, and asked, "How much longer do I have? Will I wake up or is this my last vision before death takes me?"

"That all depends on thee," said Aureas. "I gave thee all the history. I said many wizards reached a plateau and thought they had attained what they sought. I said they were missing something. It is the one thing that had been forgotten in their search for power. It is the one thing that would have made them whole and made them realize their full potential. It is something thou hast fought to ignore and as a result thou hast been defeated and now lay dying."

Kordan thought for a minute. "I fell in love. I thought that falling in love would rob me of my powers and I let it."

"That has been the great lie," said Aureas. "Love is the final component to the completion of thee and thy power. It was always there at the beginning. Magic folk fell in love, raised families, and maintained the world order with dragons. All looked out for each other; all cared for each other. Everything was in balance. Thou hast feared love would ruin thee and it did."

"I do not wish to die. I wish to tell someone I love her." said Kordan.

"I must warn thee," said the great dragon. "Thy love may not be returned, or thou may not be able to be together. But that does not change the fact that thou hast experienced the emotion that will make thee the strongest wizard who has ever lived. Thy heart is pure which is why I brought thee here. Mankind is moving away from magic and is embarking on a different path. That way will not include our kind. But for the present thou art needed. Thou art the only one who can save thyself. Thou must believe in thyself and believe in thy love. I can help thee no more."

Suddenly the cave began to spin. He could see Aureas begin to fade from his vision. He heard the golden dragon say one last thing. "Good-bye young Kordan, do not lose faith in thyself, thou art powerful."

"I am powerful," said Kordan. And as the cavern began

— 151 —

to spin faster and faster, he closed his eyes took a deep breath and screamed at the top of his lungs. I AM POWERFUL!"

Suddenly all went black. It was a few moments and through the darkness Kordan began to feel warmth in his toes, then his legs. The feeling began to creep into his chest. He could feel his heartbeat and he was aware of the pain in his ribs. The warmth kept moving up his body until it reached his brain and then his eyes. He opened his eyes. At first his vision was blurry. It slowly cleared and he could make out two figures standing by him at the bed. It was Alicanth and Serania. The feeling was now in his throat and mouth and he spoke what he needed to say. "Alicanth, I love you."

Alicanth knelt down at the bed. She was holding Kordan's hand. She smiled through her tears and said, "I love you too."

Kordan managed a weak smile and squeezed her hand and said, "I fought my way back to you," and fell into a deep sleep.

The last thing he heard before passing out was "Seriana, fetch the healer."

Kordan

Chapter 12

THE PROMISE

Kordan awoke from his deep sleep. Most of the pain in his chest had subsided and overall, he felt pretty good. He sat up and saw Alicanth's beautiful, smiling face. "Well sleepy head, it's about time you woke up. You've been asleep for two days."

"Two days?" said Kordan.

Alicanth giggled. "Yes, our healer said you might sleep for some time. He was amazed you had regained consciousness, and more amazed that you seemed to be breathing normally and your heartbeat was strong and even."

"I didn't mean to be so much trouble," said the wizard.

"You haven't been," said the Princess. "I've actually been spending quite a bit of time with Stelth. He has been asking for updates on you every few hours. He's quite intelligent and he's promised me that you will take me on a ride when you've recovered."

"Oh, he has?" said Kordan smiling. "I feel him coming this way now."

Sure enough, Kordan felt Stelth's mind reach into his. "Art thou able to speak?" were the words that Kordan's heard. He responded, "Give me a couple of hours and I will come to see you." Stelth replied, "I will wait for thee."

Alicanth bent over to give Kordan a kiss. "I have to see my father. You need to rest."

Kordan was alone in the room. He knew he was weak and needed a hand getting up from the bed. He called out for help and Darien entered. "I have strict orders to see to your safety Sir Wizard, what can I help you with?"

"Darien, it's good to see you." said Kordan. "Can you help me up? I need to wash, dress, and move around, and I need to see Stelth."

"Sir," said the guard, "I don't think the princess wanted you to leave the room."

Kordan laughed, "You can say I put a spell on you." Darien laughed back and helped the wizard to his feet. He was a little unsteady but after a moment he was able to stand without any help. "While I wash myself and dress," said Kordan, "can you get me some food, I'm famished."

Darien shook his head and left. He returned with a whole tray of fruit, bread, and cheese. Kordan devoured everything he could get his hands on. Darien stood by in wide-eyed amazement as the wizard ate. The guard didn't think anyone could eat that much.

When Kordan had finished eating, he asked Darien,

"Can you take me to the Princess? I need to speak with her."

Darien stood quietly for a moment before answering. "She is in a meeting with the King good sir. I've been told not to interrupt them."

Kordan responded, "What I have to say is important and the King will need to hear as well. I will take the responsibility for the intrusion."

Darien looked at the wizard and saw the seriousness of his statement and said, "Follow me sir."

Kordan followed and as he walked Darien commented, "Sir, I thought your leg was broken."

The wizard smiled and said, "It was." Darien shook his head and continued walking.

Kordan didn't realize how large the castle was. The two walked and walked turning from this corner to that corner, finally arriving at two large wooden doors. Darien went to knock, but Kordan stopped him and knocked instead. They waited a moment and heard the King's voice say, "Enter." Kordan pushed the heavy doors open and walked through with Darien in tow.

As they entered the room, Kordan looked around. "This must be the King's private quarters," he thought. "Ahhh, Sir Wizard," said the King. "Back from the dead I see. I am glad to see you looking well and moving as you are even with a broken leg."

Kordan smiled and bowed, also taking the time to cast a quick glance to Alicanth who was also in the room. "I am healing very quickly. My bones have mended. I am just left with a few muscle aches from the internal injuries. I am sorry for this intrusion, but I wanted to tell you of what occurred while I was unconscious. I also have some ideas for future dealings with the giants after I defeat Ningthus."

The room became eerily silent for just a moment. Alicanth jumped up from her seat "Kordan, No!" she said. Timor also responded to the wizard's statement. "Are you sure that is wise? You almost died from your last encounter."

Kordan smiled and said, "It won't be an issue this time I have regained all my magic." He raised his hand made a rose appear which he placed on the table in front of Alicanth. Her look of surprise barely covered the fact she was blushing.

Kordan then began to tell the story of his meeting with Aureaus. He told them of the history between wizard and dragon and the birth of evil wizards and rogue dragons. The struggle both good and evil had in their quest for power and the wars created as a result. When he reached the part about his defeat, he turned to Timor and said, "Sire, I did not know how to deal with my feelings, and I caused my powers to diminish. I am completely healed because I had to admit that I had fallen in love with your daughter. If I speak out of line or have caused you anger at this, I submit myself to whatever your command on this will be. But I will finish the task at hand. Once I am done, if your wish is for me to leave forever, I will. I place my future in your hands."

Timor stood from his chair and walked over to the wizard. "Rise Kordan," he said laughing. "I am aware of your feelings for her and hers for you. I may be King, but I am not blind, nor do I forget the great lengths I went to show her mother how much I loved her. Alicanth will choose who she loves, not me.

We were both summoned to King Godrin's kingdom a few days ago. She would not leave your side. I went on my own and have just returned. Godrin lays dying, and he needs to see his granddaughter. But I am curious about you and Stelth being the last of your kind. What are the implications?"

"I don't know yet," said the wizard. "I am not totally sure why that was made known to me. After I leave here, I must see Stelth. I would ask the Princess to join me if she wishes."

"I cannot," said Alicanth. "I must get ready. I leave at dawn to go to my grandfather's Kingdom. I travel light; speed is of the essence. Darien and Kir will be with me. I will return as quickly as possible. You and I have much to talk about as well."

Kordan smiled, "I will look forward to that Princess."

"Now if you both will excuse me," said Alicanth, "I must

take my leave I have preparations to make before I can depart in the morning."

As she left, she saw Kordan move closer to her father. He was speaking softly to him. Timor was listening intently and seemed quite interested. She wondered what the wizard was saying. She watched him talking. She saw the ease and confidence with which he spoke. Her heart beat a little faster for it. She took a deep breath, smiled, and went about her business.

Kordan finished his impromptu audience with the King and headed to see Stelth. Darien was still with him. "You will take care of her?" asked Kordan. "With my life Sir Wizard, with my life," said the guard.

The two men made their way through the castle courtyard where they were met by two stable hands holding horses.

"Stelth is a few miles away in the cave where he was born and lived until Ningthus captured him. It's too far to walk," said Darien.

Kordan laughed. "We will not need to ride by the time we walk to the clearing outside the castle, Stelth will be there. I have sent for him."

Kordan was right, Stelth was waiting in the clearing beyond the castle. "How did he know to come?" asked Darien.

"It is called an imprint. It is part of both of our bloodlines. I can communicate with him and he with me through our thoughts. We also know when the other is hurt. It's quite remarkable. I have asked Stelth to speak aloud so you won't be standing there wondering why we are staring at each other."

As they approached the dragon he spoke. "Thou hast called for me. It is good to see that thou art well"

"Thanks to you," replied Kordan. "I have a story of our history to tell you and something unique about the two of us." The wizard continued and told the tale as related to him by Aureus. Stelth listened carefully and waited for Kordan to finish before speaking.

"My mother did mention the name Aureus to me once when talking about the imprint. I never knew the rest. We have passed many generations to find each other. What must we do?"

"I think the first thing is to finish this uprising with the giants," said Kordan. "When that is done, we will deal with finding a way to save Peltor's library, make it available for future generations. Right now, I need to rest for another day or two, then we'll meet and plan our attack. We have to make sure you stay safe. They've found a way to harm you."

"I will wait to hear from thee." said Stelth and he flew back to his cave.

As Darien and the wizard walked back to the castle, Kordan looked at the guard. "You will keep her safe?" Darien smiled and nodded. In truth, he was concerned. He didn't trust Ningthus and he was nervous there could be trouble. Speed and secrecy were their best chances to keep the Princess from harm.

The two men spoke no more. Darien went to finish his preparations to leave and Kordan went to his room to rest. He was almost healed. He would need all his strength for what was coming.

Alicanth and her two guards, Darien and Kir left the castle just as the sun was rising. The plans were finalized just minutes before they left with only Alicanth, the two guards and King Timor aware of the details.

"We ride for twelve hours straight. We will stop twice to change out the horses," said Darien. "Kir has paid six stables to have horses ready. We will stop at only two going and two returning deciding just before which one it will be. The stable masters have been paid in full. Even those where we don't stop will have been paid for their services and more importantly their silence."

Alicanth knew that the next day would be a challenge to her strength, but she felt up to the task. She began to remember the conversation with her father as she rode. "How much time does he have?" she asked.

"His physicians believe he may have a month or two, but they're not sure. It's best you go as quickly as you can," said Timor. "He looks pale and gaunt and has lost weight. He eats and drinks little and even though he was sitting up in his chair during my visit, I believe he will soon be bedridden."

Alicanth loved her grandfather very much and knew she had to see him. Her memories of the time they spent together were some of her most cherished moments. While she rode, she thought of all the wonderful summers she had spent at his castle. She especially loved the garden where her mother played as a child and where her mother and father had met as children.

The day seemed endless. They came to the first stop and changed horses. All went smoothly and without incident. The entire process took about twenty minutes. The horses were at the ready; just a few things to switch between saddles and they were on their way again.

They made good time. Since they were just three, they could travel quickly. They came to the second stable and once again the change was quick and without incident. "At this pace," said Kir "we will make Godrin's castle just after nightfall. I think we will have made this journey in record time."

As Kir had predicted they arrived at Godrin's castle gates just a few hours after sunset. They were exhausted from their journey, but now they were safe. Alicanth asked the palace guard about her grandfather, and she was told he was sleeping peacefully. She was thankful of that, now she could go to her room, eat, clean up and get a good night's rest. She would see her grandfather tomorrow.

From his room, Kordan had been able to watch Alicanth and her guards leave. Once they were out of sight and he was sure no one saw him, he raised his right arm and said, "Venire Caeruleus." A few moments later a dark-winged figure appeared and landed on Kordan's outstretched arm. "Follow the Princess. Stay hidden and let me know immediately if anything happens." The raven cawed and flew off. The wizard felt better now that his eyes were on the situation. He just did not trust Ningthus.

Alicanth was exhausted from her long ride and slept longer than she intended. The sun was higher in the sky than she was used to seeing when she arose. She quickly washed her face, dressed, and headed to her favorite spot for her morning meal. Her mother's garden.

She was fully expecting to dine alone, but as she walked through the doors from the castle leading to the garden, she noticed someone sitting quietly by her small table. As she moved closer, she realized it was her grandfather. She surprised him with a large hug and a kiss to his cheek.

He seemed a bit startled by her approach, "Oh, my dear Alicanth you're here. I've been waiting for you," said Godrin.

"Yes Grandfather, I got in last night. You were asleep," said the Princess.

"I suppose they told you I'm dying," said the King. "Well maybe I am, but not just yet." He began to laugh and as he did his laughter turned into a deep, rasping cough, which did not look like it was going to stop. As the fit continued, he motioned Alicanth over to the table and pointed to a glass goblet filled with some sort of liquid. She picked it up and brought it to her grandfather. She carefully and lovingly held it so he could drink. After a few moments the cough subsided and Godrin spoke. "Thank you, granddaughter. I don't know what's worse the cough or that awful potion the healer gave me." He took a few more moments to calm himself and then reached out and took his granddaughter's hand in his.

"You've grown into quite a woman. Your father tells me the men are falling off their horses staring as you ride by." Alicanth blushed; Godrin continued. "I spent a good deal of time with your father last week while you looked after that wizard. Nasty business these giants. Haven't heard much out of them since your father killed their leader Ohmthus. That event set in motion all that has happened in all the kingdoms. Your father is a brilliant tactician and businessman. It is the reason I asked him to merge our kingdoms after I die. He refused, and with good reason. Commerce is based on each of the kingdom's individual strengths. The balance is not a strong one, but it is stable. That stability could be challenged by a union of our two realms. I have no son or daughter to ascend to the throne once I am gone, and I do not want to pass this on to some distant cousin or my Captain of the Guard."

Godrin paused for a moment. Alicanth kept his hand

in hers. She looked at her grandfather and was amazed at how much he seemed to have aged over the last year; how frail he looked. Her throat tightened and tears welled up in her eyes. She loved him very much and she would miss him terribly.

He continued, "Your father and I discussed all my options at length. We both came to the same conclusion. My kingdom must fall to you."

Alicanth's heart began to beat rapidly. This was not what she had planned. Maybe at some point she would take over her father's kingdom, but her grandfather's? This took her completely by surprise.

"Grandfather," she said. "This is very sudden, I...I."

He stopped her. "I told your father I could rest in peace if my granddaughter became queen. I made him promise not to tell you. I needed to have you here so I could tell you personally. You are my closest blood heir. Promise me you will do this."

Alicanth was speechless. This commitment would change her life forever. She saw the look in her grandfather's eyes as he asked; heard the pleading in his voice. She also understood the ramifications and implications among the other four realms if she refused and her father was forced to absorb this kingdom. The current peace and prosperity would be short-lived. She knew there was no other way. Too many people and livelihoods would be destroyed if she refused. She tightened her grip on Godrin's hand and said, "I promise."

A smile moved across the old King's face. "I don't have much time my dear, I wish to see you crowned as soon as possible."

"I will need to return home, can I do this in two weeks?" asked the Princess. "Do I have to have a fancy Coronation? Can't I just assume duties?"

"You can start being Queen as soon as I die, abdicate or by proclamation, the coronation is a formality," said Godrin. "I had my scribe prepare the proclamation. It is done."

"You knew I would say yes?" said Alicanth.

"Well, I hoped," smiled her grandfather.

"Be aware every single prince in the other four realms will be here looking for your hand in marriage," said the King. "Don't marry any of them. You don't want to give the impression of merging kingdoms. You work because you are my granddaughter and my bloodline. You will be operating independently of your father, and you will have to show that in the way you govern."

"Do not worry grandfather," said Alicanth. "I love someone else. And, with this now being my fate, I fear we will not be together. I have some time before I need to wed."

Godrin smiled and looked deep into his granddaughter's eyes. "It has been my experience, that things work out, one way or another. I am aware of the great sacrifice you make to take on this role. I did not ask it lightly. In the end it was the best and only choice I felt would work. I love you my dear. Please forgive me."

"There is nothing to forgive," said the Princess. "I do this for you and my father with all my heart. I will not fail you."

King Godrin called to his guard to help him to his great hall. He then summoned all his staff and his military personnel. When all had gathered, he grabbed on to his granddaughter's and his guard's arm. They both helped the feeble king to his feet. He took a deep breath and spoke with all the strength he could muster. "My loyal servants and friends. I am no longer able to rule. By Proclamation I abdicate. I am proud to introduce to you your new Queen, Her Royal Highness Alicanth."

The room was silent for a moment as the shock of the new Queen settled in. Then from the side of the room two guards spoke loudly and said, "Long Live Queen Alicanth." Soon, the whole room was echoing "Long Live Queen Alicanth!"

Alicanth stepped forward and stood tall and said, "Thank you all for that wonderful welcome. In the coming weeks I will be meeting with you all. I promise a smooth transition from my grandfather's rule to mine." She then told the guards to dismiss everyone and within a few minutes the room was once again empty.

She looked over to her right and saw her two personal guards still down on one knee. Smiling she said, "Arise you two. We leave at dawn to return to my father's kingdom."

She turned to her grandfather and with the aid of his personal guard they helped him to his room. He was exhausted. He laid down on his bed. Alicanth bent down and gave him a kiss on the forehead. "Sleep well Grandfather. I will see you when I return."

King Godrin went to sleep, and never woke up again.

The next morning, Alicanth, Darien and Kir left just before sunup. They made their final plans on where to stop to change horses. Alicanth's Captain of the Guard was very concerned for his new Queen. "There was not enough protection," he said. Darien and Kir made the argument that speed and secrecy were of the essence and that the Queen would pass safely as they did on their way in. The final decision was made by Alicanth. "I have been kept safe by these two my whole life. They will protect me." The new Captain frowned but gave in to her command.

The three were making good time and came to their first stop. The exchange was made easily and smoothly. They were pushing the horses more than they did on their first drive to Godrin's kingdom. This sense of need was coming from Alicanth. She set the tempo and her guards complied. They arrived at their final stop at just before dusk. If they could keep up this pace, they would see Timor's castle within a few hours.

The final stop was bit more out of the way than the others in fact, it was hidden from view by a series of large boulders. Darien thought this would be good for the final horse exchange as it would give them a moment to see if they were being followed. The road looked clear. "Not long now, Your Majesty," said Kir as Darien and Alicanth passed the first set of boulders. It happened quickly, from one direction a large metal net fell on top of Kir taking him and horse to the ground. He yelled, "Darien protect the Queen." Darien stopped his horse to turn when another metal net flew from behind the rocks, bringing him to the ground too. Alicanth spun around on her horse trying to find a way around the two downed guards. With high boulders on either side of her, she was trapped.

From behind the largest boulder, she heard, "Queen, did I hear him call you Queen? This is more than I could have ever hoped for."

A moment later Ningthus appeared with two more giants. "You will be a great bargaining chip Your Majesty," he said sarcastically. "But I'm afraid you will be my guest tonight and not your father's." He let out a loud laugh. "I look forward to writing your ransom note. Your life for his."

Alicanth remained quiet, she knew it was futile to try and escape or fight. She looked at both Kir and Darien who were motionless under the heavy nets as two giants had their spears pointed directly at them. "Leave my men alone, I will cause you no trouble. Please spare them."

Ningthus laughed again, "They'll not be harmed by me. They will have to answer to your father. If they were my men, I would shame them in front of the others and kill them for their failure." Ningthus motioned to his men, and they left the guards struggling to free themselves.

High in the air a small black dot could be barely seen, not that anyone was looking up. For all intents and purposes, it was invisible. The figure followed the giants to their stronghold. Unseen against the sky, the black figure saw them take the Queen inside one of the caves and saw two guards posted outside. It circled one more time and then flew back to its master.

Kordan was in his room meditating, making sure his body was fully healed when he heard the call of Caeruleus. He rose from the chair he sat in and held his arm for the raven to perch. Through the series of clicks that followed, the wizard learned of the Queen's ("Queen?" he thought) capture. When the raven had finished Kordan said "Keep watch over the stronghold; keep me informed as to the Queen's condition." Caeruleus cawed his understanding and flew off to his appointed task.

Kordan moved over to the window and stared into the night "Stelth," he thought. A moment later the dragon responded, "What dost thou need?"

"Alicanth has been captured by Ningthus," thought the wizard. "Kir and Darien are somewhere along the main road within two hours as the crow flies. Find them and bring them to the castle. Wait in the clearing outside the castle for Timor and me. We will discuss our plan of action then. Do nothing until we talk."

"It is done," was the reply.

Kordan then opened the door to leave. He encountered a guard standing outside. "Take me to the King immediately," said the wizard. The guard nodded and led Kordan to where Timor was finishing his evening meal. As Kordan entered the room, he saw the king speaking to his Captain, Irick. "Sire," said Kordan, "I bring urgent news of your daughter."

Timor looked over at the wizard his face turned white as he struggled to stand. "Out with it man!"

"Alicanth, now Queen Alicanth has been kidnapped by Ningthus on her return from her visit to King Godrin,' said Kordan. "At this moment, she is alive and unharmed."

"How do you know this?" asked the king. "How do you know about her being Queen?"

Kordan explained that he had sent his raven to keep watch over Alicanth. "He heard and saw everything," continued Kordan. "I have sent Stelth to bring Kir and Darien here so we can find out more from them, apparently Ningthus let them live. As to her being a Queen... 'Protect the Queen' was yelled by one of the two guards as the attack took place."

"Godrin must have appointed her Queen while she

was there," said Timor. "I'm surprised she said yes. I need to find out more about that. Irick, call the men we must mount an attack on the giant stronghold. I must rescue my daughter."

Irick nodded and turned to leave. Kordan stopped him. "Sire, Ningthus doesn't know we are aware of your daughter's abduction. Most certainly he will send a ransom note, and I am sure it will be today. He cannot afford to wait. Word will be getting to us quickly of his deed, especially since he did not kill Darien and Kir. If you attack you will almost certainly force his hand to harm Alicanth. When the note arrives, he will demand you come alone to exchange yourself for your daughter. I don't believe he will let either of you go. With you he captures your kingdom, with her he has two kingdoms. His goal is to conquer all of them. If the two most powerful kingdoms fall the others will not be hard to defeat. I suggest you agree to meet, but not at the stronghold but at the sight of my battle with him-Root Glade. He will agree, but he will not come alone, he will believe you will be alone because you value the life of your daughter over your own. Instead of you he will find me. He will be irritated but will have expected some sort of play to rescue Alicanth. She will be in grave danger, and we must not allow him to send any word back to the stronghold to warn them of our treachery. I can stop them from fulfilling that order. I know you will not like this, but you must remain here. If Ningthus tries a counter measure to send his troops here, you will be needed to help defend the castle. Let me handle

Ningthus. We will send Stelth to rescue the Queen. Stelth is a creature of magic, and I can channel a spell of protection through him to keep Alicanth safe once he attacks the stronghold."

Irick and Timor stared at Kordan for a moment. "You're right," said the King. "I won't like staying here, but your reasoning is sound, and if it all plays out the way you describe, it gives us the upper hand. Is Stelth aware of the part he will play?"

"Not fully," said the wizard, "but please accompany me to the clearing outside the castle, Stelth should be there with Darien and Kir. We can discuss our plans with him at that time."

"Not much privacy," said the King. "Irick, see that the courtyard is clear, and no one leaves the castle until we are done."

"As you command Sire," said Irick, and he was off to secure the area.

The King and Kordan walked through the castle gate to see Stelth and the two guards in the clearing. As Timor approached, Darien and Kir were down on their knees, "Sire, we have failed you," said Darien.

Timor walked over to both men. He put his hand out to Darien and helped him to his feet; he did the same with Kir. "There is no blame here. You have not been remiss in your duties. For eighteen years you have guarded my daughter. I have found your service to be exemplary. Now work with us to get her back unharmed."

Stelth looked down and said, "Thou art merciful, King. I will work to bring the Lady Alicanth to you safely. Kordan what must we do?"

Kordan began explaining the plan when out of the forest a lone giant walked into the clearing. He seemed to be un-armed and upon seeing Stelth, he froze in his tracks.

"I...I bring a message from Ningthus," said the messenger, "I am to wait for a reply."

Timor walked forward and accepted the message. The giant waited patiently as Timor read the note, all the while he kept looking up at Stelth. The dragon glared back down at the shaking giant and blew acrid smoke from his nostrils to add to the giant's fears.

Timor walked over to Kordan and gave him the note to read. The contents were as follows:

King Timor,

I have your daughter. If you wish to see her alive again, come to the giant stronghold tomorrow at dawn. Come alone or I will kill her and all you will have is her dead body.

Do not attempt a rescue. It will ensure her death.

Respond to my messenger.

Ningthus

Timor turned and looked at the giant and spoke. "I agree to your master's terms with these changes.

1. I will not come to the stronghold. I will meet him alone at Root Glade.

2. I will have a horse that I will ride in on. Once my daughter is safely away on the horse, I will turn myself over to him.

Do you agree to these changes?"

The giant responded. "Ningthus said you would change the conditions. He mentioned you might suggest another location. Root Glade is acceptable. He has given me permission to agree to such a change. I must return to give him your reply." The messenger turned and walked toward the forest, continually looking at Stelth to make sure he was not followed or attacked.

Once he was out of sight Kordan spoke. "Sire, that was brilliant to suggest the exchange that way. He will of course not bring her with him."

"My fear, Kordan," said the King, "is that he will see you and not even show himself."

"I know I said that he would get me instead of you," said the wizard, "but what I didn't say is that he will still think it's you. "Mutare." As he finished speaking, Kordan transformed before their very eyes. Where the wizard once stood was an exact copy of King Timor.

Timor gasped, "Egad! Is that me?"

"For the moment." said Kordan. "I can't hold this for long and I will change back the moment I use another spell. It will buy us precious time. Stelth, it will be up to you to rescue the princess. I will teach you the charm of protection so you can surround her with it. The danger is to you and their spears that can pierce your skin. I fear they have made larger ones that could kill you. You will need to be careful."

Stelth looked at Kordan. "I will save Lady Alicanth. Contact me before you leave in the morning." Stelth nodded to the King, spread his wings and was gone.

Kordan looked at Timor. "Sire," he said. "Show me the points in your castle that are the most difficult to defend, and I will place charms of protection there, making it difficult for anyone to breach those areas."

Timor smiled at Kordan. "That would be most appreciated. Darien, please show Kordan the places in the castle hardest to protect. Irick and I must meet and plan our defense."

That night while meditating in his room, Kordan reached out and contacted the dragon. "Stelth, I must give you the charm of protection. When you can see Alicanth, call her name. When she looks at you speak the word 'Custodire.' You must be looking directly at her. This will be the most dangerous time for you. Your attention will be compromised. Be careful!"

"I hear thee," said Stelth. "Wounded or not, I will bring

her back to thee and her father."

Kordan knew he would not sleep so he sat in his chair and continued meditating. His mind wandered a few times during the night, mostly wondering if Alicanth was all right. He worked his plan over and over in his head and hoped that he had read Ningthus correctly, and that all he had said to Timor would fall into place.

It seemed like it took forever for the night to end, but just before dawn, Kordan rose from his chair to prepare himself. He splashed water on his face and went to the center of his room. He raised his right hand and spoke, "Stola mea." Magically his robe appeared and slipped over him. Next, he reached out his left hand and said, "Vigram Meam." His staff floated across the room to his hand. Then, walking to the window he raised his right arm and said, "Venire Caeruleus." A few moments later the black raven appeared and updated Kordan on the status of Alicanth. When the bird was done, Kordan said, "Continue your surveillance."

"Stelth," Kordan called out.

"I hear thee," replied the dragon.

"Alicanth is tied to a stake in the stronghold courtyard. Two guards with spears are keeping watch. She is to be taken and hidden if anything goes amiss. Ningthus wants her alive. I'm leaving now."

"I leave also, I wish thee well, Kordan. I will see thee soon."

Kordan turned toward the door and said, "aperta Ianuam," and the door swung open. As he walked, he said "Mutare," and even though the wizard walked through the door, any who looked only saw King Timor. The battle had now begun.

Kordan's horse was waiting for him near the castle gate. No one was near, the horse stood alone, and the drawbridge was open. He mounted and started forward. From the top of the walkway stood a solitary guard. It was Darien. "Good luck Sire," he shouted. Kordan smiled and waved. After he crossed the bridge, he stopped, looked back at the castle one more time and headed toward Root Glade.

When Kordan reached the glade, the sun was just peaking up over the horizon. The forest was so thick around him it almost blocked out the rising sun. He was now in the spot where he had initially met Ningthus. He took a deep breath and hoped this would be over soon. He didn't have to wait long when he heard rustling all around him. As he spun in his saddle to see, he saw several giants coming out of the thick trees. They came out one by one until he was surrounded. He would be unable to escape.

In front of him Ningthus appeared. He bore his shield his sword, his spear, and he carried Timor's sword like a dagger in his belt. "You came alone, I see," said the giant. "Fool, I did not bring your daughter. Come with me quietly or I will kill you where you stand."

Kordan dismounted from his horse and said, "I would prefer not to come."

Ningthus became enraged, "take him!" The giants behind him began to move, they would take him in two steps. He raised his hands and said "Obdormiscere." All the giants except Ningthus dropped to the ground in mid step - all fast asleep. As the wizard cast his spell the face and body of Timor slowly dissolved, and Kordan stood alone once again facing Ningthus.

The giant stood motionless, speechless and Kordan could see his rage build. During that fraction of a second Kordan pulled his staff from the saddle and stood defiant and ready against the giant. Ningthus lifted his spear and hurled it at the wizard. Kordan's staff was already raised, "custodire." The spear hit the wizard's protective shield and fell to the ground. Enraged further, Ningthus pulled his sword. Kordan pointed his staff and yelled, "perdere." A bolt of lightning flew from the staff and hit the sword violently ripping it from the giant's hand. Not wasting a moment with the other hand Ningthus dropped his shield and pulled Timor's sword from its scabbard. He hurled it with all his might at Kordan.

Once more with his staff raised, he said, "festina lente," and the incoming weapon began to slow and turn until it was pointed directly at Ningthus. Kordan spoke, "volare celeriter et vera." The blade seemed to shudder for a second then moved so fast there was no time for

Ningthus to react. It buried itself deep in his chest. For a moment there was silence. For a moment their eyes met. Then the giant's eyes closed, and he fell, downed by the same sword that killed his brother.

Kordan walked over to the giant's body and said, "recogitamus," and his body flipped over. The wizard bent over and pulled out the sword and retrieved the scabbard stuck in Ningthus's belt.

After tying the scabbard and sword around his waist, he walked over to the sleeping giants. Raising his staff, he said loudly, "exsuscito." Slowly the giants began to rouse from their slumber. When all were awake and standing Kordan spoke. "Which of you is Klamdous?"

The giants were in shock. Here was this little man standing next to the body of their leader. They were frozen with fear. "Well speak up, I don't have all day." said the wizard. Finally, one giant came forward, and lowered his head. "It is I," he said.

"You will come with me, the rest of you may go," said Kordan. The wizard then walked over and mounted his horse and began heading back to the castle with Klamdous following close behind.

Stelth decided to approach from behind the stronghold. He knew the giants rarely looked in that direction or up because the mountain and caves were a natural defense barrier. His route took him in a large circle which he felt was his best choice to avoid detection. Since the sky was clear, he did not want to fly high and be seen by the giants keeping watch.

He reached the far side of the mountain behind the stronghold and flew up in the direction of his cave. He found a protected rock outcropping that allowed him a view of the courtyard down below. The rock shadows kept him well hidden. He saw the layout and saw Alicanth tied to a post just to the far side of the courtyard with two guards standing watch.

On either side of the courtyard were new weapons he had never seen. Two giant crossbows with large spears and their rock-piercing, dragon-penetrating tips. They were cocked and ready to fire. They had design features that allowed them to shift quickly to better aim and hit their target. Stelth would have to take them out first and then quickly invoke the charm of protection. This would be tricky, and his timing would have to be perfect.

He decided to fly down the mountain. Then once on the bottom, he would go by ground to the west side of the stronghold. This side had the steepest slope. It was nearly one hundred feet to the top of the wall. Then he would fly up and destroy the first turret as he crossed the wall while in the air destroy the second before they had the chance to aim and shoot. He would quickly land and call Aicanth's name, speak the charm of protection and take out the rest who would try to stop him – he was prepared to take a few spears. If he could put a line of fire between him and the others, he could grab Alicanth and be off.

His plan went without a hitch. As he called Alicanth's name and spoke the spell he felt deep searing pain as a giant arrow/spear hit him with great force piercing under the arm of his right foreleg, hitting his lung and just missing his heart. He did not see the third turret they had hidden in one of the caves. He'd been hit and hurt badly. With his lung pierced his ability to make fire was compromised. He hit the ground hard. He heard Alicanth scream, "STELTH!." The two guards tried to silence her but could not penetrate the shield.

Stelth tried to clear his head. He saw giants coming from all around and, they were coming in for the kill. But the son of Vaneera, the last dragon, was not going to fall easily. With a mighty push Stelth brought himself up to his full height towering over the giants rushing him. He spun around with all his strength and swung his tail; it took out three. Two more who were closing in were hit with the razor-sharp talons of the dragon's left claw. The rest, fearful of Stelth, stopped their approach. A few haphazardly threw their spears, but they missed the target.

Stelth stood for a moment took the deepest breath he could and laid down his line of fire. As he finished, he was coughing and spitting up blood. He turned and said, "Fin," and cancelled the spell. He sliced through Alicanth's bonds with his left talon, carefully took her in his grip and leapt into the air. He strained to gain altitude but got safely away with the Queen.

As he flew, he heard Kordan, "Stelth you've been hurt. Can you make it back? Do I need to come to you?"

"No," replied the dragon. "I will see thee soon. I have the Lady Alicanth; she is safe. I must go. It is a struggle to maintain my flight."

Stelth saw the castle and began to descend. He was beginning to black out but fought to stay awake. He landed turning to fall on his left side to protect his passenger. The giant spear was still protruding, and blood gushed from the wound.

Alicanth stepped out of the dragon's claw and saw Timor and Kordan running to her and Stelth. "Kordan," she screamed as she ran into his arms, "can you save him?"

The Wizard looked and said, "I don't know. I will do the best I can." He turned Alicanth over to her father and walked over to Stelth and examined the wound. He called to Darien and Kir, "Grab the spear and on my signal pull it straight out."

The two did as they were told. Kordan pointed his staff at the wound and whispered unfamiliar words. The wound began to glow. "Now!" said the wizard. The men pulled out the giant arrow and as they did, they saw the glowing wound seal itself. Leaving no scar.

"Now stand back everyone," said Kordan. Raising his

staff high above his head he said in a loud voice, "CURA TE IPSUM."

Static suddenly filled the air. Alicanth's hair began to rise up at the sides. Soldiers got shocked touching their swords. Onlookers felt the hair on their arms stand up as a green glow emanated from Stelth. Kordan stood there motionless with his staff raised up and he was heard whispering more strange words.

Then as quickly as it all started, it stopped. Kordan, exhausted, nearly collapsed. Alicanth rushed to his side. "Will he be all right?" she asked.

Before Kordan could answer she heard, "I thank thee for asking, my Queen. Our wizard hath much strength and power."

Alicanth walked all the length of Stelth's neck until she came face to face with him. She kissed him on the snout and said, "I thank you. You will always be welcome and have a place of honor in my kingdom."

Kordan slowly walked over to Alicanth and held her. "That was close."

They walked away together and let Stelth rest.

Chapter 13

THE ROAD

It was now afternoon and there was still much left to be done. King Timor had his guards bring Klamdous into the great hall, one of the few rooms that could house a being of that size. The giant followed peacefully, not speaking and only doing as he was instructed to do.

Kordan told Alicanth that he wished to attend the meeting her father was going to have with the giant. She agreed, as her new role as Queen of the Mid Realm gave her authority to grant the wizard's request. The bargain her father was going to try and strike with the giants today would affect all kingdoms.

"You go ahead," she said to Kordan, "I have something I need to do."

She turned and walked back to where Stelth was resting. Standing guard over the dragon were her two personal guards, Darien and Kir. As she approached both men, they bowed. Darien spoke, "Your Majesty, Kir and I have failed you. Please, we submit ourselves to you for your judgement."

Alicanth shook her head and walked over and hugged each one. "You both have been with me my whole life. You have been more like uncles than guards to me. If Godrin's Captain of the Guard had convinced you to bring more guards, it would have been less safe than what you two had planned. It was working. If Ningthus had attacked a larger group to get at me some could have been injured or killed. You made the right choice. I am deeply grateful you are still alive. I would be honored if you would both remain my personal guards. In fact, I have decided that the Captain of the Guard will report directly to you."

The men pulled their swords and touched their foreheads with the flat end of the blade, pledging their undying allegiance. "Thank you, Your Majesty."

"We will leave for King Godrin's castle in a few days. Now, see no one disturbs our dragon."

Alicanth hurried to the great hall where her father and Kordan were meeting with Klamdous. As she entered, she heard the giant speaking. He seemed more eloquent than Ningthus and she caught the tail-end of what he was saying.

".....ruled by fear. It is a hard thing to fight when you are all fearful for your lives. I am truly sorry for the grief I have had a part in playing. If you will have me, I will pledge my loyalty and service to you, and I pledge for any who follow me as well."

Alicanth walked up quietly to the smaller throne and

sat down. Her father spoke, "Klamdous, son of Mendous, your fealty is not necessary. The giants roam the outer reaches and are not subject to the governance of the five realms. However, I would like to make a proposal that I hope you will find interesting enough to take back to your people."

I am glad my daughter is here as she is now the Queen of the Mid-Realm and this proposal will affect her. I have to bring this to the council for approval, but if you agree we can do this together."

One of the hardest commodities for us to come by is wood. We are surrounded by it. Many go into the forests and chop down what they need. That is a long and time-consuming process and since it takes time, it removes people from their daily business. What would you say to the five realms partnering with the giants to produce lumber for our kingdoms?

Your people would chop trees and process the wood, and we would buy it from you. My Kingdom is willing to invest in the construction of a mill to process what you harvest. I'm sure I can convince other Kingdoms to invest as well. I believe three mills would handle the job. I would ask for ten percent of your profits for my investment. I have also spoken to the owner of the Quiet Wife, one of our local Innkeepers, to build accommodations for some of your people when they have to stay in town, and he is willing to do so. Also, whatever you take out of the ground you must plant and replace. Those may not be touched again for ten-fifteen years. What do you think?"

Klamdous stood speechless before Timor. His mouth was open and by the movement of his eyes, you could see he was searching for words. Alicanth took the break to speak. "As Queen of the Mid Realm, please let me say that I would also be willing to invest in this future partnership. Our Kingdoms are wealthy and prosperous because of my father's vision. We would be honored to work with you."

Klamdous had finally composed himself enough to speak. "King Timor, Queen Alicanth, you shame me with your proposal. Just a few hours ago we tried to take your most precious possessions away from you. You defeated Ningthus and could rightly lay claim to all that the giants have. You choose to include us. You offer trust not punishment. Were the tables turned, you would have torture, confinement, and death. Although it may not seem so, we are actually a quiet and private people. Ohmthus and Ningthus thought we should have more. Their speeches were moving and many of the younger giants were persuaded by their vision. The speeches touched them and inspired them to violence. It was only made worse by the killing of Ohmthus. Ningthus capitalized on that to incite them even more. You, good King have been loathed and hated for all this time. I am not making excuses; I just wanted you to know who you are proposing partnership to. I think this is a great idea, but I am not sure how to sell this to my people. It may take some time."

"Do you have any influence with the clan that lives in the stronghold?" asked Timor.

"Some," said Klamdous, "but with word of Ningthus's death many will scatter. Without a leader we tend to revert to the wanderers we are."

"With my proposal," said Timor, "I was hoping to change that. I was hoping to introduce to you all a better way of life. No more searching for food or shelter. I want you to establish homes and be part of a larger community. Will it help if I speak to them?"

"I do not think so," replied the giant, "but your daughter might be more persuasive."

Timor sat up a little straighter in his throne. "How so?" he asked.

"Queen Alicanth was our captive," said the giant. "The clan will understand the rescue, the damage and the deaths, even will be more accepting of Ningthus's death if she were to speak. They would see her being there as a gesture of forgiveness for her abduction and might just be willing to consider this partnership."

"How can you guarantee her safety?" said Timor. "We are not comfortable," he said glancing over to Kordan, "with her going unarmed and alone."

"No," said Klamdous, "I agree with your concern. But…if she flew in riding Stelth, it would be different. The giants are afraid of Stelth. They failed at trying to kill him.

Respect for her ability to tame the beast would certainly get their attention and they would listen to her."

Timor and Kordan both knew Stelth would die protecting Alicanth. Alicanth thought it was a great idea. Kordan and Timor reluctantly agreed.

"Now," said Klamdous, "we must see to our dead. I will expect to see the Queen in two days' time, when the sun is highest in the sky. Until then."

Klamdous bowed, turned, and left. Timor had offered to help return Ningthus's body, but the giant refused and thanked him for his kind offer.

After the giant had left, Alicanth looked at Kordan, "But we didn't ask Stelth if he wanted to do this."

Kordan laughed. "He attended this meeting through me. It is his honor, his words, to do this for you. We can fit him with a saddle that you can hold onto. He flies pretty fast." Kordan continued, "King Timor, Stelth and I will be connected through her entire visit, so I can relate to you everything that is happening. Also, Stelth knows the Charm of Protection. He can protect her at any time."

The next day brought word of Godrin's death and for Alicanth the pressure to return to her Kingdom. A single rider had brought the news ahead of the Captain of the Guard's entourage coming to escort the Queen to her new home.

She knew the escorts would be there the next day.

She hoped she would be successful in her meeting with the giants. Kordan rarely left her side. She felt his strength and support for her. Things were so hectic, she and the wizard had little time to just talk. She knew that would need to happen soon. Their future was unclear, but she knew one thing. She loved him.

At just before noon on the second day she climbed into the saddle that had been put on Stelth and grabbed the reins. "Art thou comfortable my Queen?" said the dragon. "Yes", was her response. "Then hang on tightly," instructed the dragon. He took two steps forward and was air-born.

Alicanth was amazed at how beautiful the view of the shrinking landscape was. There was a feeling of excitement and at the same time peace. The experience was one she would never forget. It wasn't long before she heard the sound of a horn and looking below, she saw the giant stronghold and a large crowd of giants. Something different caught her eye; there were women among the crowd.

Stelth circled and made his descent. He landed softly and got down on his haunches so Alicanth could step down. Klamdous walked forward and put forth his hand so she could step down more easily. The giant motioned her to a large flat stone that rested above the crowd and lifted her up. Stelth was close by and where he walked the giants backed away. Alicanth guessed there must have been nearly fifty giants present.

Klamdous turned to face the crowd, "My friends, I would like to introduce to you, Alicanth, Queen of the Mid Realm. Listen with an open mind. She offers us a great opportunity." Once he finished, he bowed and allowed Alicanth to speak.

She delivered the message. The courtyard was silent. All were listening intently to what she had to say. When she had finished, she asked. "Do you have any questions.?"

She waited moment and saw a hand from a woman rise. "Yes," said Alicanth.

"Are you saying we are being forced to do this?"

Alicanth looked at the woman and said, "No, this is not about forcing, this is a chance for you to partner with all the realms to supply lumber. You will be paid for the products you create. With the money you can buy land, raise cattle. It is your choice. We have a need. We are asking you if you want to provide for that need. We will draft an agreement and we will honor our part; you honor yours."

"When can we see the agreement?" another voice called out.

"I would suggest that Klamdous and one of our people meet and put it together. Then he can bring it back for your approval. Nothing will happen unless we both agree to it."

Then...silence, the giants started walking away saying

nothing more. Klamdous helped Alicanth down. As she started to walk over to Stelth to leave, the woman who had asked her the first question approached.

"You were brave to come," she said. "We are not a loud people; we tend to keep to ourselves. I like what you offer and if Klamdous would be willing, I would like to be part of making this agreement. Giants being quiet is a good thing."

Klamdous nodded. Alicanth smiled and thanked the woman. She looked over to Klamdous. 'My grandfather has passed away and we must see to his burial. Come to King Timor's castle one week from today in the morning, and we will start the process."

Klamdous smiled, "It will be our honor." He then helped Alicanth get into her saddle and both giants waved as Stelth flew away. "This is a great day," she thought as she took in the view from her saddle. "A very great day."

Stelth landed in the Courtyard of Timor's castle. Kordan was there to help Alicanth down from the dragon's back. Also waiting was the Mid Realm Captain of the Guard.

He walked up to the Queen. "Your Majesty, I fear you take too many chances. I cannot protect you if this creature were to turn on you. Your people need their Queen."

Alicanth looked at her Captain. "With this man," she touched Kordan's shoulder, "and with that dragon, I am safer than anywhere in the world."

The Captain lowered his head, "I meant no disrespect my Queen, I only meant...."

"I know what you meant Captain," said Alicanth. "You think me young and foolish. Tell me Captain, did you think because my grandfather had no direct heir that the kingdom would fall to you? I have started a process that will bring more prosperity and peace to all the realms. Was that foolish? I know my place and I understand my responsibilities. I thank you for your concern. You will from this point take your orders from my two top advisors and personal guards, Sir Darien and Sir Kir."

Alicanth turned to see the two men standing behind Kordan. "Gentlemen, please get the Captain's itinerary and tell him when we will leave. I believe my father will want to join us on the journey back to my castle."

The Captain was speechless. Darien and Kir came forward and began discussions with the now very humble man. After seeing the Queen in action, the men in her entourage knew without a doubt who was in charge and snapped to attention as she passed.

"Kordan," said Alicanth. "I need you to stay and start the negotiations with the giants. You know the plan you discussed it with my father. Can I count on you to do this. You have all my confidence and my authority for any decisions that must be made."

Kordan was impressed. "It would be my honor, Your Highness."

Alicanth abruptly stopped and said in a whisper, "I am not your Queen, I nearly died when I thought I lost you."

Kordan smiled and the two walked to the great hall to speak with Timor about the day's events and future plans.

After Alicanth had told her father about her meeting with the giants, Timor was quite pleased. "They'll be here in one week," said the King. "Will that be enough time for us to go and return from Mid Realm?"

"I don't think so," said Alicanth. "Our armed guards will slow us down. We might make it back in two weeks. I will have many meetings to install my government. I don't see how I can get away. I have asked Kordan to act on my behalf."

"All eyes will be on you my daughter," said Timor. "Losing that many days could cause you many problems at home. I do not advise you to leave."

Kordan thought for a minute, "I may have a solution. We have Stelth. He can travel between kingdoms I would think in about two hours. Plus, he can stay with you at your castle, and I can keep him informed of what is happening in the negotiations. Then you can decide when it is critical for you to come here. You need only be absent for a few hours."

"Would he be willing to do that?" asked Alicanth.

"I have already asked him," said Kordan. "He would be only too happy to do it."

Alicanth and Timor left the following morning. Darien and Kir had worked with the Captain to maximize speed and safety. "My Queen," said Darien, "If it meets with your approval and with King Timor, we can cut the journey to a day and a half. Since we are not at war, the men don't need to ride their horses all day. Every hour or so the men will walk alongside the horses. We can pick up an extra five to ten miles. It's better for the horse, and though the men won't like it, it's better for them too."

The Queen smiled and thanked Darien. Timor, Alicanth and Kordan had decided not to send Stelth to Mid Realm's castle until after Alicanth had arrived. No need to frighten the kingdom with a fire-breathing dragon landing in the castle courtyard.

True to their word, the Queen's entourage made the journey in a day and a half. Alicanth was surrounded as soon as she entered the castle. Darien and Kir with the help of the palace guards pushed the crowd back so Alicanth had time to organize her thoughts. Once the crowd was in control, the Queen spoke.

"This is a period of transition. We all will work together to ensure all your concerns and issues are addressed, and to the best of my ability resolved. It is not all going to happen in one day. It will require time and I ask for your patience. My first priority is to lay my grandfather, your

King, to rest. That will be all for now."

Darien and Kir moved to her side to guide her out of the hall. "I want you two to handle the Court for the next few days while I take care of Grandfather and see how things are run around here. Kir, please see to my father. Darien, Stelth will be arriving tomorrow. See that our Captain of the Guard is prepared for dealing with our special guest."

"It is going to be a long week," she thought.

Kordan was waiting outside the great hall when the two giants arrived. Klamdous introduced his companion. "This is Feybos. She is sister to Thembos. Ningthus killed Thembos for not attacking and killing you Sir Wizard. She has no love loss for Ningthus and looks with favor on those responsible for his demise. She has spoken to many who were friends to Thembos, and they find your proposal quite attractive. We have many things to add."

Kordan bade them into the Great Hall. He had food waiting and had special chairs made so the giants would be comfortable at the table. He explained why Alicnath and Timor were not there and that he had full authority to negotiate and set up the agreement. "Let us begin."

The meeting went smoothly. The giants brought some tremendous suggestions to the table. They had spent the last week giving the idea much thought. What they described was creative and remarkable. They proposed to use as much of the tree as possible. They would not just produce boards and beams and slats, but they would use smaller branches to make arrows, larger branches to make spears and long bows and when possible, crossbows. They would mulch the leaves to create fertilizer and they had a way to compress sawdust that could then be used as kindling for fireplaces. They also proposed they would cut and sell firewood for home hearths.

They would not want to compete with any townsfolk in fact, they were sure that both sides could teach each other new things. They were looking forward to an era of mutual cooperation. They would agree that King Timor or any monarch who fronted the money to build would get ten percent of the main products, but any stores they built alongside the mills selling the side products described, would not be subject to that.

They also realized there may be those who wanted to gather their own wood. They would not stand in their way and no ill will would be shown as a result. In fact, should those who cut their own wood and decide they needed help, they can bring it to them, and they will charge twenty-five percent of their agreed upon rates to process the wood.

Things went so smoothly. They had a completed agreement by the end of the day. "Will you have a problem with your people," asked Kordan, "No," said Feybos, "since you have agreed to almost all of their suggestions."

"We have three kingdoms to convince, but with King Timor and Queen Alicanth in favor, it is unlikely that any will stand against it."

After the giants left, Kordan told the royal scribes who were present during the meeting taking notes and writing everything down, "I need documents by first light. King Timor and Queen Alicanth want them immediately." The scribes grimaced but agreed to have it done.

The scribes delivered the documents to Kordan as ordered and within a few minutes he and Stelth were on their way to Mid Realm. "This will be a good test of how long this will take," thought Kordan.

"I can fly faster," responded Stelth, "But I will lose time saving thee from falling." The dragon managed to reach a good balance between speed and safety. Kordan figured they made the trip in about an hour and a half. They landed in the Courtyard to some commotion, but the palace guards were prepared and gave Stelth the room he needed.

Alicanth was informed as soon as the dragon was spotted and ran out to meet them. She threw her arms around Kordan as he walked towards her. "I didn't know you were coming too," she said. "I've missed you." Then she walked over to the dragon, "Thank you for bringing him safely to me Stelth."

Stelth lowered his head, "Of course My Queen, but he is not the only one who wishes to see thee."

Kordan and Alicanth laughed, "We wanted to surprise you," said Kordan. "The giants and I were able to complete the agreement yesterday. I had the scribes work all night. I sent one of the copies to Klamdous and Feybos. This copy, with Stelth's help can be taken to the remaining Kingdoms and have the Kings sign. As long as they see you and your father's signatures, there should be no problem. I have also thought about the mills. You and Timor can build the first, and the remaining kingdoms can split the costs and profits on the second. Klamdous feels he will have a signed agreement with his people in a few days."

Kordan and Alicanth went into her castle and then to her garden where she found her father, sitting pensively eating his morning meal. Alicanth walked up to him and hugged him. "Good morning father," she said. "Why are you sitting here all alone?"

Timor smiled at his daughter. "This garden has a special place in my heart. I first met your mother here, and every so often, I like to spend some time alone here and remember what it was like to be five years old and playing here with her. I think we loved each other from the moment we met. I never loved anyone since. Except of course for you, my daughter. I see so much of your mother in you, it gladdens my heart to know she is still with me through you." Timor took his daughter's hand and kissed it.

As the three sat chatting, Kir came into the garden. "I

apologize for the intrusion my Queen. We have a few matters that require your attention. It shouldn't be long."

Alicanth excused herself and left the two men alone. Timor looked down and spoke. "I've been wanting to talk to you since you defeated Ningthus and saved my daughter. I wanted to thank you. You are truly a remarkable young man. I have grown quite fond of you, and I admire your resolve. I know you love my daughter, and she loves you. The future for both of you is as yet undecided. Your story has yet to be told."

As he spoke, he reached into his vest and pulled out a small pouch. "There is no need to look at the contents yet. When the time comes you will know why I gave this to you."

"Sire I...," before he could finish, Alicanth had returned. The three talked, laughed and finished their meal. Afterwards they moved to the main hall where Timor and his daughter signed the agreement with the giants. "This document is fluid and will be revisited every two years to see we are each living up to its contents," said Kordan. "Alicanth," he continued, "please have your scribes make three more copies and I will go to the three remaining kingdoms tomorrow and secure the signatures."

Alicanth agreed and had her scribes complete the copies. She was glad she had sent riders out nearly a week ago to let the other kingdoms know what was going on and to expect a visit from Stelth and his rider.

The scribes completed their task by the following morning. Kordan saw Alicanth alone for breakfast and gave her a kiss. He didn't know how long it would take, but he was hoping for one day, but most likely three. A day in each kingdom. He also left Caeruleus at the Queen's disposal. "Send a note to Klamdous and find out how it goes on their end. If all continues to go smoothly, we can start construction on the first mill when I return."

Kordan had figured it correctly, he returned in three days. Each king took a day to review and then signed. None could find any downside to the plan. When the wizard and Stelth returned, Alicanth said the giants had signed the document and wanted to give it to Queen Alicanth personally. Once again Stelth was put to work, and he flew Alicanth this time with Kordan to the giant stronghold. There she was greeted warmly and with respect. She was able to inform them that all Kingdoms had signed also.

The giants seemed very excited and had actually scouted the spot where the first mill could be built. This location had ample land for the mill and storage of processed lumber and room to expand with the shops they wanted. The stream in this location had a strong waterflow and was deep enough to support and turn the water wheel that would run the saws. Alicanth couldn't have been more pleased. She introduced Kordan and said he would be helping to build the mill. Since the place the giants selected was in Timor's kingdom, the Queen saw no problem with starting as soon as they wished. Klamdous looked at Kordan. "I bear you no malice good wizard. I would like us to be friends."

Kordan looked at Klamdous and smiled. "And so we shall. Give me a few days, I have some things to attend to and Stelth and I will meet you back here to start gathering the material you need."

Alicanth added, "Please let my father know of the costs and he will supply the necessary funds you will need. I have brought one hundred gold sovereigns so you can start."

As Kordan and Alicanth left they felt good about what they had started. When they arrived back at her castle, Alicanth asked Kordan what he meant by 'few things to do.' "I thought you wanted to start right away," she said.

"I do," he said, "but I need to go back to Peltor's temple and figure out what needs to be done there. I haven't been for some time and as the last wizard, I have a responsibility to find a way to archive the volumes of books on magic and history that needs to be protected and saved. It is here in your kingdom, not far, but I do have to go. I haven't thought about it since this whole thing began."

Alicanth had forgotten about his life before he came to her. Just as she had responsibilities, so did he. "I understand," she said. "Will you be gone long?"

"No," he said, "two, maybe three days at the most. I'll leave in the morning."

Kordan left the next morning. True to his word he returned on the morning of the third day. Alicanth ran out to greet him when he arrived. "Is everything all right?" she asked. "There's more to do than I thought," he said as he gave Alicanth a kiss and a hug, "but I'll worry about that later. Tomorrow Stelth and I will take your father home and then I can work with the giants to get started on their mill."

"You look tired," said Alicanth. "Let's get something to eat and we can talk. I have several meetings scheduled for this afternoon. While I'm busy, you can rest and we can talk more over dinner."

Kordan kissed her again and they headed off to the garden for a mid-morning meal. The wizard looked distracted, and the Queen did her best to engage him and keep things light.

"This is a good time to build the mill, it's spring and outside of a few showers, the weather should be perfect," she said. "Yes, it will be," was his response." They sat quietly for what seemed like an eternity to Alicanth.

Kordan finally spoke. "I'm sorry I'm not very good company, I have a lot on my mind and I'm very tired." He reached over and grabbed Alicanth's hand, pulled her close and gave her a kiss and left.

That night at dinner, Kordan seemed quite animated, joking and engaged in conversation. Alicanth was relieved to see him like this. But he seemed different after his return from Peltor's temple. It made her nervous. He had become the one constant in her life - the one she could talk to, confide in and be herself. She was very much in love with him.

The next morning Kordan and Alicanth's very nervous father climbed up on Stelth and left for his castle. They arrived without incident. Timor was glad to be on solid ground again. He thanked Kordan and Stelth for the ride of his life, and as he walked away vowed to go by horse next time.

The giants met Kordan and Stelth at the spot they had described and began their project. Giants and men from the local town worked together drafting plans, building and creating the new mill. Stelth was great help at felling trees with his razor-sharp talons. The local blacksmith worked with the giant's Master Forger to create the saw blades. They were made of stone, crystal and metal. Giant and men shared their craft with each other and developed unique blades that never dulled or chipped.

The project took three months. Since everyone worked together it went quickly and without a hitch. It would be the model for the second mill. Kordan and Stelth returned to Alicanth's castle as often as they could at night after the day's work. As the work drew to a close and the mill was ready to begin operation, Alicanth saw that far-away look that Kordan had after visiting Peltor's temple. It seemed to weigh even heavier on him.

When the mill was completed, there was a huge

ceremony hosted by Timor and Alicanth. Tours were given and many merchants had pre-ordered stock before the mill was operational. It was destined to be a success. The biggest and best outcome of the project was that from this point, giant and man never were at odds again. They worked and lived together in harmony.

History has forgotten giants. They seemed to have slowly disappeared. No one is quite sure why. But for a time, there was peace and prosperity for both man and giant.

After the mill was completed, Kordan withdrew into himself. He always let Alicanth know he loved her, was always there when she needed him, but he seemed distant, and the feeling grew. At one point, Alicanth went to Stelth and asked him if he knew of anything that was bothering the wizard. Stelth replied, "He carries a great weight for us both."

Alicanth tried to understand. She really needed Kordan to talk to her. A few days later he asked, "Could we be alone in the garden tonight?" She responded, "Yes, of course my love."

She was understandably nervous. The day dragged on until finally... she walked through the doors into her garden. The night was clear and the stars overhead twinkled in their celestial harmony. The temperature was comfortable, and a single candle burned on her table. Next to the candle lay one rose. "How romantic," she thought.

Kordan saw her as she walked from the castle and he thought, how beautiful she was and a tear ran down his cheek. He walked over to her and kissed her deeply. When the kiss was done, and she pulled away she saw the tear on his face. "Kordan what is it?" she whispered.

He grabbed both of her hands. "Alicanth, you know how much I love you." She nodded. "So, you will understand how hard this is for me." She backed away. "I have to leave."

The words cut her like a knife. Why was he doing this to her? Didn't he know how much she loved him, counted on him, depended on him. "Kordan.." He stopped her.

"When I went to Peltor's temple. I was confronted by things I never expected. No one should have been able to enter because I had put a spell of protection around the entire temple. When my powers waned, some were able to breach the barrier. Some were looters looking for quick riches from my master. He had none. Others were old and had been servants for other wizards who have died. They overcame and threw out the thieves. Then they stayed and protected the building and its contents. When I arrived, there were many people outside the temple grounds. They were in awe that a wizard and dragon still existed. Stelth and I were mobbed. I stopped them and calmed them all down. Stelth stayed unseen in the temple courtyard, and I spoke to those who were now living in my old home."

There are hundreds of such temples as Peltor's.

Someone has to go and retrieve and protect all the knowledge of the magical arts and the histories that these wizards kept. I am the last. That task falls to me."

Kordan stopped for a moment. He wanted to hold Alicanth. She had tears in her eyes and asked. "How long will you be gone?"

"That's just it," he said. "This task is monumental. There are those that still have magic in their blood. If they find some of these books and accidentally cast a spell, people could be killed. Demons could be released into the world affecting the balance of nature as we know it. I cannot allow that to happen. I don't know when, or if I'll return."

"I wanted to ask you to come with me and we would travel the world. We could take care of this together. But your duty is as demanding and all-encompassing as mine. We are trapped by who we are. We cannot ignore the responsibilities that have fallen at our feet."

"No!" cried Alicanth. "We can't let this happen." She ran into his arms. They held each other tightly both crying and slowly realizing there was no other way. "When will you leave?" she asked.

"I will leave tomorrow. I could not bear to wait and see and feel your hurt. I will not contact you, but I will carry you with me. Your love has made me who I am, and I will love you always."

Kordan gave her another deep kiss and left. Alicanth

sat down in her chair and tried to pull herself together. She managed to control her tears so she could make her way to her room. Once there she cried herself to sleep.

She woke in the morning and heard Kordan and Stelth leave. She knew she couldn't go out to see him off. She'd never let him go. She got up and dressed. As she was leaving her room two familiar faces were out in front of her door standing guard.

"Your Majesty," said Darien. "I have a note and a present for you."

At first, she didn't want it. Then Kir spoke. "Princess, you really should open it."

Only someone as familiar as both men were with her would call her Princess. That's how they still see her, and she was glad of it. "I love you both," she said with tearful eyes. She took the small package with her to her garden for her morning meal. This morning she asked to be alone.

As she sat at her table she opened the package, inside was a note and a small string and leather wrist bracelet. It was nothing much to look at. She smiled and slipped it over her hand onto her wrist. Then she opened the letter.

My Love,

Inside is a truth bracelet. In all your dealings, if there is something that feel's amiss or someone you do not trust, speak "Verita" look at the person you want the truth from and ask a question. The person will have to tell you the truth. I hope it will be helpful to you. Even though I will not contact you, you will know I am alive as long as there is magic in the bracelet.

I will love you always

Kordan

P.S. I have spoken to Seriana, Darien and Kir. They know what has happened and why. They love you too.

Alicanth smiled at the letter and finished her meal. As usual, being Queen meant she had a busy day planned and she knew it would be helpful to keep her mind occupied.

Someone must have let it be known that Kordan and Stelth had left because it wasn't long before would-be suiters started arriving asking for the Queen's hand in marriage. She found the truth bracelet very helpful indeed.

"Verita, Why are you really here?" She asked one young prince.

"Well, your very beautiful and all, but our kingdom is bankrupt, and If I marry you, I get to keep my horse." This one caused much laughter in the hall. Alicanth politely refused and she gave the boy ten gold sovereigns to take care of his horse.

Week after week, month after month, boys and men walked into Alicanth's court asking for her hand in marriage. To be sure, some were very handsome and very interesting. She had dinner with a few, and thanks to her bracelet she was able to find out why they were really there, and once again, they were sent on their way. Some went quietly, some left relieved, and some left in tears, for not fulfilling their parent's agenda.

One day after a particularly busy day, Alicanth asked what was on the agenda for tomorrow. Kir looked at the list and said, "Another suiter your majesty." Alicanth looked at Kir and said, "Cancel tomorrow,"

It had been nearly a year since Kordan had left. She thought about him every day. She wondered what he was up to. She had worked hard to set up her government and had established herself as a strong, compassionate, and just Queen. Her subjects loved her and thrived under her rule. Tonight, she was lonely. As she sat in her garden having dinner, she asked her handmaid Seriana to sit with her.

"Seriana," she asked. "Should I wait, or should I give up and take a husband? You have been like a mother to me. Speak as you would to your daughter."

Seriana, reached over and took the Queen's hand. "Alicanth, true love is hard to find. Your mother waited for her true love to return. She thought it would be impossible to see her Stick again. He found her. Maybe yours will too."

Seriana got up and kissed Alicanth on the forehead and left. It was very quiet. Alicanth was lost in thought about what to do when she heard a sound. From over her wall a large blue-black raven flew in and landed on her table. In its beak was a small bag. She took the bag from the bird's mouth. She opened it and poured the contents onto her hand. It was a ring, a beautiful, yet simple ring with one white pebble in the center.

Alicnath could hardly breathe. Tears filled her eyes. Then she heard it. A sound she was familiar with. It was the beating of wings – Dragon Wings.

The Road

APPENDIX

List of Songs and Lyrics

Cast of Characters

Alicanth (Ali Sahnth) – Princess and daughter of King Timor

Aureas (Or E Ahss) – The First Dragon

Caeruleus (Ky Rule E Oos)-Raven and messenger for Kordan

Cilios (See lee Os)-Giant and general under Ningthus

Darien (Dare E An)-Personal guard to Prijncess Alicanth

Feybos (Fay Bose)-Giant and Sister of General Thembos

Gaylord Garland-Ranch owner in the Mid-realm

Geoff (Jeff)-Owner of The Quiet Wife Inn and Tavern

Godrin (Go drin)-King of the Mid rRealm and Alicanth's grandfather

Grimp-Giant and Master forger/blacksmith to Ningthus for

Irick (Eer Ick)-IKing Timor's Captain of the Guard

Kir (Keer)-Personal guard to Princess Alicanth

Klamdous (Klam Doos)-Giant and general under Ningthus

Kordan (Kore-dan)- Wizard, apprentice to Peltor

Lorayne (Lo rain)-Daughter of King Godrin and wife to King Timor

Mok (Mahk)-Giant-underling

Ningthus (Ning Thoos)-Giant and ruler of the giants

Ohmthus (Ohm Thoos)

Peltor (Pell Tor)-Kordan's teacher

Philip Graywater- Ranch owner in the Mid-realm

Stelth (Stealth) The Last dragon

Thembos (Them Bose)- Giant and general under Ningthus

Theros-The first Wizard

Thomas Thornberry -Ranch owner in the Mid-realm

Timor (Tee More)-King of the Northern Realm

Vaneera (Van Eer Uh)- Mother of Stelth

CPSIA information can be obtained
at www.ICGtesting.com
Printed in the USA
BVHW040054030223
657810BV00012B/33/J

The Olympic Games,
the Soviet Sports Bureaucracy,
and the Cold War

The Olympic Games, the Soviet Sports Bureaucracy, and the Cold War

Red Sport, Red Tape

Jenifer Parks

LEXINGTON BOOKS
Lanham • Boulder • New York • London

Published by Lexington Books
An imprint of The Rowman & Littlefield Publishing Group, Inc.
4501 Forbes Boulevard, Suite 200, Lanham, Maryland 20706
www.rowman.com

Unit A, Whitacre Mews, 26-34 Stannary Street, London SE11 4AB

British Library Cataloguing in Publication Information Available

Library of Congress Cataloging-in-Publication Data Available

ISBN 9781-1-4985-4118-3 (cloth: alk. paper)
ISBN 9781-1-4985-4119-0 (electronic)

♾️™ The paper used in this publication meets the minimum requirements of
American National Standard for Information Sciences—Permanence of Paper
for Printed Library Materials, ANSI/NISO Z39.48-1992.

Printed in the United States of America

Contents

Acknowledgments

There are a number of people and organizations I wish to thank, without whom I would not have completed this book. I benefitted immensely from intellectual interchange with many friends and colleagues who have read and commented on various aspects of this book. In particular, I would like to thank my advisor and mentor Don Raleigh, whose support, encouragement, and criticism were essential. I would like to thank Louise McReynolds, David Griffiths, Chad Bryant, Jeff Jones, Marko Dumancic, Christopher Ward, Jon Wallace, Sharon Kowalsky, Rosa Magnusdottir, Igor Fedyukin, Mike Paulauskas, Emily Baran, Gleb Tsipursky, Nick Ganson, Jack Langer, Adrianne Jacobs, Edward Geist, Aaron Hale-Dorrel, Dan Giblin, Mary Mellon, and Andrew Ringlee, Philipp Stelzel, Tom Goldstein, and Joseph Bryan. Special thanks also go to Brian Hill, Eric Kuntzman, and the staff at Lexington Books for their work in overseeing publication. The reader comments and criticism also greatly improved the final version of the book. I would also like to thank my colleagues and students at Rocky Mountain College who have challenged me professionally and intellectually.

Research in Moscow was much more enjoyable and productive because of weekly "meetings" at Bilingua, conversations in the GARF cafeteria, and other social gatherings with a remarkable cohort of scholars. I thank Martin Breisswenger, Liudmila Novikova, Jennifer Amos, Danielle Berman, Christine Evans, Nicole Eaton, Susan Smith-Peter, Allison K. Smith, Betsy Jones Hemenway, and Paula Michaels for their friendship, support, and exchange of ideas.

I am indebted to my colleagues in the German Scientific Network, "Integration and Disintegration: Social and Cultural History of Eastern European Sport in International Comparison" for their encouragement and expertise, especially Manfred Zeller, Anke Hilbrenner, Evelyn Mertin, Ekaterina Emeliantseva,

Kateryna Kobchenko, Carol Marmor, Christian Koller, Stefan Zwicker, Gregor Feindt, and Stefan Wiederkehr. My understanding of Soviet sport has been very much shaped by conversations and workshops with these scholars.

Several organizations provided funding for my research. I received a travel grant from the UNC University Center for International Studies (now Global Initiatives), a Doris C. Quinn fellowship from the History Department, and a Foreign Language and Area Studies grant from Center for Slavic, Eurasian and East European Studies. The Olympic Studies Center at the International Olympic Committee Headquarters in Lausanne, Switzerland awarded me a Postgraduate Research Grant. I thank Ruth Beck-Perrenoud, Nuria Puig and the archivists and support staff at the OSC for their help navigating the IOC holdings. My research in Moscow was funded by a Fulbright-Hays Dissertation Research Abroad fellowship, and many thanks go to Ed Roslof and the staff at the Russian Fulbright office for their in-country administrative support.

Many individuals helped me navigate the Russian archives and libraries. Irina Markovna Bykhovskaia at the Central State University of Physical Culture and Sport not only arranged for me to visit the university library and museum archives, but welcomed me into her home and her guidance and friendship have been very important to me. The curator and staff at the sports university museum allowed me access to their small but rich collection of documents. I would like to thank the staff at GARF, RGANI, and RGASPI for their professionalism. I am especially grateful to the reading room managers Nina Ivanovna Abdulaeva at GARF and Liudmila Ivanovna Stepanich at RGANI who were especially generous with their time and energy.

A version of Chapter 1 was previously published as "Verbal Gymnastics: Sports, Bureaucracy, and the Soviet Union's Entrance into the Olympic Games, 1946–1952," in *East Plays West: Sport and the Cold War,* Stephen Wagg and David Andrews, eds. (London and New York: Routledge, 2006), 27–44 and is used here by permission of Taylor & Francis Books (UK). The book also incorporates material that appeared in in the following publications: "Welcoming the Third World: Soviet Sports Diplomacy, Developing Nations and the Olympic Games," in *Diplomatic Games: Essays on the International History of Sport and Foreign Relations since 1945*, Heather L. Dichter and Andrew L. Johns, eds. (Lexington: University Press of Kentucky, 2014); "'Nothing but Trouble': The Soviet Union's Push to 'Democratise' International Sports during the Cold War, 1959–1962," *International Journal of the History of Sport* 30.13 (2013); "Promoting Authority through Sport by States and Societies of Eastern Europe," Hermann Beyer Thoma and Anke Hillbrenner et al. eds., *Handbuch der Sportgeschichte Osteuropas* (Wissenschaftliches Netzwerk zur Sportgeschichte Osteuropas, Universität Bonn, 2014), http://www.ios

-regensburg.de/fileadmin/doc/Sportgeschichte/Parks_Sports_and_Authority.pdf. The material is used here with permission of those presses, and I thank the anonymous reviewers of those articles for their constructive feedback. Other portions of the book were presented at the Southern Conference on Slavic Studies, the ASEEES, the UNC History Departmental Research Colloquium, and the UNC Center for Slavic, Eurasian, and East European Studies. I'm grateful for all the questions and observations I received from participants in those events.

My parents John and Sharon Parks and my sister Elizabeth have always encouraged me to excel in all my endeavors. Finally, I can't express how much the love and support of my husband Scot Ninnemann have meant to me. For working tirelessly on every draft of every chapter, for accompanying me to Switzerland and Russia, and for encouraging me at every stage of my career, this book is dedicated to him.

Introduction

On 19 July 1980, before a crowd of 100,000 in the Grand Arena of Moscow's Central Lenin Stadium at Luzhniki, the president of the Organizing Committee of the Games of the XXII Olympiad, Ignatii Novikov, proclaimed, "We have tried to make the Olympic Games in Moscow a large-scale and representative celebration where athletes of all continents could show their achievements, as much as we wished that these Games would give a new impetus to the development of the Olympic movement, fostering dissemination of the lofty Olympic ideals: strengthening of mutual understanding, friendship, and peace between nations."[1] Athletes from sixty-four countries marched behind their national flags as they entered the stadium to take part in and enjoy the display of protocol and pageantry. After Soviet premier Leonid Il'ich Brezhnev pronounced the Games officially open, millions of spectators, in person or on television, were dazzled by the elaborate festivities. Hundreds of dancing boys were dressed as Moscow mascot Misha the bear, girls danced with dolls, and groups from every Soviet republic performed folk dances in their national dress. All of this took place against a backdrop of a human wall of moving colored tunics and placards, switching seamlessly between Soviet and Olympic symbolism (see Figure I.1). As the first Olympic Games hosted by a socialist country, the well-organized and exquisitely coordinated festival was designed to show off the strengths and progress of the Soviet sports system and demonstrate to the world the role of the Soviet Union as a disseminator of Olympism, peace, and international friendship. Despite the absence of sixty countries, due to the U.S.-led boycott, the Games were regarded by Soviet authorities and the International Olympic Committee (IOC) as a great success.

The road to Olympiada-80 was not a straight or uncontroversial one. Olympic idealism, however, provided the common ground necessary to welcome

Figure I.1. Created by spectators waving colored placards, the image of Misha, the mascot, oversees the Opening Ceremonies of the Moscow 1980 Olympic Games, 1980. Courtesy of International Olympic Committee.

the Soviet Union into the Olympic family despite rising Cold War tensions. That same idealism also offered a linguistic and theoretical framework that could be used to further Soviet policy goals through international sports, paving the way for the Soviet capital city to mount a successful bid to host the 1980 Summer Games and welcome the world to see their socialist experiment first hand. Each of these achievements was proposed and championed by a group of dedicated sports administrators working within the Soviet party-state apparatus. Standing at the intersection between state and society, between Soviet political goals and their execution, and between Olympic sport and Marxist-Leninist ideology, Soviet sports bureaucrats provided the impetus, expertise, and experience necessary to realize the Soviet Olympic project.

Through analysis of archival materials of the All-Union Committee on Physical Culture and Sport of the Soviet Union (Sports Committee), the Communist Party of the Soviet Union (CPSU), and the IOC, this book traces the activities of the Soviet Sports Committee from the years leading up to the Soviet Union's Olympic debut in 1952 through the 1980 Summer Games in Moscow. From their entrance into the Olympic Games, Soviet athletes were a dominant force in the world sporting community. Coming in a very close second place to the United States with 71 medals in 1952, the Soviet national team went on to "win" almost every Olympic Games in which they competed until the break-up of the Soviet Union in 1991. The Soviet Union managed to out-medal its chief Cold War rival in the overall medal count in all but two of their meetings in the Summer Olympics between 1952 and 1980. With the U.S. team absent from the 1980 Summer Games, athletes of the Soviet Union racked up an impressive 195 medals before the home crowd in Moscow, including 80 gold.

Besides their dominance in the medal count, the Soviet Union's entrance into the Olympic Movement in the early 1950s changed the shape of international sports. Through the efforts of Soviet representatives, the International Olympic Committee (IOC) expanded dramatically, welcoming more members from socialist and developing nations into the organization. The number of countries participating in the Olympics also increased markedly between 1952 and 1980. In the 1952 Helsinki Games, 69 countries competed, compared to 121 in the 1972 Games in Munich. The Soviet Union's entrance into the Olympics also sparked worldwide interest in women's sport. Only 519 women competed in Helsinki, 10 percent of the total 4,955 competitors. In the 1980 Moscow Games, women made up 21 percent of the athletes, or 1,115 out of 5,179. The number of Olympic events for women also doubled during that period, from twenty-five to fifty. This evolution of the Olympic movement was due in large part to the persistence of Soviet representatives.

This study seeks to understand the role that sports administrators played in the Soviet Union's participation in the Olympic Games, the pressures they encountered from the Soviet leadership and the international sporting community, and the means they used to negotiate the different and often competing Soviet and Olympic visions of sports in order to maintain both Soviet dominance in Olympic competition and enhance Soviet influence within international sports organizations. Despite entering the international arena rather late and doing so as lesser partners to their Western European and American counterparts, Soviet representatives, over the course of only a few decades, became a dominant and respected voice within international sports circles, actively promoting Olympic ideals abroad even as they transformed those ideals to better align with Soviet goals. In the process, Soviet sports contributed to the evolution of Olympic sport, integrating the Soviet Union into an emerging global culture, and contributing to transformations within the Soviet Union.

As a longitudinal, archival study of mid-level decision-making in the Soviet sports apparatus, spanning the years of late Stalinism through the Khrushchev and Brezhnev years, this study stands at the intersection of three bodies of historiography: the emerging field of Soviet sports history, the "new" Soviet political history of internal political practices and culture, and the study of international exchange and the cultural Cold War. Examining the party-state apparatus and its functionaries who oversaw Soviet sport also helps break down the binary thinking that has often characterized interpretations of the Soviet Union.[2] Many of these commonly held dichotomies—modern/backward, communism/capitalism, East/West—predate the Soviet Union, but became entrenched during the period of revolutionary social, cultural, and political formation, as Communist Party leaders and intellectuals, as well as technical and scientific experts, sought to create an entirely new type of civilization.[3]

Physical education and sport were important to the new society being forged in the Soviet Union. As in other fields of Soviet culture, physical culture was meant to demonstrate "the autonomous, exceptional and superior nature of socialist society in comparison to and in distinction from capitalism," but the creation of a new "proletarian" style of sports was shaped by institutional conflict, theoretical contestation, and the changing needs of the government.[4] Public health, education, and military preparation were key needs of the nascent Bolshevik state in the aftermath of the Civil War, and the state and party bureaus overseeing these areas vied for influence over physical culture in the 1920s.[5] Meanwhile hygienists prioritizing "personal and social health" and *proletkul'tists* advocating a distinctly non-competitive proletarian physical culture "free of bourgeois influences" sought public support for their initiatives.[6] Ultimately, the practical needs of mobilizing the masses politically and physically in the construction and defense of the nascent workers' state meant that competition and material incentives became imbedded in Soviet sport. Soviet athletes became analogous to the Stakhanovite "labor heroes" who were rewarded for meeting and surpassing the production goals established by the five-year plans, receiving awards and prestige for sporting achievements and serving as role models for Soviet youth.[7]

Just as Josef Stalin's industrialization drive provided new impetus for competitive sport, Soviet aspirations for leading world proletariat revolution inspired the creation of a workers' alternative to the Olympic Games. Promoting upper-class notions of leisure and sport, Olympic founders distinguished between elite, amateur sport, and professional, worker or lower-class sport.[8] To counteract what they saw as an attempt to prevent workers from competing, Soviet leaders rejected the Olympic Movement and formed the Red Sport International (*Sportintern*) to promote revolutionary class-consciousness abroad through athletic meets with communist sporting organizations.[9]

By the early 1930s, however, presumably to increase their influence in Europe, Soviet leaders encouraged sports organizers to take advantage of the mass appeal of sporting matches and to strengthen the "progressive" (i.e., socialist) elements in national sports federations.[10] *Sportintern* also served as a challenge to the Western-bourgeois concept of the modern nation-state, and its dissolution marked the acceptance by the Soviet Union of the Western standard of international recognition and authority.[11] A 1933 mandate to "catch up and overtake bourgeois records" strengthened the move toward assimilation with Western sports, and sports organizers began to implement European tactics and training methods and to compete against mainstream European teams.[12]

Despite these developments, the Politburo of the CPSU denied the All-Union Committee on Physical Culture and Sport's (Sports Committee) request to officially join several international federations.[13] Impending war and domestic terror halted Soviet formal participation in the international sports movement, and Soviet leaders placed all sports organizations, institutes, and societies under the military, requiring all physical education in schools to focus on military preparedness.[14] As the country moved to a military footing, the Soviet Olympic debut would have to wait until after the war, but the process of integrating the Soviet Union into a Western-dominated sports movement had begun.[15] Rather than an entirely new socialist sport, the sports system established during the 1920s and 1930s combined socialist elements of "labor gymnastics, excursions, [and] mass displays" with the competitive drive of "bourgeois" sport.[16]

After the cancellation of the Olympic Games during World War II, the combined allied victory over Nazism inspired IOC members and Soviet officials to contemplate Soviet participation in the Olympic Movement. However, the emerging Cold War divided postwar Europe conceptually between two seemingly opposite socio-economic systems. In this context, Soviet propagandists continued to promote a distinctly socialist sport, and Western perceptions of sport tended to highlight the "exceptional" nature of Soviet sport on negative terms, contrasting the state-run, Soviet-style sports regimes of the East with the "free" institutions of the West. The USSR's eventual participation in Western international sports and the Olympic Games also renewed tension within Soviet sports between promoting mass participation in sport (*massovost'*) and training elite athletes—who could achieve sporting mastery (*masterstvo*), set world records, and win Olympic medals. The Central Committee declared that Soviet sports would both "spread sport to every corner of the land" and "help Soviet athletes win world supremacy in major sports in the immediate future."[17] Official ideology held that the success of Soviet elite athletes stemmed from a society mobilized in pursuit of widespread sporting participation, and Western scholars echoed this idea as they sought to understand how the Soviet sports "system" functioned in Soviet society.[18] While Western observers admired the sporting successes of socialist countries, they often criticized the socialist sport system as dehumanizing, speculating that Soviet success had less to do with the pursuit of an active and healthy citizenry, and more to do with a collectivist ethos, pharmaceutically enhanced men, and "ball bearing females" who were either hormonally altered or simply men in women's clothing.[19] Since the 1980s, this perception has been reinforced as former coaches, athletes, and officials exposed severe training methods, performance enhancing compounds, and the use of material incentives to secure world records and medals.[20] Such accusations also associated the Soviet Union with the Nazi regime and its successor state the GDR, supporting the totalitarian model that dominated much of the Soviet history field for decades.[21] As evidence of the East German state-run drug program surfaced, it seemed to confirm suspicions about the Soviet Union as well, upholding the Cold War construction of good Western societies where doping was an "aberration" versus the evil communist system of the Eastern Bloc.[22] Examining Central Committee archives, Mikhail Prozumenshchikov has shown that the party-state apparatus did seek to control its sports practitioners through repressive measures.[23] But sport in the Soviet Union could also undermine state authority by providing a less controlled venue for expressing dissatisfaction with state-imposed activities through spontaneous outbursts of sporting fandom, as well as an avenue for local and regional administrators to exert their authority outside of—and in some cases in opposition to—the central state and party organs.[24] Analysis of Soviet sport can also move beyond dichotomies of state repression and popular resistance, demonstrating that while local and regional clubs as well as individual fans could and did promote their own authority through sport in opposition to the state, groups and individuals also at times reinforced state power by participating in official, state-organized competitions and couching their demands for autonomy in official language and ideology.[25]

My work builds upon the emerging field of "new Soviet political history," applying the study of formal and informal policies and practices in order to "reconstruct" the political world of the sports bureaucracy.[26] The activities of sports administrators illuminate how decisions were made within the Soviet party-state, further complicating persistent assumptions of Russian backwardness vis-à-vis Western political development which contrast Soviet politics to a Weberian ideal of modern rational-legal forms of governance.[27] Recent works on post-war Soviet science, music, and politics have revealed how "unofficial networks" and "informal interactions" intersected with "official" bureaucratic procedures, providing a means for lower-level administrators to influence party leaders. Patronage politics helped cut through the red tape and get things done, but cultivating relationships with party leaders subjected administrators to bureaucratic intrigues, reorganizations, and intra-party conflicts, as actors on all levels of the party-state apparatus struggled to reconcile their professional pursuits with Marxist-Leninist ideology.[28] The reports, memoranda, and meeting minutes of the Sports Committee reveal insights about the formal and informal network of rules and relationships through which bureaucrats understood, enacted, and shaped their roles within the party-state power structure. Soviet sports administrators pushed the leadership to enter the Olympic Games despite the increasing anti-Western and isolationist domestic and foreign policy during Stalin's last years in power. Demonstrating a significant degree of maneuverability, sports administrators utilized personal contacts and other informal channels as well as formal procedures as they promoted Soviet participation in the Olympic Games during the period of postwar Stalinism.

Using the Soviet Olympic program as a means to examine the dynamics of politics and decision-making after Stalin and determine how the "rules of the game" evolved with changing circumstances, my study further breaks down binary conceptions of state and society and between the "public" and the "private."[29] Bureaucrats were both part of "the state" and part of "society." They were impacted by social and economic developments that affected Soviet society as a whole, and they were not immune to the social and political upheavals that marked the Soviet period. Nikita Sergeyevich Khrushchev's (1953–64) policies of de-Stalinization and cultural thaw created new opportunities for state administrators even as they brought them under increased scrutiny. The unevenness and changing nature of reforms left Soviet party-state functionaries to speculate at the priorities of the CPSU leadership as they implemented confusing and changing party directives.[30] While the relative openness in the Soviet cultural realm opened up "roomier pockets" for administrators to advance their own interests, de-centralization and reorganization of the Sports Committee renewed, temporarily, turf battles over sport governance.[31]

Khrushchev's promotion of peaceful coexistence with the West provided a new impetus for Soviet international sports, dramatically expanding the number of athletes, trainers, and sports officials traveling abroad and lending more authority to those in the Sports Committee overseeing international sports. Higher standards of living, increased opportunities for travel, and expansion of educational opportunities allowed state functionaries to pursue the "Soviet Dream" of a good job, a decent apartment, a loving family, and consumer goods.[32] Physical culture institutes and sports universities began to produce graduates who would go on to careers in the Sports Committee apparatus, sports federation administrations, and the Organizing Committee for the Moscow Olympic Games, and expanded sports exchanges during the period allowed hundreds of Sports administrators to travel abroad via international conferences and sporting events. As a result, many functionaries on all levels of the party-state apparatus appear to have become more interested in their own professional and social stability than in supporting dramatic initiatives from the party leadership.

The rise to power of Leonid Il'ich Brezhnev in 1964 and the movement toward détente with the West in the 1970s marked the heyday of the Soviet Olympic program. During this time, the Central Committee gave its approval for a bid to host the Olympic Games in Moscow while improved relations between East and West generated international interest and support for a Moscow Olympiad. Brezhnev's support of détente also helped the sports bureaucrats to smooth over international political issues that could have hampered their chances of hosting the Games. The propensity for stable careers, consumer perks, and a fulfilling private life also became more pronounced under Leonid Brezhnev, whose "stability of cadres" policies privileged technical skills and expertise, and these in turn provided job security.[33] At the same time, sports bureaucrats' working interactions, which in some cases accounted for the vast majority of their waking hours, had a profound impact on their sense of self, their sense of their role in larger regime goals, and the importance of their work. Lifetime tenure certainly allowed for lethargy, obstructionism, and resistance to reform, but it also provided the experienced cadres needed to make the 1980 Olympic Games in Moscow a success.

My study also helps to complicate the concept of stagnation that has colored interpretations of the Brezhnev era and the period of late socialism. Scholars of this period have begun to challenge the stagnation label and the "false dichotomies" in which it is rooted, including public versus private, and vitality versus torpor.[34] The organization of the 1980 Olympic Games in Moscow contradicts the claim that official proclamations of happy Soviet citizens enjoying the fruits of developed socialism simply masked the realities of economic crisis, social malaise, and widespread disaffection among the population, revealing "a peculiar paradox at the core of the Soviet system" that was "everlasting and steadily declining, full of vigor and bleakness, dedicated to high ideals and devoid of them."[35] Late Soviet socialism was marked by "greater repression *and* greater experimentation," and while Soviet citizens challenged official ideology, finding new meanings and avenues for creative expression not necessarily tied to the political goals of the system, this did not necessarily equate to a fundamental rejection of socialism in the abstract or the system as a whole.[36] As with other big projects of the Brezhnev era, the Organizing Committee had to overcome significant bureaucratic barriers, political paralysis, and economic decline in order to make the Games happen, and these difficulties called into question the official pronouncements of the Soviet state's achievements.[37] But also as in other sectors of the Soviet party-state, sports administrators "remained committed to the ideological foundations of the state, recognized the challenges that the system faced, and embarked on a creative search for solutions."[38] As Kristin Roth-Ey notes, "Inconsistency is not necessarily the same thing as cynicism."[39] Soviet sports officials could sincerely promote Olympism and Olympic philosophy while acknowledging that their own chief mandate was Soviet excellence. They could do everything within their power to ensure Soviet success internationally without abandoning their firm beliefs—in Marxist-Leninist tenants of sport for all, or in the power of Olympism to promote peace and friendship throughout the world. They could also work tirelessly to ensure the success of the Moscow Olympiad, even as they leveraged their position in the Organizing Committee for a larger office or apartment. One of the best example of the paradox of late socialism is the decision to send Soviet troops into Afghanistan on the eve of the Olympic Games. The Organizing Committee leveraged all their political clout to ensure maximum participation in the Moscow Olympiad, even as a reckless decision by an aging and out of touch leadership threatened to undermine their efforts.

Displaying a significant degree of maneuverability and autonomy and an ability to advance their own priorities, the Sports Committee's leading personalities represented a new kind of Soviet bureaucrat, who emerged in the late years of Stalinism and helped to shape Soviet political practices throughout the period of my research. Through their own reports and their participation in crafting Sports Committee, Central Committee, and Council of Ministers decrees, state bureaucrats found an avenue whereby they could exert authority over the decision-making process. This upward flow of information served as a source of influence for state functionaries, as well as a marker of their skills and experience that could earn them a promotion within the Soviet administrative apparatus. At the same time, the realm of activity for Soviet bureaucrats remained circumscribed by the limitations of the command economy, the rigid party-state apparatus, and the extent to which their recommendations found support from top party leaders—official reports and memoranda did not completely replace personal connections, informal communiqués, and back channels as means for getting things done in the Soviet Union.[40] However, success internationally translated into increased authority within the Soviet party-state power structure so that, by the summer of 1980, when Moscow welcomed the world to the XXII Olympiad, Soviet leaders relied upon the accumulated knowledge and expertise of its sport administrators to ensure that the first Olympic Games hosted by a socialist nation would be the biggest and the best.

Sports bureaucrats also had to navigate the ebbs and flows of international, political tensions, and their experience helps to break down the Cold War binary of East and West. Placed under the Department of Agitation and Propaganda of the Central Committee of the Communist Party (Agitprop), international sports became an important propaganda tool in the cultural Cold War.[41] Complicating the idea that the United States won this cultural competition by "raising" or "parting" the iron curtain by destabilizing Soviet society with Western cultural exports, my research shows that this influence flowed in both directions.[42] Kirill Tomoff demonstrates that Soviet success in international music competitions, "led some Westerners to adopt and adapt select Soviet values and practices, partially realizing Soviet goals of expanding global influence and transformation." However, he argues that Soviet dominance "masked the gradual, long-term integration of the Soviet Union into the U.S.-dominated global system."[43] Gyorgy Pietri also contends that international exchange revealed "the deep embeddedness of the socialist project in (capitalist) modernity and the profound unity of the *modern* world."[44] Barbara Keys suggests that "sports competitions opened up a 'back door' to subtle but arguably significant openings to global culture, eventually playing a role both in undermining the closed nature of the Soviet system and in spurring the kinds of global cultural flows that led to the current era of globalization."[45] These trends can certainly be seen in the realm of Soviet sport. In order to be successful, Soviet sports organizations had to obey international rules and uphold international standards. Soviet administrators therefore had to be well-versed in these requirements and, in this way, acted as envoys of the IOC and the International Federations (IFs) that governed international sport in the Soviet Union, even as they worked to shape those organizations' rules to enhance Soviet successes.

While Soviet participation in the Olympic Games did open the Soviet Union to Western conceptions of modern sport, Soviet representatives also transformed those ideals as they rearticulated both Olympic and Marxist-Leninist philosophy in terms that made them mutually understandable, rendering their contradictions less significant than their overall commonalities, and participating in the "process of consensus construction of values in the world of global sport."[46] Soviet administrators and the IOC developed a shared understanding that sport helped create an orderly society, regulated by observable and measurable achievements, defining progress both in terms of enhancing the level of competition and in advancements in technology, sports science, equipment, modern facilities, systematization, and an overall sense of the ability to shape the body and the person—to improve humanity through sport.[47] Soviet and IOC officials envisioned Olympic sport as a civilizing mission that strove to pull everyone toward modern society, and the "magnificent organization" of the Moscow Olympiad appears as a pinnacle of modern sporting pageantry, evidence of the self-ascribed vision of what modern society should be—and, by 1980, what the Soviet Union had officially become.[48]

The organization of the book is largely chronological, beginning with the Soviet Union's entrance into the Olympic Games in 1952 and ending with the 1980 Moscow Olympiad. Chapter 1 offers a comprehensive look at the Soviet Union's Olympic debut in 1952, focusing on the role of the Sports Committee in the decision to enter the Games, in the procurement of approval from the IOC, and in the preparation of the first Soviet Olympic team between 1945 and 1952, the years of postwar Stalinism. The second chapter looks at how Soviet administrators responded to tensions between Olympic and Soviet sports ideologies in order to attain Soviet political goals within the International Olympic Committee and other international sports organizations. Chapter 2 also explores the impact on the Sports Committee of expanded international sports ties during the Khrushchev period, determining how travel abroad by the administrators themselves affected the work of the Sports Committee and how sports exchanges influenced changing relationships and expectations within the Soviet bureaucracy during this period.

Tracing the evolving role of Soviet representatives in international sports, the book's final three chapters provide an examination of the 1980 Summer Games in Moscow. Chapter 3 analyses the Soviet bid to host the Olympic Games in Moscow. Chapter 4 outlines the ambitious task of organizing the Olympic Games in a socialist country. The fifth chapter focuses on the international diplomacy, political conflict, and propaganda efforts surrounding the organization of the Games during the era of the boycott. The book concludes by examining the fate of Soviet Olympic sports after 1980, tracing the evolution of the "rules of the game" through the 2014 Winter Games held in Sochi, Russia.

NOTES

1. *Official Report of the Games of the XXII Olympiad*, vol. 2: *Opening and Closing Ceremonies*, 288, available from http://library.la84.org/6oic/OfficialReports/1980/or1980v2pt1.pdf.

2. In his sweeping analysis of Soviet historiography and cultural exchange, Michael David-Fox advocates for "a middle ground between the binary oppositions entrenched in this field, most notably the one between exceptionalism and shared modernity." Michael David-Fox, *Crossing Borders: Modernity, Ideology and Culture in Russia and the Soviet Union* (Pittsburgh: Pittsburgh University Press, 2015), 17.

3. See Katerina Clark, *Petersburg: Crucible of Cultural Revolution* (Cambridge: Harvard University Press, 1995), 20, 214. Clark argues that early Soviet cultural formation was the result of dialogue between competing intellectual groups and the party and state authorities. The two major points of common ground she sees between the intellectual groups and the party are a hatred for the role of the market place in culture which threatened the purity of political and cultural life, and "evolutionary impatience," or the sense that they have to create an entirely unique culture and they have to do it right now. See also Stephen Kotkin, *Magic Mountain: Stalinism as Civilization* (Berkeley and Los Angeles: California University Press, 1994), 2.

4. Gyorgy Peteri, "Sites of Convergence: The USSR and Communist Eastern Europe at International Fairs Abroad and at Home," *Journal of Contemporary History* 47.1 (2012): 4. For a detailed analysis of the early development of physical culture and sport see Susan Grant, *Physical Culture and Sport in Soviet Society: Propaganda, Acculturation, and Transformation in the 1920s and 1930s* (New York and London: Routledge, 2012) and "The Politics and Organization of Physical Culture in the USSR during the 1920s," *Slavonic and East European Review* 89.3 (2011): 494–515.

5. Grant, "The Politics and Organization of Physical Culture," 499.

6. Ibid., 502.

7. John Hoberman, *Sport and Political Ideology* (Austin: University of Texas Press, 1984), 192; and James Riordan, *Sport in Soviet Society: Development of Sport and Physical Education in Russia and the USSR* (Cambridge and New York: Cambridge University Press, 1977), 132–33.

8. Allen Guttmann, *The Olympics: A History of the Modern Games, 2nd ed.* (Urbana and Chicago: University of Illinois Press, 2002), 12.

9. Barbara Keys, "Dictatorship of Sport: Nationalism, Internationalism, and Mass Culture in the 1930s" (PhD Diss., Harvard University, 2001)," 191.

10. Ibid., 207–8.

11. Andre Gounot, "Between Revolutionary Demands and Diplomatic Necessity: the Uneasy Relationship between Soviet Sport and Worker and Bourgeois Sport in Europe from 1920 to 1937," in Pierre Arnaud and James Riordan, *Sport and International Politics: The Impact of Fascism and Communism on Sport* (New York: Routledge, 1988), 201.

12. Ibid., 214, 224.

13. Ibid., 244.

14. Riordan, *Sport in Soviet Society*, 155.

15. See Barbara Keys, "Soviet Sport and Transnational Mass Culture in the 1930s," *Journal of Contemporary History* 38, 3 (2003): 416. Keys asserts that while modern Western sport in some ways became modified or "Sovietized" as it was adapted to fit the Soviet context, the price for participating in Western sport was the "opening [of] Soviet culture to internationalist currents often subversive of broader regime goals."

16. Grant, "The Politics and Organization of Physical Culture," 501–3.

17. Victor Peppard and James Riordan, *Playing Politics*: *Soviet Sport Diplomacy to 1992* (Greenwich, CT: JAI Press, 1993), 62.

18. See James Riordan, *Sport in Soviet Society*, and Henry W. Morton, *Soviet Sport* (New York: Collier Books, 1963).

19. Rob Beamish and Ian Ritchie, "Totalitarian Regimes and Cold War Sport: Steroid '*Ubermenschen*' and 'ball-bearing females,'" in *East Plays West*, 20–21. See also Barbara Carol Cole, "The East German Sports System: Image and Reality," Ph.D. diss., Texas Tech, 2000; and Steven Ungerleider, *Faust's Gold: Inside the East German Doping Machine* (New York: Thomas Dunne Books, 2001). These speculations led to invasive and controversial physical, genetic, and hormonal "sex verification" examinations of female athletes in international sport. See for example, Stephan Wiederkehr, "'We Shall Never Know the Exact Number of Men Who Have Competed in the Olympics Posing as Women': Sport, Gender Verification and the Cold War," *International Journal of the History of Sport* 26.4 (2009).

20. James Riordan, "Rewriting Soviet Sports History," *Journal of Sport History* 20.3 (1993). See also see Yuri Brokhin, *The Big Red Machine: The Rise and Fall of Soviet Olympic Champions* (New York: Random House, 1978).

21. Beamish and Ritchie, 14–16.

22. Paul Dimeo, "Good versus Evil? Drugs, Sport and the Cold War," in *East Plays West*, 149–50. For a balanced and thorough treatment of doping in Olympic sport, see Thomas M. Hunt, *Drug Games: The International Olympic Committee and the Politics of Doping, 1960–2008. Terry and Jan Todd Series on Physical Culture and Sports* (Austin, TX: University of Austin Press, 2011). The recent report commissioned by the World Anti-Doping Agency, alleging collusion between the Russian Federation drug testing lab and state authorities to cover up a government-sponsored doping program begun in 2011, again conjures up Cold War assumptions.

23. Prozumenshchikov, *Bol'shoi Sport i Bol'shaia Politika* (Moscow: ROSSPEN, 2004). Unlike the East German case, so far there have been no revelations from the former Soviet archives to confirm or disprove the assumption of widespread state-run doping in the Soviet Union.

24. See Robert Edelman, *Serious Fun: A History of Spectator Sports in the USSR* (New York: Oxford University Press, 1993); *Spartak Moscow: A History of the People's Team in the Workers' State* (Ithaca: Cornell University Press, 2009), and "A Small Way of Saying 'No': Moscow Working Men, Spartak Soccer, and the Communist Party, 1900–1945," *American Historical Review* 107, no. 5 (2002): 1441–74; Katzer et al. eds., *Euphoria and Exhaustion: Modern Sport in Soviet Culture and Society* (Frankfurt: Campus Verlag, 2010); Manfred Zeller, "'Our Own Internationale,' 1966: Dynamo Kiev Fans between Local Identity and Transnational Imagination," *Kritika* 12:1 (2011): 53–82; Vilma Cingiene and Skaiste Laskiene, "A Revitalized

Dream: Basketball and National Identity in Lithuania," *International Journal of the History of Sport* 21.5 (November 2004): 762–79; William D. Frank, *Everyone to Skis! Skiing in Russia and the Rise of Soviet Biathlon* (DeKalb: Northern Illinois University Press, 2013); Arie Malz, Stefan Rohdewald, Stefan Wiederkehr, *Sport zwischen Ost und West: Beiträge zur Sportgeschichte Osteuropas im 19. und 20. Jahrhundert* (Osnabrück: fibre Verlag, 2007).

25. Nikolaus Katzer et al. eds., *Euphoria and Exhaustion*, especially Christina Kiaer, "The Swimming Vtorova Sisters: The Representation and Experience of Sport in the1930s" and Manfred Zeller, "'Our Own Internationale,' 1966," 62.

26. See Sheila Fitzpatrick, "Politics as Practice: Thoughts on a New Soviet Political History," *Kritika: Explorations in Russian and Eurasian History* 5.1 (2004): 27–54. Pierre Bourdieu claimed that "an adequate analysis of political discourse must be based on a systematic reconstruction of the field within which such discourse is produced and received . . . and its relation to the broader social space." Pierre Bourdieu, *Language and Symbolic Power*, ed. with an introduction by John B. Thompson, trans. Gino Raymond and Matthew Adamson (Cambridge, MA: Harvard University Press, 1991), 29.

27. In Max Weber's seminal work, he described modern bureaucracy as a hierarchical world in which bureaucrats advance through "thorough and expert training" based upon "general rules which are more or less stable" and governed by written documentation. H. H. Gerth and C. Wright Mills, *From Max Weber: Essays in Sociology* (New York: Oxford University Press, 1946), 196–99, 203, quoted in Karl W. Ryavec, *Russian Bureaucracy: Power and Pathology* (Lanham, MD: Rowman and Littlefield, 2003), 4. See also Max Weber, *Economy and Society: An Outline of Interpretive Sociology*, vol. 2 (Berkeley: University of California Press, 1978).

28. Kiril Tomoff, *Creative Union: The Professional Organization of Soviet Composers, 1939–1953* (Ithaca, New York: Cornell University Press, 2006), 36. For the case of science, see Alexei Kojevnikov, "Rituals of Stalinist Culture at Work: Science and the Games of Intraparty Democracy circa 1948," *Russian Review* 57 (1998): 25–52 and *Stalin's Great Science: The Times and Adventures of Soviet Physicists* (London: Imperial College Press, 2004); Nikolai Krementsov, *Stalinist Science* and *The Cure: A Story of Cancer and Politics from the Annals of the Cold War* (Chicago: University of Chicago Press, 2002); Ethan Pollock, *Stalin and the Soviet Science Wars* (Princeton: Princeton University Press, 2006). See also Yoram Gorlizki and Oleg Khlevniuk, *Cold Peace: Stalin and the Soviet Ruling Circle, 1945–1953* (Oxford: Oxford University Press, 2004).

29. Malte Griesse, "Soviet Subjectivities: Discourse, Self-Criticism, Imposture," *Kritika: Explorations in Russian and Eurasian History* 9.3 (Summer 2008): 24. Griesse highlights the importance of not assuming that one sphere of interaction (for instance, "public" vs. "private") is "more 'true,' 'real,' or 'relevant' than the others." He also maintains that breaking out of such "binary reasoning" that artificially creates a tension between the public and private self can also help to break down the underlying "opposition of the Soviet Union and the 'west.'"

30. Polly Jones, ed., *The Dilemmas of De-Stalinization: Negotiating Cultural and Social Change in the Khrushchev Era* (Abingdon and New York: Routledge, 2006),

14. As Poly Jones notes, "[dilemmas over de-stalinization] led to the paradoxical combinations of liberalism and conservatism, iconoclasm and preservation of Stalinist norms in party policy . . . . These paradoxes were mirrored in the uncertainty which gripped the Soviet population, as it held its own debates about the Stalin cult, terror, post-Stalinist identity and the post-Stalinist system, unsure of the limits of discussion, and of the uncertain answers which emerged."

31. Kristin Roth-Ey, *Moscow Prime Time: How the Soviet Union Built the Media Empire That Lost the Cultural Cold War* (Ithica and London: Cornell University Press, 2011), 13. Daniel Tarschys, "Management by Duplication: Some Observations on Soviet Bureaucracy," *Nordic journal of Soviet and East European Studies* 3, no. 2 (1986): 42.

32. Donald J. Raleigh, *Soviet Baby Boomers: An Oral History of Russia's Cold War Generation* (Oxford and New York: Oxford University Press, 2012), 168. For more on travel and consumerism in the Khrushchev period see Anne E. Gorsuch and Diane P. Koenker, eds., *Turizm: The Russian and East European Tourist under Capitalism and Socialism* (Ithaca and London: Cornell University Press, 2006); and Susan E. Reid, "Cold War in the Kitchen: Gender and the De Stalinization of Consumer Taste in the Soviet Union under Khrushchev," *Slavic Review* 61.2 (2002): 211–52.

33. Nikolai Mitrohin, "'Back Office' Mikhaila Suslova ili Kem i Kak Proizvodilas' Ideologiia Brezhnevskogo Vremeni," *Cahiers du Monde Russe* 54.3–4 (2013): 409–40. See also Steven l. Solnick, *Stealing the State: Control and Collapse in Soviet Institutions* (Cambridge: Harvard University Press, 1998; Stephen Kotkin, *Armageddon Averted: The Soviet Collapse 1970–2000* (Oxford, UK: Oxford University Press, 2001).

34. Christine Evans, *Between Truth and Time: A History of Soviet Central Television* (New Haven: Yale University Press, 2016), 5.

35. Alexei Yurchak, *Everything Was Forever until It Was No More: The Last Soviet Generation* (Princeton: Princeton University Press, 2005), 282.

36. Evans, 7; Yurchak, 283; Kristin Roth-Ey, *Moscow Prime Time*, 23–24.

37. Christopher J. Ward, *Brezhnev's Folly: The Building of BAM and Late Soviet Socialism* (Pittsburgh: University of Pittsburgh Press, 2009), 3, 152–53.

38. Dina Fainberg and Artemy M. Kalinovsky eds., *Reconsidering Stagnation in the Brezhnev Era: Ideology and Exchange* (Lanham, MD: Lexington Books, 2016), xii–xiii, xvi.

39. Roth-Ey, 20.

40. Karl W. Ryavec, *Russian Bureaucracy: Power and Pathology* (Lanham, MD: Rowman and Littlefield Publishers, 2003), 5–6.

41. See Heather L. Dichter and Andrew L. Johns, eds., *Diplomatic Games: Sport, Statecraft, and International Relations since 1945* (Lexington: University Press of Kentucky, 2014); Peppard and Riordan, *Playing Politics*; Stephen Wagg and David Andrews, eds., *East Plays West: Sport and the Cold War* (London and New York: Routledge, 2006); Prozumenshchikov, *Bol'shoi Sport i Bol'shaia Politika*; Toby C. Rider, *Cold War Games: Propaganda, the Olympics, and U.S. Foreign Policy, Sport and Society* (Champaign: University of Illinois Press, 2016); Thomas M. Hunt,

"American Sport Policy and the Cultural Cold War: The Lyndon B. Johnson Presidential Years," *Journal of Sports History* 33.3 (2006): 273–97; Evelyn Mertin and Christoph Bertling, eds., *Freunde oder Feinde? Sportberichterstattung in Ost und West während des Kalten Krieges* (Köln: Gütersloh Medienfabrik Gütersloh, 2013); Malz, Rohdewald, and Wiederkehr, *Sport zwischen Ost und West*.

42. See Walter L. Hixon, *Parting the Curtain: Propaganda, Culture, and the Cold War, 1945–61* (New York: St. Martin's Press, 1997); Yale Richmond, *Cultural Exchange and the Cold War: Raising the Iron Curtain* (University Park: Pennsylvania State University Press, 2003); David Caute, *The Dancer Defects: The Struggle for Cultural Supremacy during the Cold War* (New York and London: Oxford University Press, 2005).

43. Kiril Tomoff, *Virtuosi Abroad: Soviet Music and Imperial Competition during the Early Cold War, 1945–58* (Ithaca and London: Cornell University Press, 2015), 14–15.

44. Peteri, "Sites of Convergence: 5.

45. Barbara Keys, "The Soviet Union, Cultural Exchange and the 1956 Olympic Games," in Malz, Rohdewald, and Wiederkehr, *Sport zwischen Ost und West*, 133.

46. Dikaia Chatziefstathiou, "The Changing Nature of the Ideology of Olympism in the Modern Era," (Ph D. diss., Loughborough University, Leicestershire, UK, April 2005), 1.

47. Allen Guttmann, *From Ritual to Record: The Nature of Modern Sports* (New York: Columbia University Press, 1978), 15, quoted in Chatziefstathiou, "Ideology of Olympism," 26–72. Guttmann compiled a list of seven "distinguishing characteristics of modern sport" based on a Weberian framework, including "secularism, equality of opportunity to compete and in the conditions of competition, specialization of roles, rationalization, bureaucratic organization, quantification, [and] the quest for records."

48. Samaranch to Novikov, telegram, 14 January 1981, COJO 1980 Correspondence 1980–1993, IOC Archives.

Chapter One

Verbal Gymnastics

The Soviet Union Enters the Olympic Movement

On a rainy day in Helsinki in the summer of 1952, the Soviet Union made its Olympic debut. Before a crowd of around 70,000 in the Olympiastadion (Olympic Stadium), 295 competitors—255 men in all-white suits and forty women in navy blue—marched around the field behind weightlifter Yakov Kucenko, who carried a red flag emblazoned with the gold star, hammer and sickle. Taking their place among the nations of the world, the athletes of the Soviet Union would go on to take part in 141 events in eighteen sports, securing a total of seventy-one medals, twenty-two of them gold. Yet, a year earlier, the prospect of Soviet Olympic participation had remained unclear. In this chapter, I consider the evolution of attitudes surrounding the Soviet Olympic project, as well as the changing relations between the Soviet organizers and the IOC that allowed the Soviet entrance into the Games.

After a twelve-year hiatus, the Olympic Games resumed in 1948 amid a period of volatile international relations. As the wartime partnership between the Soviet Union and its Western Allies broke down over competing visions of the postwar order, a series of actions and incidents on both sides led to a new division of Europe. Western Europe benefitted from American aid and protection through the Marshall Plan and Truman Doctrine, while Eastern European nations fell increasingly under the economic, political, and ideological dominance of the Soviet Union. Many IOC members thought that inviting the Soviet Union to join the Games would prove the vitality and appeal of Olympic ideals. However, IOC regulations demanded that athletes be amateurs and that IOC members act independently of political interference, and worries that the USSR's state-run sports system would violate these standards made Soviet participation a divisive issue.

Domestically, the postwar period in Soviet society was a time of hopes and disappointments. Many Soviet citizens expected their wartime sacrifice and

1

victory over the Nazis to bring about a period of peace and stability. Such hopes were soon quashed by renewed political purges and further economic sacrifices resulting in widespread poverty, insecurity, and famine. In her landmark study, Elena Zubkova argues that new people rose to important positions during and just after the war, bringing a high level of professionalism, initiative, and willingness to take risks in their new roles. As these new cadres sought solutions to the many problems facing the USSR, Soviet leaders, fearing a loss of control, answered initiative with interference and repression.[1] Stalin's leadership during this period has been described as a "neo-patrimonial" attempt to combine regular, rational-legal forms of administration in lower levels of the hierarchy with informal, repressive forms of control based on personal loyalty within his inner circle. While decisions in the Central Committee and Politburo more and more often were made by Stalin's personal entourage in meetings at his dacha or over late-night phone calls, work in the Council of Ministers and the state bureaucracy became more routinized and systematic.[2] At the same time, "unofficial networks" and "informal interactions" intersected with "official" bureaucratic procedures throughout the party-state apparatus during this time.[3] As the Soviet Union moved from wartime cooperation to political, economic, and ideological confrontation with the West, the party leadership sought to purify the country ideologically, igniting rivalries between members of the intelligentsia and party-state functionaries in Soviet scientific, educational, and cultural institutions. Scientists, musicians, and other specialists, as well as their administrative counterparts, cultivated personal connections with powerful patrons in the higher ranks of the party-state apparatus in order to advance their professional priorities. By couching their proposals within the overall priorities of the Politburo and using Marxist-Leninist discourse as a "negotiating language," intellectuals and apparatchiks achieved a certain degree of autonomy and agency in advancing their own interests. At the same time, these tactics rendered them vulnerable to squabbles within the higher party leadership.[4]

Appointed by the Central Committee as chairman of the Sports Committee, Nikolai Romanov reported to the Agitation and Propaganda department of the Central Committee (Agitprop), headed by Andrei Zhdanov, and later Mikhail Suslov as well as the secretary of the Central Committee in charge of hiring party cadres, Georgii Malenkov.[5] The Sports Committee comprised departments overseeing each sport and a department for international sporting relations. The National Olympic Committee (NOC) of the USSR, formed in 1951, was in theory a separate, independent body, as required by IOC regulations. However, the NOC president, Konstantin Andrianov, and corresponding secretary, Petr Sobolev, also held positions within the Sports Committee; Andrianov was vice-chairman, and Sobolev headed the department of international sporting activity. In addition, each of the fifteen constituent republics of the USSR had a committee that mirrored the role of the Sports Committee but was subordinated to it. At the local level, voluntary sport societies had been established in the 1930s under the supervision of trade unions, the NKVD (Soviet security police), and the Red Army. This structure appears to have been revived after the war.[6] Headed by N. A. Mikhailov, the Soviet Communist Youth Organization (Komsomol) oversaw youth sports and physical education in schools.

The three men most responsible for the Soviet Union's Olympic debut belong to a generation of Soviet functionaries who began their professional lives in the 1930s as beneficiaries of Stalin's Cultural Revolution and rose to prominence during or just after World War II.[7] A Communist Party member since 1937, Romanov worked with physical culture training in the Komsomol before the Second World War.[8] Andrianov joined the CPSU in 1931, and by 1941 had risen to the position of vice chairman of the Sports Committee, having headed the Moscow city committee.[9] Both men spent the war training reserves for national defense before rebuilding the Sports Committee and initiating the push to enter the Olympic Games.[10] Having completed secondary school with honors in Arkhangelsk, Petr Sobolev graduated from the Moscow Institute of History, Philosophy and Literature in 1941. In 1943, Sobolev joined the First Belorussian Front of the Red Army and participated in the Battle of Berlin under G.K. Zhukov, attending the signing of Germany's capitulation as a translator. Having served as a people's correspondent for the newspaper *Pravda severa* before the war, Sobolev became a sports journalist in the postwar years and joined the Sports Committee as the head of international sports relations while also working in the Ministry of State Security (MGB—successor to the NKVD and precursor to the KGB).[11] With the Great Fatherland War as their formative experience, these men represented new cadres who brought experience, independence, and creativity to solving the problems of postwar reconstruction.[12]

During this period of possibility and uncertainty, Soviet sports administrators promoted Olympic participation as an opportunity to show the world the superior technique and training achieved by the Soviet system, as well as the value of the Soviet way of life. Working in a volatile international setting as well as a potentially dangerous internal political climate, these men represent a new kind of Soviet bureaucrat, whose skills and personality presaged the style of governing of Stalin's successors. Like their counterparts in other bureaus, sports administrators exploited the relationship "between the regular, orderly, impersonal operation of established bureaucratic procedures and the personalized, individual interventions" that helped them "navigate that bureaucracy more successfully" in order to send a Soviet team to the Olympic Games.[13] Reflecting the optimism of the time, The Soviet Sports Committee under the leadership of Nikolai Romanov argued that the Soviet Union should join the Olympic Movement, taking full advantage not only of the position of the Soviet Union but of the popularity of the Olympics to carve a place within that movement for Soviet interests. Down the hierarchy of the Sports Committee were other bureaucrats who also demonstrated varying degrees of autonomy, finding ways to advance their own projects by relating them to their superiors' priorities. The Soviet Union eventually entered the Olympics because individuals were willing and able to step up and make things happen while operating in a difficult, repressive, and often dangerous environment.

However, the Soviet leadership's demands for victory above all else, and the increasingly xenophobic atmosphere of Soviet and international politics during the early days of the Cold War, imperiled Soviet participation in international sports and complicated the Soviet Olympic debut. Correspondence on both sides of the Iron Curtain betrayed attitudes of confrontation, superiority, and suspicion between competing ideologies. At the same time, both Soviet organizers and the IOC championed the Olympic ideals of fair play and international understanding that provided the necessary common ground, allowing the ambitious project of entering the Olympic Games to succeed during the period of post-war Stalinism.

"A MOST EMBARRASSING CONTROVERSY": AMATEURISM AND ANXIETY IN THE IOC

Founded in the decades leading up to World War I and motivated by "deep feelings among Europeans that were rooted in anxieties about war and peace," the Olympic Games represented for their organizers an apolitical and universal remedy to increasing international tensions.[14] Having seen those ideals tested twice by brutal worldwide conflicts, many members of the IOC were eager to resume after the Second World War and expand the Olympic Movement to the Soviet Union. However, ideological differences had kept the Soviet Union out of the Olympic Games before the war and threatened to continue to prevent Soviet participation in the 1940s. Founded in 1892 on commonly held ideas of nineteenth-century Western liberalism, the modern Olympic Movement idealized individual liberty within the context of the modern nation-state. The brainchild of Baron Pierre de Coubertin, the modern Olympic Games hoped to build a better world through the internationalization of sport, but this idealism masked attitudes of superiority to the "lower classes" characteristic of the early IOC's socioeconomic milieu.[15] Promoting upper-class notions of leisure and sport, Olympic founders distinguished between elite, amateur sport, and professional, worker or lower-class sport. While the IOC did not continue the Victorian definition of amateurism that sought "to exclude the 'lower orders' from the play of the leisure class," economic constraints tended to limit participation and many IOC members looked down upon those who competed for material incentives instead of purely for the love of sport.[16] This attitude became more entrenched during the interwar period, as growing worker unrest fueled fears of war and revolution.

Following the destruction of World War II, many IOC members thought that welcoming the Soviet Union into the Olympics would demonstrate the power of sport to gather nations together in peace and friendship. As IOC member from Hungary Ferenc Mező insisted in 1951, "the future Olympic Games can only be of value if the prominent young people of the Soviet Union, one of the greatest sports powers, take part."[17] Many in international sporting circles began to reach out to the USSR. Arguing that "young athletes all over Europe [were] crazy to have the Russian athletes participate," Sigfried Edström, president of the IOC and the International Amateur Athletics Federation (IAAF), began to harbor hope that the USSR would compete in the 1948 Olympic Games.[18] Similarly, Lord Burghley, IOC member from Great Britain, visited the Soviet Union in 1947 to learn about its sports system and to encourage the country's participation in the London Games of 1948.[19] On his visit, Burghley attended an elaborate physical culture parade featuring more than twenty thousand athletes. Staged for the second time since World War II, the festivities surrounding Physical Culture Day impressed the English visitor and served as a powerful tool to garner support for Soviet sports internationally.[20] A conservative, anti-communist, self-made businessman from Middle America, the Vice President of the IOC, Avery Brundage, remained skeptical about Soviet participation. However, even he had to admit that, if the IOC was to live up to the Olympic ideals of internationalism and maintain its prestige, "it [was] necessary that National Olympic Committees be organized in all countries as soon as possible."[21]

Despite the enthusiasm of some IOC members, an enduring anti-socialist bias and revelations about the state-run sporting system in the USSR fueled a debate already raging within the IOC over amateurism. In 1947, a special IOC committee headed by Brundage defined an amateur as "one whose connection with sport is and always has been solely for pleasure and for physical, mental and social benefits he derives therefrom and to whom sport is nothing more than recreation without material gain of any kind, direct or indirect."[22] Brundage proved a vocal proponent of Olympic amateurism. He opposed a proposal by Swedish members of the IAAF to change the federation's amateur rules to allow athletes to receive compensation for "broken time" to make up for wages lost due to missed work days resulting from travel to sporting competitions.[23] Similarly, Brundage took on the American Hockey Association, asserting that the organization's athletes were "tainted by professionals" and served commercial interests.[24] Brundage's strict definition of amateurism seemed incompatible with the Soviet system where, according to Edstrøm, "athletes who are intended for participation in international sport matches are concentrated in training camps. They are freed from their jobs, are well paid by the governments and receive—with their families—more and special food."[25] The Soviet Union officially ceased giving out cash prizes to athletes in July 1947.[26] The IOC, however, remained convinced that Soviet athletes were professionals paid by the state and worried that athletes from Eastern Europe would have similar state support.[27] Soviet officials maintained that their athletes worked full time as students, soldiers, or factory workers, but in reality their time was spent training.[28] The revelations over the Soviet state-run athletic system, coming at a time when amateurism was the issue of the day, made the Soviet Olympic entrance highly contestable for Brundage and the IOC.

With the reputation of the IOC at stake, Edstrøm and Brundage felt pressure from both sides. Unable to reconcile the Soviet Union's possible entrance with the Olympic amateur ideal, Brundage found refuge in the IOC's bureaucratic process. Perceiving astutely that a decision either way could damage the IOC's reputation, Brundage assured Edstrøm, "We cannot keep them out but we can be prepared to be just as tough as they are in enforcing our rules and regulations. One rotten apple can do a great deal of damage to the rest of the barrel."[29] Before the Soviet Union formed a National Olympic Committee (NOC) and petitioned the IOC for recognition in 1951, Brundage could avoid dealing with the challenge to the Olympic amateur ideal and focus instead on the more clearly defined rules of the IOC. No country lacking a National Olympic Committee would be invited to participate in the Olympic Games.[30] Having invited the Soviet Union informally to join the Olympic Games, Edstrøm now made several attempts to persuade the chairman of the Soviet Sports Committee, Nikolai Romanov, that the Soviet Union would be allowed to participate in the Olympic Games only if it followed IOC rules and formed a National Olympic Committee.[31] The many missives Edstrøm sent to Romanov went unanswered, creating further anxiety for the IOC president and vice-president. Hearing nothing from their Soviet contact, Edstrøm and Brundage worried that Soviet athletes might arrive at the Helsinki Olympics without the IOC's prior approval. Reminding Edstrøm of the Soviet Union's unexpected appearance at the 1946 European Track and Field Championships in Oslo, Brundage stated, "It would not surprise me if they tried the same stunt at Helsinki in 1952. . . . Not only the IOC but also our Finnish friends must be prepared for this contingency in order to avoid finding ourselves in the middle of a most embarrassing and dangerous controversy."[32] Romanov's silence, however, had more to do with indecision within the Soviet party-state bureaucracy than with a plot to enter the Olympics on their own terms.

"IF YOU ARE NOT READY":
INTERNAL RETREAT AND THE NEED FOR TOTAL VICTORY

If the Olympic project were to be realized, Soviet sports administrators would need to balance demands from international sporting organizations and the IOC with conditions placed upon them by the Soviet leadership. How could the committee make the Soviet-style sports system conform to international standards while promoting the ideological and political goals of Stalin and the Central Committee? The years from 1946 to 1951 saw tremendous upheaval within the Soviet leadership, and this put added pressure on mid-level bureaucrats as they sought patrons within the Politburo. Uncertain as to what approach might induce his superiors to approve an Olympic team, Romanov proceeded with caution as he petitioned for a team to compete in the 1948 London Games.

Soviet sports administrators defended Olympic participation by highlighting their athletes' ability to act as ambassadors for socialism, to bring glory to the Soviet Union, and to promote peace internationally, being careful to frame their proposals within the prevailing ideological platform of the Stalinist leadership. Soviet leaders established the Cominform in 1947 at a meeting of communist leaders in Europe as a means to counter the growing influence of the United States on the continent, represented by the Truman Doctrine and Marshall Plan unveiled earlier that year. At the founding meeting of Cominform, propaganda chief Andrei Zhdanov declared that the world had been divided into two irreconcilable camps and that "communists must be the leading force in the effort to enlist all anti-Fascist, peace-loving elements in the struggle against the new American expansionist plans for the enslavement of Europe."[33] Condemning the "imperialist and anti-democratic" United States, Zhdanov painted the Soviet Union as the leading defender of peace and democracy to an international audience.[34] When Nikolai Romanov asked Zhdanov for permission to prepare a Soviet team for the 1948 Olympic Games, he framed his request in these terms. Stressing the huge popularity of the Games throughout the world, the increasing number of countries joining the Olympics, and the idealized message of the Olympic Movement, Romanov argued, "Considering . . . that the Olympic Games are a symbol of peace, the participation of the Soviet Union in the 1948 Games becomes particularly desirable."[35]

Convinced that only the guarantee of a first place victory would induce the Soviet leadership to send athletes to compete abroad, Romanov also suggested that the country's athletes had a good chance of winning in a wide range of events, insofar as sports had developed so much under the Soviet government.[36] According to Romanov, he had to personally guarantee victory before sending Soviet athletes abroad.[37] Stalin believed that even the second place finish of Soviet wrestlers' at the 1946 European Championships discredited the Soviet Union, and he chastised Romanov for sending a team to the competition, saying, "if you are not ready, then there's no need to participate."[38] So, when Romanov asked Politburo member Andrei Zhdanov for permission to send a team to the 1948 London Games, Romanov couched his request in terms of "total team victory." Conceding that the Soviet Union could not surpass the United States in medals, Romanov asserted nonetheless that by competing in every sport on the program and placing in the top six in those sports, the Soviet team could secure full team victory based on the "unofficial" points system observed by competing nations and the international press.[39]

Despite the obstacles imposed by the party leadership, Romanov and the Sports Committee thought that Soviet athletes and sports officials could serve as important vectors for promoting Soviet interests internationally. As early as 1944, the head of the international division of the Sports Committee, K. I. Nepomniashchii, posited that sporting exchanges should fulfill "concrete diplomatic tasks," that one must not consider sport exchanges as "entertainment," but as "important, difficult, and extremely critical work" for which the "most suitable representative is a specially trained, responsible worker" of the Sports Committee.[40] Nepomniashchii listed the key diplomatic skills that all Soviet sports representatives should possess. According to him, delegation leaders should not only understand the political climate and the priorities of Soviet foreign relations with the country being visited, but should know foreign languages and be able to work comfortably in a foreign environment.[41]

Romanov's request, however, came during a period of Cold War confrontation, xenophobia, and factional politics that made the future of the Olympic project and his own position doubtful. In 1946, Zhdanov initiated an ideological campaign against anyone with affinities or ties with Western culture. As the Stalinist leadership purged from their posts, arrested, and imprisoned people for "kowtowing to the West," student athletes, sports educators, sports scientists, and other officials fell victim.[42] Soviet leaders had also begun to lose interest in international organizations by March 1946, fearing that continued participation would suggest capitulation to a U.S.-led postwar order.[43] Moreover, the Sports Committee journal *Fizicheskaia Kul'tura i Sport* (Physical Culture and Sport) reiterated Soviet opposition to the Olympic Games on the grounds that they were run by capitalists and aristocrats who wished to exclude workers from competing.[44]

The events surrounding Romanov's demotion and reinstatement reveal how the careers of party and state functionaries were shaped by rivalries and factional intrigues within the Politburo. After Zhdanov's death in August 1948, his enemies within the Politburo, Georgii Malenkov and Lavrentii Beria, orchestrated a purge of Zhdanov's former associates in the Leningrad party apparatus. The Olympic project stalled under Zhdanov, but after his downfall, Lavrentii Beria, Georgii Malenkov, and the new propaganda minister, Mikhail Suslov, exhibited more interest in and exerted more control over sports matters. An avid sports fan, Beria in particular used his political position to enhance the secret-police-run sports club Dinamo.[45] After a mixed performance by Soviet speed skaters at the 1948 world championships in Helsinki, Romanov was soon replaced by Nikolai Apollonov, then deputy security chief and head of Dinamo.[46] Romanov, however, remained active in the Sports Committee's work. According to his memoir, soon after his removal as chairman, Romanov received a phone call from Politburo member Georgii Malenkov informing him that Stalin wanted him to remain in the Sports Committee and, on 2 February 1949, he was appointed vice-chairman upon Apollonov's recommendation.[47]

Under Apollonov, the Sports Committee became less assertive in campaigning for Olympic participation. Despite a December 1948 Central Committee resolution, charging all sports committees to "spread sport to every corner of the land, to raise the level of skill and, on that basis, to help Soviet athletes win world supremacy in major sports in the immediate future," international meets occurred rarely between 1948 and 1950.[48] Even socialist sporting contacts, common since the late 1920s, occurred less frequently during that time.[49] Rather than requesting that Soviet athletes compete in London, Apollonov proposed that a group of forty-one sports experts attend the "Olympic Congress" held during the London Games "to study sporting techniques, training methods, and other technical and organizational questions pertaining to the competitions."[50] The contingent, led by Gleb Baklanov, also intended to forge ties with international sport federations and coordinate socialist countries within the sports movement. Noting that his group's late arrival denied it the opportunity to meet with members of international federations or representatives from Eastern Europe, Baklanov lamented that "not a single front of democratic sporting interests was established."[51]

Apollonov's tenure as Sports Committee Chairman revealed tensions between the two purposes of the Soviet sports system—*massovost'* (mass participation in sports) versus *masterstvo* (sporting mastery). The party resolution of 1948 encouraged both expanding sports participation throughout the country and breaking world records. In practice, however, training of elite athletes and promotion of widespread participation often came into conflict. Romanov tells us in his memoir that the Sports Committee became heavily involved in expanding sports education and local sports organizations between 1949 and 1951, founding pedagogical departments, increasing the number of physical culture collectives, and expanding sports curriculum in schools.[52] During this time, the Soviet press emphasized the need to create sports clubs in every village and to expand the number of young people achieving physical fitness minimums.[53] Soviet articles also promoted a distinctly Soviet style of sports and physical education, contrasting the "strength of the collective" in Soviet boxing to the drive for profit in capitalist sport, and insisting on the superiority of "Russian hockey" to the more physical Canadian ice hockey.[54] Even though official discourse linked *massovost'* to the pursuit of world supremacy in sport, expansion of local-level sports no doubt drained the resources allotted to the Sports Committee, thereby limiting the funds available for international travel to competitions.[55] Until Romanov's reinstatement as chairman of the Sports Committee in 1951, preparations for Olympic competition appear to have been a low priority for the Central Committee.

Apollonov appears as a purely political appointee who lacked the qualifications for his job and did not enjoy the confidence and support of his colleagues or underlings. The Sports Committee leadership received considerable criticism about Apollonov from within its ranks, and from other departments and organizations, over the lack of Soviet participation in international sports and his personal management style, revealing conflicting priorities within the party-state apparatus. First Secretary of the Central Committee of the Komsomol, N.A. Mikhailov, complained that Apollonov was perpetually on vacation, and that in his absence "the current staff, for all practical purposes, was doing nothing."[56] In June 1949, Mikhailov again denounced the Sports Committee leadership for failing to send Soviet athletes to compete abroad, "damage[ing] the prestige of Soviet sport" and "[bringing] harm to our Soviet state."[57] Agitprop workers agreed with these assessments. Considering the failure to develop international sports ties as a reflection of poor documentation and oversight by the Sports Committee leadership, they gave Apollonov one month to submit a "suitable plan" for training Soviet athletes for international competitions in 1950.[58]

Apollonov's attempts to address the perceived weaknesses of his committee failed to impress his critics or his superiors. Apollonov sent a proposal to reorganize the Sports Committee, requesting additional funds to improve "material conditions" for Sports Committee workers in order to attract "the most highly qualified specialists." Apollonov also asked for additional facilities for training bases and a new building for the State Central Order of Lenin Institute for Physical Culture, but these measures were apparently not enough to please his detractors.[59] At a meeting of the Party Organization of the Sports Committee in February 1950, members condemned him for everything from lack of proper "criticism" and "self-criticism" to his "bureaucratic leadership style."[60] Many attendees at the meeting complained about the working conditions, blaming Apollonov for poor office space and the lack of training and support available for young workers "to raise their business qualifications" and gain promotions.[61] Many bemoaned that planned sports schools and institutes remained unfinished as well as the lack of physical culture development in villages, trade unions, and republican sports ministries.[62] In July 1950, Agitprop reported further criticism of Apollonov from several Sports Committee workers who condemned Apollonov's handling of international sports relations.[63] A complaint from boxer Korolev reached the desk of Beria, who asked Malenkov to look into it.[64] Apollonov even angered sports writers and football fans when he approved the transfer of *Spartak*'s star Sergei Sal'nikov to *Dinamo*.[65] By early 1951, it was clear that Apollonov "did not enjoy authority among masters of sport and many leading physical culture workers," and Romanov, the chief promoter of the Olympics, again headed the Sports Committee.[66]

Soon after the reinstatement of Romanov, the Soviet Union officially joined the Olympic Movement. On 14 December 1950, the Sports Committee submitted to the Central Committee a request to form a Soviet Olympic Committee.[67] Hearing no response to the request, on 18 April 1951, Romanov reminded the Central Committee that the Vienna session of the IOC would take place in May and that if the Soviet Union had not formed an NOC by that time, Soviet athletes could not compete in the Helsinki Games the following year.[68] On April 23, the Central Committee International Department recommended to Stalin that the Sports Committee request be accepted.[69] That same day, Petr Sobolev sent a telegram to the IOC requesting recognition of the newly formed Soviet National Olympic Committee.[70]

Soviet sports administrators applied for IOC recognition as the Soviet Union began to consolidate its sphere of influence in Eastern Europe, and they hoped to use sports to promote Soviet influence internationally. Once the Soviet NOC formed, Romanov advocated wider participation by Soviet representatives in International Federations, to "allow the widening influence of Soviet sports organizations in the international sports movement, popularization abroad of Soviet sports achievements, and study of the experience of top-level foreign athletes by Soviet masters of sport."[71] Promoting a united communist front in a global confrontation with the West, Soviet leaders hoped to exert influence on international sports organizations through a coordinated effort with East European representatives. In fact, the prospect of the IOC recognizing a West German NOC in part motivated the Central Committee to finally approve a Soviet Olympic Committee.[72] Romanov observed that the Soviet representatives had already made considerable strides in international sports, and that getting into more IFs would not only promote participation in the Olympic Games but, according to Romanov, also would provide "the opportunity to further invigorate the [Soviet] drive for democratization of the international sports movement."[73] Similarly, Petr Sobolev reported that despite the "fascist" and "reactionary" views of several prominent members, "[the IOC] could and should be used by representatives of the Soviet Union and the peoples' democracies as one means of drawing athletes of all countries into the struggle for peace throughout the world."[74] Though motivated by Cold-War concerns, Romanov recast Soviet aims to fit within the discourse of the Olympic Movement. Soviet sports administrators exploited the rhetoric of peace, common to both Olympism and Soviet communist ideology, to justify the Soviet presence in the Olympic Movement to both the Central Committee and the IOC.

"WHO DO WE KNOW IN RUSSIA?"
THE SOVIET UNION JOINS THE "OLYMPIC FAMILY"

Soviet goals, however, came into direct conflict with the prevailing effort of the IOC to combat nationalism within the Olympic family. Officially, IOC members represent the interests of the Olympic Movement to their native countries and do not serve as their nations' representatives to the IOC. Fearing an unwelcome intrusion of state interests, the IOC sought to maintain its independence from state politics by choosing carefully its representatives in communist countries. Concerned that East European NOCs were falling under the control of government ministries, Brundage wrote to Edstrøm in late 1947, "it looks like we're in for a bitter struggle to maintain our freedom."[75] In fact, nationalism was nothing new to the Olympic Movement. As athletes represented their nation, marched under their nation's flag, and heard their nation's anthem played when they won a medal, the Games were imbued with nationalism. Still, Brundage blamed the Soviet Union and its East European neighbors for bringing politics and nationalism into the Olympic Games in the postwar period.

The real problem, however, was that the IOC was traditionally self-perpetuated through social networks that did not extend to the Soviet Union. As Brundage noted, "aside from all this who do we know in Russia?"[76] Edstrøm too agonized over this question declaring, "The greatest trouble will be to find men that we can have present in the IOC. I do not feel inclined to go so far as to admit communists there."[77] Indeed, much of Brundage and Edstrøm's objection to the Soviet Union's participation reflected a personal disdain for what they perceived as boorishness and ignorance of commonly held values and modes of conduct. When his many missives to the Soviet Union went unanswered by Romanov, Edstrøm complained, "Perhaps he does not care, but probably he does not know that one should answer a letter."[78] Brundage too portrayed an elitist attitude toward Romanov and his cohort when he wrote, "As you know, I have kept my fingers crossed on the efforts to bring [the Soviets] into the Olympic family. Not understanding fair play, good sportsmanship and amateurism, I am sure they will bring with them nothing but trouble."[79] More than a desire to uphold the ideals and rules of the IOC, these statements reveal prejudice against the Soviet representatives as people who did not share his background and values.

When the IOC discussed recognition of the new Soviet National Olympic Committee in May 1951, Brundage and others expressed concern over the professional status of Soviet athletes. To ensure that the Soviet state-run sports system did not conflict with the Olympic Charter, one committee member suggested that the Soviet NOC be required to present its regulations for inspection. Lord Burghley of Great Britain, who had encouraged Soviet participation on his visit to Moscow in 1947, proved to be the leading supporter of the Soviet NOCs recognition. Arguing that they had never asked for the rules of other nations, he spoke out against investigating Soviet sports regulations.[80] Sobolev's telegram requesting recognition by the IOC stated simply, "We inform you that an Olympic Committee was created in the USSR. This Olympic Committee examined the rules of the IOC and declares them accepted."[81] Ultimately, the IOC members decided to rely on Sobolev's assurances. The question over the amateur status of Soviet athletes remained unanswered, and the IOC recognized the Soviet Union's Olympic Committee by a vote of thirty-one in favor with three abstentions.

THE SOVIET UNION'S MAN IN THE IOC: KONSTANTIN ALEKSANDROVICH ANDRIANOV

Once the Soviet NOC was recognized, the IOC members considered the nomination of Konstantin Andrianov as a Soviet member of the IOC. Andrianov proved a strong candidate for the position from the perspective of the Soviet leadership. As the former chairman of the Moscow city sports committee and the vice chairman of the national Sports Committee since 1941, he had traveled abroad to Bulgaria, England, France, Czechoslovakia, Norway, Holland, and Hungary. He also had the proper class and party credentials as a former mill operator and regional Komsomol secretary, and he had just completed at degree at the Higher Party School.[82] Oddly enough, there was no discussion within the IOC over Andrianov's independence from government control or his ability to represent the ideals of the IOC in the Soviet Union.[83] When his nomination was put up for debate, the only objection was that he did not speak either of the official languages of the IOC. Once again Lord Burghley came to the Soviet delegate's defense, declaring that Andrianov was a true sportsman and "that is much more important for [the IOC] than knowledge of languages."[84] Upon entering his first IOC meeting, Andrianov assured his fellow members that he would "cooperate sincerely with the IOC for the good of the Olympic Movement in [his] country and for world peace."[85] Andrianov overcame hesitancy among IOC members by presenting himself as a sports authority and keen promoter of Olympism.

The ease with which the IOC recognized Soviet membership and ratified Andrianov's nomination may seem unexpected, but it reveals important things about the way the IOC operated. Personal ties were essential for securing a positive vote within the IOC. The spectacular physical culture parade that Lord Burghley attended in 1947 no doubt made an impression and encouraged his advocacy for Soviet Olympic participation. Olympic idealism also played a key role amid the changing international environment. By 1951, the Soviet Union had detonated an atomic bomb, Mao Zedong's Communist Party had come to power in China, Eastern Europe had become a part of the Soviet bloc, and the Korean War had begun. Accepting the Soviet Union's bid during a time of highly charged tensions internationally could give the Olympic Games credibility as a vehicle for international understanding. For Brundage and the IOC, Olympic internationalism proved a more powerful motivator than anti-communism.[86]

Andrianov proved very adept at reading the political atmosphere within the IOC, couching his aims in terms that seemed likely to garner support, and employing a series of strategies to convince Brundage and other IOC members of his authority as a sports administrator in the Soviet Union. Key to Andrianov's influence in the Olympic Movement was his ability to adopt the language of Olympism and adapt to the political traditions and practices of the IOC and other international sports organizations. At times, Andrianov served as a rule watchdog, reminding IOC members of the IOC Charter and By-Laws and exposing actions that seemed to go against IOC regulations. Andrianov also cultivated a wide array of personal relationships and networks with other IOC members, and when questions arose over what was happening "behind the Iron Curtain," Andrianov ensured that IOC members would look to him for answers.

Andrianov used his growing influence to further "democratize" international sports. Immediately upon his election to the IOC, Andrianov began to push for greater representation in the Olympic Movement by countries within the Soviet sphere of influence, supporting the bids for IOC recognition by the Peoples' Republic of China (PRC) and the German Democratic Republic (GDR). Stressing Olympic principles of international cooperation, democracy, and freedom, Andrianov spoke out vociferously in favor of officially recognizing a separate East German NOC. He argued that refusing to do so would place the East German athletes "under the domination of the committee of the West," effectively "ignor[ing] a region of 22 million inhabitants."[87]

Establishing Soviet authority abroad had direct implications for political maneuvering within the Soviet Union, and the way Andrianov pushed Soviet political agendas in the nominally apolitical IOC evoked criticism from other Soviet administrators. In a report to the Central Committee, the editor of *Sovetskii Sport*, N. Liubomirov, accused Andrianov of "serious mistakes" in his activities in the IOC. According to Liubomirov, Andrianov had "showed complete political shortsightedness, took the side of bourgeois sports leaders, [and] misled public opinion" when he failed to achieve permission for the athletes from the PRC and the GDR to compete in the Helsinki Games.[88] When his report went unanswered he followed it up with a letter to Komsomol head N. A. Mikhailov maintaining that, "Andrianov's behavior . . . brought great damage to the campaign to strengthen the position of the Soviet Union and peoples' democracies in the international sports movement."[89] Couching his criticism of Andrianov within the overall goals of Soviet sports organizations in international sporting politics, Liubomirov employed a common practice of postwar Stalinist politics: making personal appeals to higher party authorities to settle professional disagreements.

Andrianov successfully defended himself against Liubomirov's accusations by convincing the party leadership that he knew best how to solve the East German and Chinese questions in the IOC. Insisting that Soviet representatives and those from the "people's democracies" could only exert influence by working with "bourgeois" members who recognized the "eminent authority" of Soviet sports, Andrianov shifted the blame to the GDR representatives, K. Edel and A. Strauss, who, he said, "were extremely inexperienced to solve such a critical problem."[90] He also upheld his "correct" approach in exploiting the "differences of opinion" existing in the IOC to win support for Soviet proposals from members "who do not want the dictates of the pro-American group."[91] On the question of China's recognition, Andrianov noted that the Chinese representative "was completely unprepared for the decision, not knowing the rules and regulations of the IOC" and that he had scored "a huge victory," by helping to secure the opportunity for his "Chinese comrades" to meet with IF delegates.[92] Dismissing Liubomirov's charge as an "irresponsible document that demonstrates the thoughtlessness of its author in resolving serious problems," Andrianov argued that Soviet representatives "objectively and properly informed the Sports Committee" of all aspects of the discussion regarding the PRC and GDR questions.[93] Following an inquiry, Romanov and Stepanov in Agitprop concluded that Liubomirov based his allegations on his "personal impressions" since he was "unfamiliar" with Andrianov's directives.[94] The Central Committee relied upon Andrianov's expertise and based its directives on his observations and recommendations which, unlike Liubomirov's, were not merely his "personal impressions" but informed opinions based on clearly documented evidence of his dealings in the IOC.

"THANKS TO GREAT COMRADE STALIN": SOVIET BUREAUCRACY, THE POLITBURO, AND OLYMPIC PREPARATIONS

The election of Andrianov to the IOC and the recognition of the Soviet NOC cleared one hurdle to Olympic participation. The Soviet leadership, however, continued to withhold permission for a team to be sent to the Games. As debate raged within the Sports Committee over the strength of the Soviet Olympic training program, invitations to compete in both the Winter Games in Oslo and the Helsinki Summer Games remained unanswered. At the same time, budget constraints and continued avoidance of foreign sporting contacts further jeopardized the Olympic project. Just as personal contacts and the regulatory nature of the IOC helped the Sports Committee secure a voice in the IOC, bureaucratic skill and connections within the Politburo helped Romanov and Andrianov to navigate the obstacles facing them and to assemble an Olympic team. A close reading of their correspondence in the months leading up to the Soviet Olympic debut helps to illuminate the relative authority of officials in the sports bureaucracy.

Following his reinstatement in 1951, Romanov spearheaded Olympic preparations and distinguished himself in his ability to balance relations with the IOC and the Politburo. Romanov also relied heavily on Andrianov and other leaders within the Sports Committee to maintain control over Olympic training measures. In June 1951, the official invitation to participate in the 1952 Winter Games set off a flurry of in-house memos and reports deliberating the Soviet athletes' chances for success.[95] A report from the scientific-sporting administration stated that Soviet skaters and skiers could expect to win their competitions.[96] The Sports Committee, however, wanted a more precise idea of Soviet chances. With the decision to compete in either the Winter or Summer Games still up in the air, Andrianov called on various departments in the sports apparatus to compare their athletes' achievements to those of foreign athletes to assess the state of Olympic training.[97] Setting 1 November 1951 as the deadline, Andrianov hoped to gather all necessary information so that a decision could be reached regarding Olympic participation.

Following Andrianov's memorandum, trainers and department heads tried to make their voices heard through letters to Romanov, Suslov, and even to Stalin's son and personal secretary, Vasilii Iosifovich, defending their ath-

letes' preparedness and thereby their personal efforts to train them successfully. Romanov, however, remained unconvinced that Soviet athletes could
dominate the winter Games in Oslo. Proclaiming that the time had come to
realize the Central Committee resolution of 1948, head of the Department of
Skating, Z. V. Kuchmenko promised "a successful appearance in the upcoming Olympic Games" from his skaters would "raise the authority and power
of the Soviet state even higher."[98] Similarly, the head of the Department of
International Sporting Affairs, Sobolev, petitioned Romanov on behalf of
Soviet hockey players maintaining "no doubt" that the Soviet team would
medal.[99] Sobolev, like Kuchmenko, situated his project within the overall
objectives of the Soviet leadership, emphasizing the importance of winning
a full team victory. Yet Romanov held his ground, maintaining that without
"firm certainty" that Soviet athletes would win first place, "participation in
the Olympic Games is pointless."[101] Afterward, Soviet hockey and skiing
trainers and officials went over Romanov's head, challenging Propaganda
Minister Mikhail Suslov to uphold the 1948 "historic decision of the Central
Committee," and reconsider sending a team to Oslo.[100] Warning him against
an egregious political mistake, these appeals got Suslov's attention: he asked
Romanov and two members of the Department of Agitation and Propaganda
to reexamine this question.[102] When Romanov rebuffed the skating and skiing
administrators, they appealed to Stalin's son and personal secretary.[103] Arguing that Romanov's estimation of Soviet chances was wrong, Chairman of the
Department of International Sporting Relations Sobolev and his vice-chairman, Senkevich argued that as first-timers, "winning second or third place . . .
would be considered good since no novices have ever achieved such results."
Contending that full team victory was unnecessary, Sobolev and Senkevich
warned that since "refusal to participate in the Winter Olympics would be
widely used in the bourgeois press to promote hostility toward the Soviet
Union," causing "even more harm than an unsuccessful performance."[104] Unfortunately, by emphasizing the potential benefits of winning only second or
third place, Sobolev and Senkevich undermined their own efforts. Citing the
lack of international competition and the underdevelopment of winter sports,
Romanov contends that the Sports Committee decided to forego the Winter
Games to better prepare for the summer ones.[105] That this last petition went
unheeded suggests that Romanov gauged the opinions within the Politburo
more accurately than his rivals and enjoyed the support of important members
of the Soviet leadership.

The limits imposed on international competition left Romanov and the
sports administrators in a desperate situation as they tried to prepare a winning team for the 1952 Summer Olympic Games. In August 1951, Komsomol head Nikolai Mikhailov complained in a letter to Malenkov of the

serious deficiency in studying foreign training methods and the lack of adequate guides and reference books. Calling for the incorporation of Western
training methods into the Soviet sports system, he proposed that the Department of International Relations of the Sports Committee be strengthened and
that trainers be sent to Sweden, Norway, Finland, Hungary, England, Italy,
and France to study their training methods and athletic achievements. He
also asked that the Sports Committee be allowed to publish foreign sports literature and that the Ministry of Internal Affairs (MVD) help gather information from countries preparing for the Olympic Games.[106] On 30 April 1952,
less than two months before the opening of the Games in Helsinki, Romanov
wrote to Malenkov requesting that the Ministry of Foreign Affairs (MID)
provide information to the Sport Committee about the Olympic training of
foreign athletes, specifically those from the United States, England, Switzerland, and France.[107] The dearth of foreign sporting contacts continued in
the months leading up to the Helsinki Olympics, forcing Romanov to obtain
through the MID what his committee had been unable to get through international competition and trainer exchanges. Soviet sports leaders struggled
with the question of international experience almost to the eve of the Soviet
Olympic debut.

As president of the Soviet NOC, Andrianov was forced to balance the
demands of this position with his subordinate one as vice-chairman of the Soviet Sports Committee, and this dual role placed particular pressure on him.
As the primary contact for the IOC and Olympic organizing committees, he
often fielded questions regarding training measures and plans to participate,
but the high level of centralization of the Soviet bureaucracy meant that he
needed approval from his superiors before making any statements to foreigners. Seeking information on Soviet chances in Helsinki, Andrianov sent out
a memo in October 1951 to several departments requesting information on
training progress.[108] From the head of the economic administration of the
committee, he ordered a detailed report of training camps, including equipment and dietary considerations. From the heads of the educational-sporting
administration and the administration of sporting games, Andrianov wanted
a list of Olympic participants and trainers by type of sport, a list of potential
judges for the Games, inventory and uniform needs, and a plan for athletes'
training by sport. These departments, along with the heads of the Central
Scientific-Research Institute of Physical Culture and the Department of International Sporting Relations, were to draw up the comparison reports of
Soviet and foreign athletes mentioned above. In October 1951, the head of the
press service of the Organizing Committee of the 1952 Winter Games in Oslo
asked Andrianov whether the Soviet Union intended to participate.[108] Then,
in November, the president of the Organizing Committee in Helsinki, Erik

von Frenckell, wanted to know if a decision had been made about the Summer Games.[109] The following month, Andrianov gave Frenckell preliminary acceptance of his invitation to participate in the Helsinki Games but delayed reporting any final decision until just before their opening.[110] He hesitated because he was not given leave to send a definitive answer. In a letter dated 2 June 1952, Andrianov requested instructions from the MVD on how to answer an urgent demand from Frenckell on whether the Soviet Union would participate in the Helsinki Games.[111]

When Olympic training began in earnest in 1951, the Sports Committee had to resort to Soviet-style *shturmovshchina*: a rushed, sporadic production spurt in order to prepare a team for Helsinki. In the months leading up to the Helsinki Games, Romanov convinced his superiors in the Politburo to augment the Sports Committee's budget and to fund Olympic training. In February 1952, Politburo member Mikhail Suslov authorized the ministries and departments to release all Olympic athletes from work and school with pay for the six months leading up to the Games and to send doctors and nurses to the training camps. In addition, Suslov endorsed an increase in the number of athletes by two hundred and the hiring of another fifty-five employees to the Sports Committee.[112] Then in May, Romanov appealed to Malenkov for an increase in the daily food expenditure from fifty to sixty-five rubles for athletes in the most draining sports—including boxing, soccer, swimming, and long-distance running, among others.[113]

While training progressed in the Olympic camps, the Sports Committee remained busy answering questions, hearing complaints, and solving problems brought to its attention by the trainers on the ground. Since the goal was to compete in every sport, each difficulty encountered threatened the entire Olympic debut. For instance, the head of the Department of Water Sports, Nikolai Adamovich, complained that the Soviet Ministry of State Security and the MGB of Estonia refused access for all parasailers to train on the Baltic Sea and that the necessary forms had not been sent to join the international federation for water sports.[114] Similarly, one month before the Games, Andrianov received a reminder from the Helsinki Organizing Committee that the Soviet Union had not yet officially joined the International Equestrian Federation.[115] Later Adamovich reported that several of his yachtsmen had not received any salary and threatened to go home if the problem with their pay was not resolved.[116] Complaints about improper equipment also came in from trainers for shooting, yachting, equestrian events, pentathlon, and fencing.[117] These trainers hoped to pressure Romanov to rethink the priorities of the Sports Committee and attend to their equipment and training needs.

As the central authority over sports, the Sports Committee oversaw every aspect of the training regimen, especially when it came to questions of personnel, equipment, and diet (*pitanie*). While the Russian word *pitanie* encompasses a variety of items concerning nutrition and diet, the documents demonstrate that, in the context of Olympic training, the word also meant special "vitamins" and "tablets"—in other words, drugs. Andrianov received a report in May from the track and field training base near Kiev requesting authorization for a "special supplement in tablet form" for the marathoners and race walkers and permission to try stimulants.[118] The report indicates that researchers had already submitted data on these new tablets to the committee. Later that month, the Presidium of the Scientific-Methods Council of the Sports Committee issued a protocol advising the manufacture of "special concentrations" for the nourishment of the marathoners so that they will become accustomed to the new concentrations during training.[119] Responding to the pressure to produce a full team victory, the Sports Committee authorized the use of experimental drugs on Soviet athletes less than two months before the opening of the Games.

Soviet scientists were not alone in their development of performance-enhancing drugs. At an international conference on sports and health held in Norway in February 1952, the Norwegian director of public health called for a united effort against "the use of dope in the amateur sports world."[120] After the games, American scientists denied that doping took place in the Helsinki Games, claiming that modern scientific training and diet accounted for the surprising numbers of world records set during the event. Despite this denial from their chief rival's science personnel, Soviet athletes endured speculation that they had been sniffing an unknown substance before their events.[121] The U.S. weightlifting coach Bob Hoffman left Helsinki convinced that Soviet lifters had been taking testosterone.[122] After the formulation of a synthetic alternative, steroid use in American sports became widespread, and doping became a fixture of the Cold War Olympics.[123] Whether the Soviet scientists learned the advantages of doping from studying Western methods or vice versa, by including experimental drugs into the Olympic-training program, the Sports Committee was in step with the international sports community.

Faced with logistical problems and complaints from the training camps, Romanov and his staff still had to convince the Politburo that the Soviet team would win the competition. In the end, the Soviet Union's chances of victory came down to an elaborate game of numbers. While the IOC does not recognize rankings by country, Soviet leaders demanded a prediction of Soviet success based on an unofficial point system by which to calculate national rankings. Romanov predicted that the Soviet team would win eight events and the U.S. seven in the Helsinki Games.[124] The rest they would split equally. The following month, Romanov held a meeting with sports leaders, trainers, and athletes who offered their personal testimonies to the Soviet team's potential.[125] One of the coaches guaranteed that "thanks to the concern for our athletes on the part of the Soviet government, party, and great Comrade Stalin," his cyclists had received "excellent preparation for the upcoming competition."[126] Romanov and the Sports Committee could do nothing at this point but cross their fingers and wait for the results.

"NOT JUST ANOTHER EVENT": THE SOVIET UNION'S OLYMPIC DEBUT

The Soviet Union's entrance into the Olympic Games turned them into a competition dominated by the United States and the Soviet Union. As president of the United States Olympic Committee, Brundage met a potential head-to-head competition between American and Soviet athletes with trepidation. He worried that Soviet success would damage the U.S. reputation abroad in much the same way the Soviet leaders feared a U.S. victory. Believing that state funding gave the Soviet athletes an unfair advantage over U.S. athletes, who relied on "the generosity of the sport loving public" for funding, Brundage wrote to President Harry Truman in the months leading up to the Helsinki Games to request the president's endorsement of the Olympic Committee's fundraising efforts. [127] As he put it, "Now that Russia and the countries behind the Iron Curtain are all sending large government subsidized teams to the Olympic Games, it is more than ever important that we send the strongest team possible."[128] Truman echoed Brundage's sentiments: "This competition is not just another event. It requires the finest American athletes we can send, it requires the fullest support Americans can give. The eyes of the world will be upon us."[129]

The Soviet sports organizers demonstrated similar apprehension over their image abroad. As the Helsinki Olympics drew near, Romanov reported to Politburo member Malenkov that the "bourgeois press" believed that this Olympics would surpass all previous ones and had suggested that the USSR's team was one of "the teams to watch." He also informed Malenkov of the huge influx of foreign tourists expected. According to Romanov, the organizers had sold 50,000 tickets and expected to sell 30,000 more, and they anticipated up to 2,000 foreign correspondents to attend, with more than 200 from the United States. Realizing that participation in such a conspicuous event as the Olympic Games could also open the Soviet Union to unfavorable publicity, Romanov asked that all information related to international sport be released by TASS (the Soviet news agency) solely with the agreement of Agitprop. His stated reason was to "keep secret" and "avoid divulgence" of materials related to the Soviet athletes' training.[130] Romanov wanted control of the Soviet Union's image to rest with the Central Committee and not with Western journalists.

While Romanov worked to "avoid divulgence" of Soviet preparations, Western press agents pressured Andrianov for information on the Soviet athletes' training. Reuters correspondent Andrew John Steiger bombarded Andrianov with a number of questions regarding Soviet Olympic preparations. Steiger requested information on everything from whether special training camps existed, to what the athletes were planning to eat and whether the Soviet delegation would stay in the Olympic Village.[131] Since he was not free to give a simple "yes, we will participate" to the Olympic organizers, Andrianov surely could not have answered detailed questions about the Soviet Olympic plans from a Western journalist. Sobolev prepared an answer to Steiger, but the letter was never sent.[132]

Characteristic of a closed society, Soviet administrators hesitated to inform the foreign press and Olympic organizers about their training regimen. This silence, however, was broken periodically with well-organized, strategically timed displays of hospitality designed to further increase the Soviet Union's international prestige. While publicly denouncing the IOC for its bourgeois elitism, Andrianov and the newly recognized Soviet Olympic Committee tried to win IOC president Edstrøm over with vodka and caviar.[133] Romanov and Soviet sports officials tried the same tactic with a group of U.S. athletes and trainers, treating them to a lavish dinner replete with steak, wine, vodka, and caviar.[134] The image of the IOC and Western sports as elitist was therefore not just a critique used to denounce the West in Soviet propaganda, but represented an attitude among the Soviet sports administrators that influenced their interchange with IOC members. The Soviet leaders hoped to win friends abroad by catering to the social attitudes of the international sports community.

In both the air of secrecy and the displays of generosity, Romanov and the Sports Committee served as the primary conduit of information and the guardians of the Soviet Union's image. Romanov again found himself in this uncomfortable position as the Games progressed in Helsinki. To encourage the Soviet and eastern bloc athletes, the Soviet officials in Finland constructed a scoreboard in the eastern bloc Olympic village, keeping a running tally of the unofficial points as each event ended. Just before the end of the Games, however, the Soviet side took down the scoreboard.[135] The reason for this becomes clear as one looks at discrepancies in the unofficial point totals of the United States and the Soviet Union. At the end of the Olympic Games in Helsinki, *Pravda*, the official newspaper of the Communist Party, proclaimed victory without reference to point totals.[136] On the same day, the *New York Times* claimed a win for the United States based on a score of 614 to 553 1/2.[137] Upon his return to Soviet Union, Romanov told the members of the Politburo that, while the United States had won more medals in the Games, the Soviet Union tied with the United States in number of points with 494. This revised total appeared in the *New York Times* on 7 August.[138] Part of the disparity comes from the use of two different point systems. Romanov calculated his results assigning seven points for first place, five for second, four for third, and so on, but the U.S. system gave ten points for first place. Hours after Romanov's appearance before the Politburo, Malenkov called to confirm the totals. Satisfied with the assurance that the United States had not won outright, the Politburo declared its first Olympic Games an adequate success, and Malenkov told Romanov to "Relax. Go home. Rest."[139]

CONCLUSION

While the Olympic ideal promoted peace and understanding among nations, the Soviet leaders saw Olympic participation as an opportunity to show the world the superior technique and training achieved by the Soviet system of mass, collective physical culture. Burdened by a leadership that was hesitant to open up to the West by sending athletes and trainers abroad, the sports administrators mustered all the resources at their disposal and sought to convince Soviet leaders to send their athletes to the Olympic Games. The trainers and sports administrators on all levels demonstrated a degree of maneuverability within the Stalinist system to achieve their own ends, finding ways to advance their own projects by relating them to their superiors' priorities.

New studies of Soviet academies, bureaucracies, and other administrative units provide additional insight into how changing dynamics within the Politburo affected the articulation and implementation of policy in the Soviet Union. In his monograph on Stalinist science, Nikolai Krementsov describes how personal contacts within the party-state leadership provided scientific administrators with a means to influence decisions to achieve their own ends while leaving them vulnerable to the constant bureaucratic intrigues and reorganizations.[140] As a result of this system of personal patronage, the most successful scientists rose through the party apparatus becoming hybrids of a sort, both members of the scientific community as well as party functionaries.[141] A similar process can be seen within the Sports Committee. Both Romanov and Andrianov rose to prominence in the Komsomol before moving to the state sport apparatus, and both benefitted from the support of powerful patrons within the Politburo. Sobolev's wartime record earned him trust within the party leadership, and he combined work in the security apparatus with his role in the NOC. Well-versed in the politics surrounding Olympic sport, he acted independently, appealing to higher-level officials and even breaking from the official script of "full team victory." When lower-level administrators questioned their decisions, Romanov's and Andrianov's contacts in the Politburo supported their authority and implemented their recommendations. All three men outlasted their apparent patrons in the Soviet party-state apparatus, demonstrating skills and tactics that presaged the governing style of Stalin's successors.[142] The years of the Soviet Union's first steps into international sport could be seen as the beginning of a new era rather than the last years under Stalin.

Central planning was both an asset and an obstacle to getting things done in the Soviet Union under Stalin, and the Olympic preparations are a case in point. Having set itself the goal of competing successfully in as many events as possible, the party-state mustered more athletes and expanded the Sports Committee personnel, thereby increasing the number of people working on Olympic preparations. When party leaders hesitated to expose their athletes to foreign influences, centralization of resources allowed the Soviet Union to assemble the best athletes and make an impressive debut despite faulty equipment and lack of international competitive experience. This centralization of power and resources also affected the way administrators did their jobs: they had to get permission before they could act. When their targets proved to be inadequate for training, the pentathlon coaches brought the problem to the attention of the Sports Committee and, failing to get satisfaction there, moved on to other influential men in the party apparatus. This reliance on the party hierarchy resulted in long periods of delay and inactivity punctuated by spurts of productivity and last minute measures, *shturmovshchina*. The Olympic project succeeded because individuals took initiative and convinced the leadership to authorize the expense, pooling its resources to organize a successful team.

Romanov, Andrianov, and Sobolev displayed great political skill in their dealings with the Politburo, but their approach to the IOC was no less successful. Securing Andrianov as a member of the IOC allowed Romanov the space necessary to negotiate between the pressures from the Soviet leadership and the international sporting community. Key to their success in dealings with the IOC was their ability to adopt the language of Olympism and their keen sense of the importance of personal connections in the IOC political culture. This bureaucratic skill to co-opt ideological language and to cultivate personal patronage was perfected in the Soviet party-state system and transferred easily to the Olympic arena.

The Soviet Union's entrance into the Olympic Games represented an important development in the Cold War by providing a venue for peaceful contact and exchange to balance the highly charged climate of international politics. The issues of amateurism and nationalism were never resolved after the Soviet Union's entrance into the Olympic family, but as long as Soviet members of the IOC were able to promote the Olympic ideals, real tensions created by their state-run system proved less significant. The Soviet Union was not kept out of the Games despite the fundamental political differences it accentuated within the IOC because all could agree on the ideals of Olympism. Even anti-communist Avery Brundage could come to terms with the Soviet Union's entrance once he saw for himself "the vast physical training program and the progress that has been made in the USSR."[143] Dazzled by elaborate sports parades on his visit to the USSR in 1954, Brundage convinced himself that the reports he had heard of grim-faced sporting automatons were unfounded. Becoming a key promoter of the excellence of the Soviet athletes, he remarked, "They weren't forced. They were having a wonderful time."[144] John Hoberman argues that, in the face of division, the IOC adopted a "language in which Olympic officials and communist functionaries [felt] supremely comfortable," but warns that "such language also serves as a screen behind which the voice of conscience is sacrificed to a myth of global consensus."[145] Yet, as long as Andrianov could proclaim that "the Soviet athletes treat the Olympic Games not 'as a major battle in the Cold War' but as an international forum for dissemination of the noble Olympic ideas of peace and consolidation of friendship between the nations," he and the IOC could at least give the impression of working together for peace.

NOTES

1. Elena Zubkova, *Russia After the War: Hopes, Illusions, and Disappointments, 1945–1957*, trans. Hugh Ragsdale (Armonk, NY and London: M. E. Sharpe, 1998).

2. Yoram Gorlizki and Oleg Khlevniuk, *Cold Peace*.

3. Tomoff, *Creative Union*, 36.

4. Krementsov, *Stalinist Science*, 254. See also See David Holloway, *Stalin and the Bomb: The Soviet Union and Atomic Energy, 1939–56* (New Haven: Yale University, 1994); J. Eric Duskin, *Stalinist Reconstruction and the Confirmation of a New Elite, 1945–1953* (Houndmills, Basingstoke, and Hampshire: Palgrave Macmillan, 2001); Pollock, *Stalin and the Soviet Science Wars*; Alexei Kojevnikov, "Rituals of Stalinist Culture"; and Tomoff, *Creative Union*.

5. Nikolai Romanov served as committee chairman from 1945–1948 and again from 1951–1952. During the interim, Arakadii Apollonov was chairman, and Romanov served as vice-chairman.

6. Riordan, *Sport in Soviet Society*, 125.

7. See Sheila Fitzpatrick, "Stalin and the Making of a New Elite, 1928–1939," *Slavic Review*: 38.3 (1979), 377–402.

8. Romanov, *Trudnye dorogi k Olimpu* (Moscow: Fizkul'tura i Sport, 1987), 14–15.

9. I.T. Novikov to TsK KPSS, 21 January 1980, GARF f. 9610, op. 1, d. 484, ll. 5–6.

10. Romanov, *Trudnye dorogi*, 19–20.

11. "Znamenitye urozhentsy Emetskoi zemli," Emetsk online: Site of Emetsk Arkhangel'skoi oblasti, available at http://www.emezk.ru/forum/topic.aspx?topic_id=23&page=6.

12. Zubkova, *Russia after the War*, 89.

13. Kiril Tomoff, "'Most Respected Comrade . . .': Patrons, Clients, Brokers and Unofficial Networks in the Stalinist Music World," *Contemporary European History* 11.1 (2002): 36.

14. John Hoberman, "Toward a Theory of Olympic Internationalism," *Journal of Sports History* 22, no. 1 (1995): 11, 12.

15. Guttman, *The Olympics*, 2.

16. Guttmann, *The Olympics*, 12.

17. Ferenc Mezö, "Olympic Peace—World Peace," *Bulletin du Comité International Olympique* 29 (1951): 24.

18. Edstrøm to Brundage, 4 December 1946, Avery Brundage Collection, University of Illinois Archives Record Series 26/20/34 (hereafter ABC), Box 42. See also Edstrøm to Brundage, 31 October 1946.

19. Arthur E. Porrit of the British Olympic Association to Brundage, 24 July 1947, ABC Box 130.

20. Aksel' Vartanian, "Sekretnyi arkhiv Akselia Vartaniana," *Sport-ekspress*, 2 September 2002, http://www.sport-express.ru. On the 50th anniversary of the Soviet Olympic debut, Vartanian published a collection of archival documents concerning the Soviet Union's decision to enter the Olympics in a Russian sports online newspaper *Sport-ekspress* (Sports Express) under the title "Sekretnyi arkhiv Akselia Vartaniana" (The Secret Archive of Aksel' Vartanian). See also Nikolai Romanov, *Trudnye dorogi k Olimpu* (Moscow: Fizkul'tura i sport, 1987), 42.

21. Report to IOC by Sydney Dawes, Miguel Moenck and Avery Brundage, 25 April 1949, ABC Box 76.

22. Sydney Dawes report of IOC meeting with international federations, 26–27 June 1947, ABC Box 75.

23. "Men from 45 Olympic Nations Expected to Attend Amateur Congress–US Among Opponents to Swedish Proposal," *New York Times*, 6 June 1946, 29.

24. "Brundage Expects Decision on Hockey to Be Far-Reaching," *New York Times*, 25 January 1948, 1(S).

25. Edstrøm to Brundage, 12 November 1947, ABC Box 149.

26. Riordan, "Rewriting Sports History," 248.

27. Brundage to Mayer, 10 February 1951, ABC Box 46.

28. Riordan, "Rewriting Sports History," 252.

29. Brundage to Edstrøm, 30 October 1947, ABC Box 42.

30. "The Position of Soviet Russia," *Bulletin du Comité International Olympique*, 25 (1947): 26.

31. Edstrøm to N. Romanov, November 25, 1946, ABC Box 42.

32. Brundage to Edstrøm, 12 July 1950, ABC Box 149. Edstrøm had invited the Soviet Union to become a member of the International Amateur Athletic Association and to participate in the competition, but he received no reply prior to the arrival of the Soviet contingent in Oslo. Edstrøm to N. Romanov, 25 November 1946, ABC Box 42.

33. Quoted in "Soviet Bloc Peace Defense Laws," *American Journal of International Law* 46.3 (1952): 538.

34. Politburo Member Andrei Zhdanov, "Speech at the Inauguration of the Cominform," late September 1947, House Committee on Foreign Affairs, *The Strategy and Tactics of World Communism*, 216–17, 223–24, 229, quoted in Michael H. Hunt, *The World Transformed: 1945 to the Present A Documentary Reader* (Boston and New York: Bedford/ St. Martin's, 2004), 34.

35. Romanov to Zhdanov, early 1947, GARF, f. 7576, op. 1, d. 623, ll. 2–7; Vartan'ian, "Sekretnyi arkhiv," 2 September 2002.

36. Ibid.

37. Romanov, *Trudnye dorogi*, 57.

38. Ibid., 64.

39. Romanov to Zhdanov, 1947, "Sekretnyi arkhiv," September 2, 2002.

40. K.I. Nepomniashchii to V.V. Snegov, 4 January 1944, GARF, f. 7576, op. 2, d. 248, ll. 152, 155–56.

41. Ibid.

42. For some idea of the scope of such purges in the sports bureaucracy see Riordan, "Rewriting Sports History," 250.

43. Vladislav M. Zubok, *Failed Empire: The Soviet Union in the Cold War from Stalin to Gorbachev* (Chapel Hill: University of North Carolina Press, 2007), 51–52.

44. Riordan, "Rewriting Sports History," 249. Riordan does not cite the date of the article only that it appeared soon after a rumor began to circulate that the Soviet Union would participate in the 1948 Games.

45. Edelman, *Spartak*, 165–66, 186–87. See also Amy Knight, *Beria: Stalin's First Lieutenant* (Princeton: Princeton University Press, 1995), 159–60.

46. Romanov, *Trudnye dorogi*, 66–69. Soviet women won their events, but no one on the men's team came in third place with no one ranking higher than twelfth place in their individual events.

47. Ibid., 71. See also D. Shepilov and K. Kalashnikov to G. M. Malenkov, 28 March 1949, RGASPI, f. 17, op. 132, d. 264, l. 35. The documentary evidence supports Romanov's version of events. According to the Sport Committee meeting minutes for 1950, Romanov led the discussion every time international sports ties were discussed, see GARF, f. 7576, op. 1, d. 755a, ll. 1–24.

48. This statement became a battle cry in sports reporting after the resolution. I have used James Riordan's translation. See Riordan, *Playing Politics*, 62. Riordan maintains that the resolution was issued in 1949, but Apollonov gives the date as 27 December, 1948. Arakadii Apollonov, "Stalinskaia zabota o protsvetanii fizicheskoi kul'tury v SSSR," *Fizkul'tura i sport*, December 1949, 4. For more on the rarity of international meets during this time, see Edelman, *Serious Fun*, 96 and Romanov,

Trudnye dorogi, 152. The documentary evidence supports these impressions. Whereas international sports delegations were barely mentioned in the Sports Committee meeting minutes for 1948, the minutes for 1951 mention hardly anything else. See GARF, f. 7576, op. 1, d. 654 and 826.

49. Edelman, *Serious Fun*, 96.

50. Apollonov to Mikhail Suslov, 7 July 1948, RGASPI, f. 17, op. 132, d. 99, ll. 1–2; Vartan'ian, "Sekretnyi arkhiv," 2 September 2002.

51. Baklanov to Central Committee of the Communist Party USSR, 25 August 1948, RGASPI, f. 17, op. 132, d. 99, ll. 44–59; Vartan'ian, "Sekretnyi arkhiv," 2 September 2002.

52. Romanov, *Trudnye dorogi*, 84–89.

53. See, for example, Nikolai Apollonov, "[?] zadachi sovetskogo sporta," *Fizkul'tura i sport*, June 1948. (The first word of the article's title was ripped out of the copy I examined.)

54. K. Grandopolov, "Stil' sovetskogo boksa," *Fizkul'tura i sport,* May 1948; G. Solovov, "Sistema rasteleniia," *Fizkul'tura i sport*, November 1949; "Russkii khokkei," *Fizkul'tura i sport*, February 1948.

55. "For massovost', for novye rekordy!" *Fizkul'tura i sport*, June 1948.

56. N. Mikhailov to G. M. Malenkov, 24 January 1949, RGASPI, f. 17, op. 132, d. 264, l. 31.

57. N. Mikhailov to G.M. Malenkov, 4 June 1949, RGASPI, f. 17, op. 132, d. 264, l. 41.

58. Kalashnikov and Sushkov to G.M. Malenkov, 22 August 1949, RGASPI, f. 17, op. 132, d. 264, l. 51.

59. Apollonov to the Council of Ministers, 7 February 1950, RGASPI, f. 17, op. 132, d. 447, ll. 18, 23.

60. Kalashnikov and Sushkov to M.A. Suslov, 28 November 1950, RGASPI, f. 17, op. 132, d. 447, ll. 14–15.

61. Ibid., l. 16, 15.

62. Ibid., l. 16.

63. A. Sushkov to Secretary of the Central Committee P.K. Ponamarenko, 15 July 1950, RGASPI, f. 17, op. 132, d. 447, ll. 119–21.

64. Korolev to L. P. Beria, 7 June 1950, RGASPI f. 17, op. 132, d. 447, ll. 117–8.

65. Edelman, *Spartak Moscow*, 183–7.

66. A. Sushkov to Secretary of the Central Committee P.K. Ponamarenko, 15 July 1950, RGASPI, f. 17, op. 132, d. 447, l. 121. The exact date of Romanov's reinstatement as chairman of the Sports Committee is unclear. Romanov states in his memoir that his replacement Apollonov "was recalled to his previous post" in December 1950, and that he was reinstated "within a short time." Romanov, *Trudnye dorogi*, 72. The documentary evidence supports this account, showing that by February 1951, Romanov was acting chairman and by August 1951, Romanov was again the chairman of the committee. Romanov signed a February 1951 letter to Grigor'ian as acting chairman. See N. Romanov to V. G. Grigor'ian, 10 February 1951, RGASPI, f. 17, op. 137, d. 557, l. 12. In August 1951, Romanov received a report as chairman on the status of Soviet skaters. Scientific-sporting Administration to Romanov, 21

August 1951, Vartan'ian, "Sekretnyi arkhiv," 23 September 2002. I found no record of Apollonov's dismissal, but it is probably safe to assume he was dismissed because of his poor performance.

67. Apollonov to Grigor'ian, 14 December 1950, RGASPI, f. 17, op. 137, d. 237, ll. 125–26. Although Apollonov signed the request, it seems reasonable to assume that Romanov was behind it.

68. N. Romanov to V. G. Grigor'ian, 18 April 1951, RGASPI, f. 17, op. 137, d. 237, l. 164.

69. V.G. Grigor'ian to I.V. Stalin, 23 April 1951, RGASPI, op. 163, d. 1583, l. 130. Quoted in Andrei Sorokin, "Olimpiada-52 v Zerkale Partiinykh Dokumentov," *Rodina* 1 (2014), 66–75, available at http://rgaspi.org/nauka/rodina.

70. Sobolev to Edstrøm, telegram, 23 April 1951, Vartan'ian, "Sekretnyi arkhiv," 16 September 2002. See also GARF, f. 7576, op. 2, d. 667, ll. 6–7.

71. N. N. Romanov to V. G. Grigor'ian, 15 November 1951, RGASPI, f. 17, op. 137, d. 557, l. 62.

72. Report on the IOC sent to Central Committee 8 December 1950, 14 December 1950, RGASPI, f. 17, op. 137, d. 237, l. 157.

73. N. N. Romanov to V. G. Grigor'ian, 15 November 1951, RGASPI, f. 17, op. 137, d. 557, l. 64.

74. Ibid., l. 11.

75. Brundage to Edstrøm, 15 November 1947, ABC Box 149.

76. Brundage to Edstrøm, 6 April 1947, ABC Box 42.

77. Edstrøm to Brundage, 3 September 1947, ABC Box 42.

78. Edstrøm to Brundage, 4 December 1946, ABC Box 42.

79. Brundage to Edstrøm, 27 September 1948, ABC Box 43.

80. 45me Session du CIO, Vienna, 7 May 1951, ABC Box 90.

81. Sobolev to Edstrøm, telegram, 23 April 1951, Vartan'ian, "Sekretnyi arkhiv," 16 September 2002. See also GARF, f. 7576, op. 2, d. 667, ll. 6–7.

82. Report on Konstantin Aleksandrovich Andrianov, 10 May 1950, ibid., l. 27.

83. 45me Session du CIO, Vienna, 7 May 1951, ABC Box 90.

84. Ibid.

85. 45me Session du CIO, Vienna, 7 May 1951, ABC Box 90.

86. Hoberman, *The Olympic Crisis: Sport, Politics and the Moral Order* (Rochelle, NY: A. D. Caratzas, 1986), 54.

87. 45me Session du CIO, Vienna, 7 May 1951, ABC Box 90. See also Hill, *Olympic Politics* (Manchester and New York: St. Martins Press, 1992), 35.

88. Report of N. Liubomirov, September 1952, RGANI, f. 5, op. 16, d. 649, l. 95.

89. Ibid., 96.

90. Andrianov to V. M. Molotov, G. M. Malenkov, V. G. Grigorian, 21 June 1951, ibid., l. 102.

91. Ibid., ll. 100–101.

92. Ibid., l. 100.

93. Ibid.

94. V. Stepanor and P. Romanov to Central Committee 31 March 1953, RGANT, f. 5, op. 16, 649, l. 118.

Chapter One

95. President and General Secretary of the Oslo Organizing Committee to NOC USSR, telegram, June 1951, Vartan'ian, "Sekretnyi arkhiv," 23 September 2002.

96. Scientific-sporting Administration to Romanov, report, 21 August 1951, Vartan'ian, "Sekretnyi arkhiv," 23 September 2002.

97. Frenckell to Andrianov, 22 November 1951, Vartan'ian, "Sekretnyi arkhiv," 20 September 2002. Andrianov to Sports Committee, memorandum, October 1951, GARF, f. 7576, op. 2, d. 658, ll. 64–65; Vartan'ian, "Sekretnyi arkhiv," 23 September 2002.

98. Kuchmenko to Romanov, 23 November 1951, GARF, f. 7576, op. 2, d. 659, ll. 123–27; Vartan'ian, "Sekretnyi arkhiv," 23 September 2002.

99. Sobolev to Romanov, 17 December 1951, GARF, f. 7576, op. 2, d. 659, ll. 167–69; Vartan'ian, "Sekretnyi arkhiv," 23 September 2002.

100. Romanov to Malenkov, report, 12 January 1952, Vartan'ian, "Sekretnyi arkhiv," 23 September 2002. Vartanian states that this report was to Suslov, but the document itself quoted by Vartanian indicates the report was sent to Malenkov. Because the wording of this report is similar to a later one sent by Romanov to Suslov, it seems logical that Romanov was the author of the January 12 report. In his reference to the later report, Vartanian states that Suslov underlined in red a certain sentence. This suggests that the reports could have been sent to Suslov who then forwarded them to Malenkov. It seems clear, however, that Romanov authored both reports.

101. Korotkov, Tarasov, Babrov, Egorov, and Chernyshev to Suslov, 14 January 1952, RGASPI, f. 17, op. 132, d. 571, l. 9; Vartan'ian, "Sekretnyi arkhiv," 23 September 2002. Andreev, Khimichev, and Senkevich to Suslov, January 1952, RGASPI, f. 17, op. 132, d. 571, l. 1; Vartan'ian, "Sekretnyi arkhiv," 23 September 2002.

102. Suslov to Romanov, Stepanov, and Sushkov, 15 January 1952, RGASPI, f. 17, op. 132, d. 571, l. 8; Vartan'ian, "Sekretnyi arkhiv," 23 September 2002.

103. Romanov to Suslov, 17 January 1952, RGASPI, f. 17, op. 132, d. 571, ll. 5–6; Vartan'ian, "Sekretnyi arkhiv," 23 September 2002.

104. Sobolev and Senkevich to V. I. Stalin, January 1952, Vartan'ian, "Sekretnyi arkhiv," 23 September 2002. Vartanian suggests that Andrianov was behind this letter, but his evidence for this assessment is unclear.

105. Romanov, *Trudnye dorogi*, 152–53.

106. Mikhailov to Malenkov, 28 August 1951, Vartan'ian, "Sekretnyi arkhiv," 30 September 2002.

107. Romanov to Malenkov, 30 April 1952, RGASPI, f. 17, op. 132, d. 571, ll. 113–16; Vartan'ian, "Sekretnyi arkhiv," 30 September 2002.

108. Andrianov to Sports Committee, memorandum, October 1951, GARF, f. 7576, op. 2, d. 658, ll. 64–65, Vartan'ian, "Sekretnyi arkhiv," 23 September 2002.

109. Walter Firp to Andrianov, 8 October 1951, Vartan'ian, "Sekretnyi arkhiv," 23 September 2002.

110. Frenckell to Andrianov, 22 November 1951, Vartan'ian, "Sekretnyi arkhiv," 30 September 2002.

111. Frenckell to Andrianov, December 1951, Vartan'ian, "Sekretnyi arkhiv," 30 September 2002.

112. Andrianov to Plakhin, Vice Minister of European Affairs, 2 June 1952, Vartan'ian, "Sekretnyi arkhiv," 21 October 2002. GARF, f. 7576, op. 2, d. 741.

113. Minutes of meeting with Suslov, 9 February 1952, Vartan'ian, "Sekretnyi arkhiv," 7 October 2002. See also RGASPI, f. 17, op. 132, d. 571, ll. 24–43.

114. Romanov to Malenkov, 20 May 1952, Vartan'ian, "Sekretnyi arkhiv," 30 September 2002. See also Romanov to Suslov, 20 May 1952, RGASPI, f. 17, op. 132, d. 571, ll. 119–20.

115. Adamovich to Sports Committee, undated, and Adamovich to Sports Committee, 8 May 1952, Vartan'ian, "Sekretnyi arkhiv," 7 October 2002 (GARF, f. 7576, op. 20, d. 1).

116. Balkama to NOC USSR, 16 June 1952, Vartan'ian, "Sekretnyi arkhiv," 7 October 2002.

117. Vartanian, "Sekretnyi arkhiv," 7 October 2002. Vartanian does not provide particulars on this report, but cites it as part of a summary report compiled at the yachting training camp. See also Romanov to Malenkov, 28 April 1952, RGASPI, f. 17, op. 132, d. 571, ll. 108–10.

118. Chekarev to Semichastnoi, 27 June 1952, Vartan'ian, "Sekretnyi arkhiv," 7 October 2002.

119. Report to Andrianov, 5 May 1952, Vartan'ian, "Sekretnyi arkhiv," 7 October 2002.

120. Protocol of the Presidium of the Scientific-methods Council, 25 May 1952, Vartan'ian, "Sekretnyi arkhiv," 7 October 2002.

121. "Fight Against Doping of Amateur Athletes Asked as Health-Sports Conference Starts," *New York Times*, 26 February 1952, 30.

122. "Science Takes Bow for Many Records," *New York Times*, 2 August 1952, 8.

123. Hunt, *Drug Games*, 7–8.

124. Ibid., 9.

125. Romanov to Suslov, report, 10 May 1952, RGASPI, f. 17, op. 132, d. 571, ll. 148–70; Vartan'ian, "Sekretnyi arkhiv," 21 October 2002.

126. Minutes of Sports Committee Conference, 5 June 1952, Vartan'ian, "Sekretnyi arkhiv," 21 October 2002.

127. Ibid.

128. Brundage to Truman, 27 October 1951, ABC Box 332.

129. Brundage to President Truman, 5 June 1952, ABC Box 332.

130. Truman to Brundage, 10 November 1951, ABC Box 332.

131. Romanov to Malenkov, 30 April 1952, RGASPI, f. 17, op. 132, d. 571, ll. 113–16; Vartan'ian, "Sekretnyi arkhiv," 30 September 2002.

132. Steiger to Andrianov, 21 February 1952, GARF, f. 7576, op. 2, d. 699, ll. 29–31; Vartan'ian, "Sekretnyi arkhiv," 30 September 2002. See also GARF f. 7576, op. 2, d. 742, ll. 4–12.

133. NOC USSR to Steiger, February 1952, GARF f. 7576, op. 2, d. 742, ll. 5–6.

134. Edstrøm to Andrianov 29 May 1951, Vartan'ian, "Sekretnyi arkhiv," 16 September 2002.

135. "Soviet Hospitality Goes Unreturned," *New York Times*, July 28, 1952, 20.

136. "Olympic Arithmetic," *New York Times*, 3 August 1952, sec. 4, p. 2E.

137. "Na olimpiiskikh igrakh," *Pravda*, 4 August 1952, 4.

138. "Unofficial Scores," *New York Times*, 4 August 1952, 19.

139. Harrison Salisbury, "Russians Recount Then Recant," *New York Times*, 7 August 1952, 16.

140. Romanov, *Trudnye dorogi*, 283. Romanov's point tally became the official word for the next fifty years. See "The 50-th anniversary of the Helsinki Olympics," *On-line Pravda*, 19 July 2002, available from http://english.pravda.ru. In October 2002, however, Aksel' Vartanian recalculated the points and found that even by Romanov's point system, the United States came out on top with a score of 495 to 487. See Vartanian, "Sekretnyi arkhiv," 21 October 2002. The fact that his point totals remained unchallenged for fifty years indicates the security of Romanov's position and the influence he enjoyed in the Politburo.

141. Krementsov, *Stalinist Science*, 283.

142. Ibid., 285.

143. See Zubkova, *Russia after the War*; and Gorlizki and Khlevniuk, *Cold Peace*.

144. Brundage to Andrianov, 9 November, 1954, ABC Box 113.

145. Hoberman, *Olympic Crisis*, 55.

146. Ibid., 7.

Chapter Two

Leveling the Playing Field

Soviet Sports Administrators Abroad and International Sports Exchanges under Khrushchev, 1953–1964

In August 1960, Nikita Sergeevich Khrushchev sent a message of goodwill and good luck to all the participants of the Summer Olympic Games held in Rome that year. In his letter, Khrushchev highlighted the significance of international sports exchanges to his foreign policy of peaceful coexistence. As he wrote, "Encounters by athletes of the different countries contribute to rapprochement and mutual understanding between peoples. Thus they play an important role in strengthening universal peace. The Soviet government attaches great significance to such encounters and lends every possible support to them. We are assured that the XVII Olympic Games will be a new step on the road to strengthening confidence and friendship between the peoples of all countries."[1] Khrushchev's support of international cooperation marked a significant transition from the days of postwar Stalinism. Unlike Stalin, who regarded peaceful engagement with the West as a show of weakness, Khrushchev saw increased interaction with international circles as a way to cement the Soviet Union's status as a superpower, able to challenge the United States not only militarily but also culturally and morally as a proponent of peace, freedom, and international cooperation. Soviet athletes rose to the challenge, out-medaling the United States in Rome by 103 to 71, securing 43 gold medals to the U.S.'s 34. Yet, Khrushchev's time in power was also marked by contradictions. Just four years earlier, revolution in Hungary left thousands dead at the hands of Hungarian security forces and Soviet soldiers. These tensions also played out in the Olympic arena as Soviet and Hungarian water polo players faced off in a highly volatile match that left Hungarian athlete Ervin Zàdor bloodied. Forty-five of the 175 Hungarian Olympians sought to remain in Australia after the Games, calling into question the Soviet commitment to peace and friendship.[2]

The Khrushchev years were a period of optimism, dislocation, and uncertainty. During this period, the Soviet leadership decried the crimes of the Stalin years and embarked on a series of reforms to dismantle the police state, build the Soviet economy, and advance the country toward communism. Khrushchev's call for "peaceful coexistence" with the West ushered in a period of increased engagement with world affairs, opportunities for travel, embrace of Western culture, and consumerism.[3] The Khrushchev period also was marked by notable successes in the goal for superpower status. The launch of Sputnik and Iurii Gagarin's first manned spaceflight signaled important firsts for the Soviet Union in the race to the moon. Moreover, during this period, Soviet athletes secured their status as the dominant sports power, winning the most medals at every Olympic Summer and Winter Games held between 1956 and 1964.

At the same time, reactions to Khrushchev were mixed, just as Khrushchev's policies were uneven. The leadership worried that attacking the policies and actions of the Stalinist years in whole would harm Communist Party authority and state stability, and the liberation and rehabilitation of former prisoners produced anxiety as well as relief.[4] Many Soviet citizens longed for stability and peace of mind, and Soviet state administrators often found Khrushchev's style unnerving.[5] As writers pushed the boundaries of the cultural thaw and ordinary people expressed dissatisfaction in various ways, Soviet authorities arrested or otherwise silenced those whose criticism went too far.[6] Khrushchev's push for a shift of resources from the military to domestic consumer industry ran up against entrenched interests in the military-industrial complex.[7] As Khrushchev's agricultural policy failed to invigorate agricultural production, labor protests, sparked in 1962 by the regime's efforts to raise food prices, resulted in violent repression.[8]

Internationally, Khrushchev's perplexing foreign policy and tendency toward brinkmanship led to a number of crises. Pressure from East German comrades inspired the construction of the Berlin Wall in 1961.[9] The Cuban Missile Crisis of 1962 threatened nuclear war between the superpowers, convincing Khrushchev to abandon his failed attempt at nuclear diplomacy.[10] Uprisings and protests in East Germany, Hungary, and Poland were answered with repression and military action, demarcating the limits of de-Stalinization in Eastern Europe.[11] Also, Soviet relations with the People's Republic of China soured as Chairman Mao Zedong felt Khrushchev betrayed basic tenants of Marxism, embracing ideological heresy and abandoning the worldwide socialist movement by pursuing warmer ties with the United States.[12]

Having to navigate unpredictable internal and international political waters, Soviet sports administrators continued to push for expansion of international contacts and greater representation of socialist and developing nations in the international Olympic Movement. As the Cold War competition moved to the cultural front, sports became an important avenue of public diplomacy, which Geoffrey Cowan and Nicholas J. Cull define as "an international actor's attempt to advance the ends of policy by engaging with foreign publics."[13] The Soviet Communist Party leadership as well as leaders of various state organs increasingly recognized the potential of sports competitions, exchanges, and aid programs as important avenues through which to exercise their "soft power" by attracting potential client states who sought to follow the Soviet model, "admiring its values, emulating its example, and/or aspiring to its level of prosperity and openness."[14] Sports diplomacy was especially valuable because the "ambiguity and ambivalence" in sports formulations can convey "more than one message simultaneously."[15] As John Hoberman notes, "[sport] is a humanism that expresses itself in a carefully guarded international code of platitudes analogous to the highly abstract language of diplomats."[16] Soviet sports administrators massaged that ambiguity very carefully, emphasizing both the Olympic ideal of "sport for all" as well as Marxist-Leninist ideology of women's equality and anti-colonial struggle as they promoted the expansion of the Olympic Movement. Soviet bureaucrats used sport "to build a picture of the Soviet state as a place that valued expression, cultivated excellence, and tolerated diversity."[17] Soviet military aggression, however, undermined sport's ability to convince the world of Soviet peaceful intentions. Other works have suggested that international exchange weakened domestic support for the ruling regime as well by opening up the Soviet Union to Western influence that highlighted its internal contradictions.[18] However, cultural exchange also integrated the Soviet Union into a global modern culture, and Soviet athletes, officials, and administrators helped to transform international sports in the process.[19]

During this period, Soviet representatives to international sports organizations promoted two interconnected and mutually fulfilling aims: building the authority of the Soviet Union and of its representatives in international sports, and "democratizing" the international sports movement. To Soviet sports administrators, "democratization" meant transforming the IOC and IFs from Eurocentric gentlemen's clubs into egalitarian, truly international bodies including representatives from all regions of the world, especially from those sympathetic to the Soviet project. They also advocated for the expansion of women's sports in the Olympic Movement. At the same time, growing tensions and cleavages within the socialist bloc began to play out in international sports, complicating the jobs of Soviet sports administrators. As Cold War cultural policy shifted toward the developing world, Soviet administrators enjoyed some success in attracting states sympathetic to the Soviet project while other emerging independence leaders pursued their own agendas. Building Soviet authority in international sports organizations during this time required an increasingly sophisticated set of diplomatic skills on the part of Soviet representatives. Through leadership transitions and changing international conditions, these officials reshaped their roles both in the Olympic Movement and within the party-state apparatus, cultivating their own personal authority and status as experts while advancing Soviet influence and prestige.

"ELIMINATING DEFICIENCIES" IN INTERNATIONAL SPORTS RELATIONS

As Stalin's health eroded in the last year of his life, KGB chief Lavrentii Beria, Chairman of the Council of Ministers Georgii Malenkov, and First Secretary of the Central Committee of the CPSU Nikita Khrushchev emerged to take on collective leadership of the country.[20] This political transition, ending with Khrushchev out-maneuvering his colleagues to become the new top party leader, brought a shift in foreign policy priorities from confrontation to peaceful coexistence. This new course encouraged cultural exchanges with Western nations, giving more significance to international sports ties. At the same time, it brought closer attention to the Sports Committee.

In the early 1950s, the Central Committee instructed the Sports Committee to take a more active role in overseeing international sports relations. Based upon Secretary of the Central Committee N. A. Mikhailov's concerns that the Sports Committee's Department of International Sports Relations (*Upravlenie mezhdunarodnykh sportivnykh sviazei*, UMSS) "underestimate[d] the political importance of international sports relations," Agitprop conducted an investigation of the UMSS and directed Vice Chairman of the Sports Committee M.M. Pesliak and UMSS head Petr Sobolev to "eliminate the deficiencies" in the department.[21] After the death of Stalin in 1953, the Sports Committee was placed under the aegis of the Ministry of Health. Though perhaps inspired by the inefficiencies unearthed by the Central Committee's investigation into the workflow of the Sports Committee, this move seems to have done little more than alter the titles of the leading figures of the Sports Committee, leaving the general structure and responsibilities of the committee largely intact. Nikolai Romanov, now a deputy minister of health, remained the chairman of the physical culture and sport section, and Andrianov and Mikhail Pesliak both stayed on as vice chairmen of the new body.[22] Also assuming the role of Vice President of the NOC, Pesliak joined Andrianov and Sobolev as one of the key administrators overseeing Soviet involvement in international sports organizations.[23]

In 1955, the Soviet National Olympic Committee designed an institutional structure for overseeing the activities of Soviet representatives in international sports organizations, answering the need to improve their international work with bureaucratic oversight. Approving the creation of an International Sports Relations Commission, the NOC would now supervise relations with international sport organizations, including proposals for attending meetings, international sport exchanges, reports from IF meetings, and plans for holding official IF events in the USSR.[24] At their December 1955 plenum, the USSR NOC put forth expectations for international sports representatives. Underscoring the "great deficiencies," including the continued non-recognition of the PRC and GDR by International Federations and the IOC, underrepresentation of colonial and newly independent states, "serious impediments" to the development of certain sports, and lack of women's participation, NOC Vice President Pesliak pushed Soviet sports sections to "take measures" to improve their work to democratize international sports.[25] To achieve these goals, the NOC established protocols for participating in the work of International Federations, requiring timely proposals and reports of IF meetings and encouraging all-union sports sections to replace representatives who were "unsatisfactory" with "more effective comrade[s]" who could secure leadership positions and further Soviet goals in those organizations.[26] Specifically, the NOC wanted Soviet representatives to be elected to the executive boards of the gymnastics, rowing, canoeing, cycling, sailing, equestrian, modern pentathlon, and the Union of European Football federations.[27]

According to the plan for the Sports Committee in 1956, the UMSS would serve as a hub of information on international sports, determining the strategies and plans of action for achieving Soviet goals in international sport. The UMSS worked in other Soviet sports sections and the USSR NOC to determine who would lead delegations travelling abroad, and to coordinate the actions of Soviet representatives to the IOC and IFs. With the main goal of "democratization" in mind, the UMSS advocated the expansion of the Olympic Movement. But the UMSS also involved itself in various aspects of Soviet sports propaganda, including supervising the study of foreign sports and publicizing Soviet sports results and achievements in the domestic and international press.[28]

As Soviet representatives to International Federations tried to implement their plans to democratize international sports, they began to gain traction in international sports organizations by employing a variety of strategies to increase Soviet authority. Chief among those practices, private meetings and personal connections helped Soviet sports administrators exploit informal networks of power and influence on the international scene. The Soviet delegation leader to the International Skating Union congress, Tolmachev, "organized a luncheon" with the president and general secretary of the ISU, promising Soviet support for their reelection if they would endorse a number of Soviet proposals and "conduct work" among the ISU members to elect Soviet, Hungarian, and Czechoslovak representatives to leadership positions within the organization.[29] To break into the gentlemen's club of international sports, Soviet representatives determined that in order to be taken seriously, they needed to demonstrate to the current IF membership that they truly belonged. The Soviet representative to the International Fencing Congress (FIE), Popov, found it "unpleasant" to tell other FIE members he stayed at a "third class" hotel while they enjoyed "first class" accommodations. Popov contended that his election to the executive committee failed "because he was not well known" by congress members.[30] Popov and other Soviet bureaucrats played up a sense of inferiority to obtain better accommodations during their travels abroad. However, they encountered real snobbery in international sports organizations and became attuned to the value of personal ties to overcome discrimination and gain influence.

To secure the necessary votes for Soviet candidates to leadership organs or even to pass Soviet-backed proposals within IFs, Soviet representatives needed to promote themselves as leaders in the development of their sport. Sending teams to international competitions not only demonstrated the sporting superiority of Soviet athletes, but also helped democratize "bourgeois" sport by opening a space for Soviet and other socialist sports representatives to gain influence within conservative international organizations. This could be especially important as Soviet sports sections joined more international federations. On the advice of the Italian representative to the FIE, Doctor Bertolli, Soviet athletes participated in the World Fencing Championships for the first time in 1955.[31] Similarly, the Soviet representative to the International Football Federation (FIFA), Granatkin, argued "that successful performances" of Soviet soccer teams and "regular participation" at FIFA meetings helped build Soviet authority in the organization.[32]

The work of Soviet representatives in IFs was designed to ensure greater success for their athletes, and sporting success internationally in turn reinforced Soviet influence in international sports federations. As cultural exchanges expanded, Soviet representatives abroad increasingly submitted to international standards. Like their colleagues in other cultural fields, such as music, Sports Committee administrators believed that as long as referees from Western Europe and America supervised most of the international competitions, their athletes would not stand a fair chance. As Kiril Tomoff notes, Soviet music officials regarded "objective judging" as synonymous with "Soviet success," because of their confidence "in the superiority of their system."[33] Similarly, sports administrators worked to get more Soviet representatives qualified as judges by international standards to allow for "more objective refereeing and the creation of better conditions for the performance of our [Soviet] athletes."[34] Soviet representatives also worked within international sports organizations to achieve rule changes that would benefit the Soviet style of sports training and increase the successes of Soviet athletes. At their 1955 plenum, the Soviet NOC recommended that Soviet all-union sections propose changes and additions to the existing rules governing international sports organizations, work to expand the program of the Olympic Games to include new sports for women and volleyball for men and women (events in which Soviet athletes had proven international success), and draw up proposals for improving conditions of sports competitions (judging, scoring systems, and evaluation of technical results).[35] These steps would lead to more Soviet victories and increased influence of Soviet sports administrators internationally. At the same time, Soviet success helped to transform international competitions. Just as Soviet dominance of music competitions led to the "standardization of music repertoire and performance practices," which emphasized "technical accomplishments," Soviet athletes' success ensured that "an emphasis on technical perfection would remain a lasting Soviet legacy" in international sports as well.[36]

The Soviet Sports Committee also considered holding international competitions and hosting high-level sports officials inside the Soviet Union as an important tool in their democratization drive. Such events enhanced Soviet authority abroad, allowing foreign sports leaders to see Soviet achievements firsthand. IOC President Avery Brundage's visit to the USSR in 1954 helped convince him of the expertise and organizational ability of his Soviet counterparts. Putting great stock in first-hand knowledge, Brundage appreciated "the many courtesies extended" to him in the USSR, where he witnessed "undoubtedly the greatest gymnastic display [he had] ever seen."[37] At its Plenum in 1955, the USSR NOC made inviting IF representatives to the Soviet Union and hosting international events key strategies for strengthening relations with international sports federations.[38] As part of this initiative, Soviet representatives recruited International Federations to join the International Friendly Sports Youth Games as part of the World Youth Festival in Moscow in 1957.[39] The Soviet Olympic Committee proclaimed that these games would be held "in full correspondence with the rules and regulations of the International Federations and the Olympic Spirit, serving the development of ties and strengthening friendship between nations."[40] The festival did promote friendships, as Soviet citizens and foreign visitors danced in the streets to jazz and rock and roll and exchanged stories about life in their respective countries. The spontaneous atmosphere, however, exposed Moscow residents to international currents and Western cultural products.[41]

The World Youth Festival served as another example of an era of expanded international ties ushered in by Khrushchev's foreign policy initiative of peaceful coexistence. As a result of this shift in priorities, sports exchanges, including competitions with Western nations, increased dramatically after the death of Stalin. In 1952 Soviet officials sent only 44 delegations abroad and invited only 67 foreign delegations to the USSR.[42] In 1954 more than 100 Soviet sports delegations traveled abroad while more than 140 foreign delegations visited the Soviet Union.[43] Peaceful coexistence also meant opening up the Soviet Union to tourists and officials from the West. In the second half of 1955 tourists from England, France, Holland, Finland, Sweden, West Germany, and the United States, including several dozen U.S. Congressmen, joined tourists from Eastern Europe whose countries had been visiting the USSR since the 1940s.[44] Even cultural exchanges between the United States and the Soviet Union became more regular during the 1950s and 1960s, providing an opportunity for the Soviet press to highlight friendly encounters between the superpowers and to promote the success of Soviet sports and society to a Western audience who "return[ed] to their homelands convinced of the peace-loving politics of the Soviet government . . . because they saw our life, became familiar with our people and became their friends."[45] To further peaceful coexistence, the Soviet Union signed a cultural exchange agreement with the United States in January 1958. While the agreement provided a formal channel for American culture to enter the USSR, it also allowed Soviet influence on international culture.[46] One result of this agreement was a series of track meets between the two superpowers, held between 1958 and 1985, which not only led to the rapid and significant expansion of women's track and field sports in the United States, but "created stars, [and] facilitated television coverage," sparking conflict between the sport's governing authorities and leading to the professionalization of track.[47]

AVOIDING "PARALLELISM": REORGANIZATION AND THE NEW SOVIET SPORTS BUREAUCRAT

Conceived as a means to mobilize the grass roots of the party membership and to eliminate bureaucratic abuses, Khrushchev's attempt to decentralize administrative power changed the working world of sports bureaucrats. Seeking to bring the state apparatus under tighter party scrutiny and undermine Georgii Malenkov's base of support, the bureaucratic shuffle left officials vulnerable to intra-party rivalries and inter-bureau conflicts, as well as garnering resentment from entrenched interests that resisted his reforms.[48] As part of Khrushchev's decentralization, in 1959, the Central Committee disbanded the Sports Committee and created in its place the Central Soviet of the Union of Sports

Organizations and Societies which encompassed representatives from both state and public sports societies. Once the apparatus had been reorganized, former Sports Committee administrators—especially the Soviet NOC—took a hard look at how they ran the sports system and how best to achieve their obligations. Khrushchev's admonitions to the Soviet populace to engage in more self-policing and take more responsibility found echoes in Sports Committee discourse.[49] While the Stalin years placed emphasis on criticism and self-criticism as a means to "eliminate deficiencies" in bureaucrats' work, "personal responsibility" became an important addition to the bureaucratic lexicon and the Sports Committee had to demonstrate accountability for their activities.

There is evidence that the Central Soviet of Sport Organizations and Societies was set up in 1959 specifically to encourage regional, republican, and provincial administrations to become more involved in promoting physical culture and sport by building more sports facilities and providing more resources for ordinary Soviet citizens to participate in sports on the local level.[50] Expansion of *massovost'* (mass sport) was seen as a tool for increasing worker production, especially in the provinces and villages. The reorganization was also designed to encourage the Komsomol and the All-Union Council of Professional Unions (Profsoiuz) sports organizations to take a more active role in sports matters. Bemoaning that "Some comrades fear that the trade unions will be unable to organize physical culture work and that a state inspector is required," Khrushchev argued that people could participate in physical culture without "state inspector[s]."[51] Nikolai Romanov transferred out of the Central Soviet to chair Profsoiuz, taking the trade union's work in physical culture very seriously, complaining to the Central Committee that the Central Soviet was trying to cut the trade unions out of the sports movement in the country.[52]

The 1959 reorganization opened up debate within the Olympic Committee over what the committee's role should be within the new structure and how the reorganization would affect its work. Because NOCs were to be independent organizations not under the political or economic control of any other organization or body, according to IOC rules, the new USSR NOC constitution made no mention of its relationship to the Central Soviet. In reality, the Soviet Olympic Committee was under the leadership of the Central Soviet just like any other sports organization in the country.[53] In its official charter, however, the status of the Olympic Committee was left ambiguous. It never constituted a distinct department of the Central Soviet but comprised representatives from Soviet sports federations, city and regional sports committees, former athletes, and other sports administrators from various agencies and organizations. In this sense it was partially independent. However, the president, vice-president, and secretary of the NOC—Andrianov, Pesliak, and Sobolev respectively—all occupied posts in the Central Soviet apparatus. Furthermore, the NOC was funded by the central sports administration, and members of the committee received salaries from the sports apparatus through their full-time positions. Despite this, Andrianov quite prudently made sure that on paper the committee functioned as an independent body.[54]

As members of the USSR NOC debated what role, if any, the Olympic Committee should have in the day-to-day operations of physical culture and training of athletes, they highlighted the need to avoid "duplicating" work already being done in the sports federations and other organs of the Central Soviet. Expressing relief that, one year after the decision to reorganize the physical culture movement, they did not "have to wait another year" to decide what direction the Olympic Committee's work should take under the new system, Petr Sobolev told the 1960 Plenum of the USSR NOC that the primary focus of their work should be directed toward expanding international sports relations, democratization of the IOC and IFs, and publicizing more widely in the domestic and foreign press the activities of the USSR NOC for fighting discrimination in sport and promoting the Olympic ideals abroad.[55] While some suggested the committee take a more active role in training athletes for competition, others argued that would create a "parallelism," duplicating work that was already being done effectively by experts and specialists well-versed in training theory and methodology.[56] IOC member Aleksei Romanov emphasized that the Olympic Committee had suffered from a basic lack of direction since its inception. He noted that many Presidium members failed to show up to meetings. Remarking that this might be because they found the meetings "uninteresting," Aleksei Romanov argued that the USSR NOC should motivate its membership to take an active role in the work of the committee.[57] Agreeing that the NOC should avoid duplicating functions handled by other departments, Andrianov declared that the NOC's "chief task" should be to make international sports organizations "correspond to the spirit of the age" and use those organizations to support the country's struggle for peace."[58]

Ultimately, the reorganization had little effect on the functioning of the Department of International Sports Relations (UMSS) other than serving as partial inspiration for its drive to democratize the IOC. Despite the added layer of bureaucracy, the Central Soviet functioned much like its predecessor, the Presidium of the Sports Committee. Sport leaders continued to report to the propaganda section of the Central Committee and the overall focus of the international activities of the sports administration remained largely the same.

By the end of the 1950s, international sports ties had become a key part of Soviet foreign policy. The Central Committee and the Soviet Ministers issued a joint decree in 1959 declaring the goal of international relations in sport to "strengthen friendship and cultural cooperation of the Soviet Union with foreign countries."[59] This was to be accomplished through a wide variety of foreign sports exchanges and contacts including participation in world championships and Olympic Games, exchanges of physical education specialists, sending Soviet sports specialists to developing countries, participating in international scientific congresses and meetings, exchanging training literature and films, lending help to foreign countries in the training of sports personnel, building sports arenas and playing fields, developing sports equipment, and, "last but not least," participating in meetings of international sports organizations. By 1960, the Soviet Union could boast of sending 399 Soviet delegations abroad and hosting 407 foreign delegations, prompting M. Pesliak, vice chairman of the Central Soviet, to declare that "the exchange of sports delegations ha[d] become one of the most important channels of international relations."[60]

In order to achieve Soviet goals, the USSR chose its delegates carefully, and close working relationships with foreign sports leaders, once regarded with suspicion under Stalin, became an asset and a key qualification of Soviet IF and IOC representatives. Learning the working languages of international organizations played a key role in raising the authority of individual Soviet representatives by facilitating communication with IF leaders in private meetings and negotiations. Therefore, a 1955 Soviet NOC decree called for Soviet representatives to study foreign languages.[61] The same year, the vice chairman of UMSS, B. Seregin, requested permission to organize language courses in French and English for his department's workers through the Ministry of Foreign Affairs, because knowledge of those languages was "necessary for their daily work, and also for travel abroad as part of Soviet sports delegations."[62] In their reports from international meetings, Soviet representatives themselves highlighted the need for IF delegates to learn foreign languages.[63]

Because it was not always possible to find effective representatives who also spoke foreign languages, many delegations relied heavily upon recruiting skilled interpreters not only fluent in a particular foreign language, but also competent enough in sports terminology and the political priorities of the Soviet leadership to facilitate discussion. In July 1964, the Soviet representative to the International Amateur Basketball Federation (FIBA), N. Semashko complained that the absence of an interpreter made it difficult for them to fulfill their assigned tasks.[64] Semashko again noted the importance of interpreters "on whom the success of our delegations greatly depends," at the FIBA congress later that year.[65] The Sports Committee representatives working with the East German delegation at the USSR Sports Parade in 1954 praised interpreter Nina Bykova for her ability to conduct meetings involving political issues and "general questions of the physical culture movement" despite her lack of specialized education in sports.[66] By contrast, the interpreter assigned to the Czechoslovak delegation drew criticism for abandoning her post and upsetting the Czechoslovak guests.[67]

The increasing demand for their diplomatic skills also made interpreters natural candidates for advancement. V. M. Chubarov, for example, began work in the Sports Committee as a rank-and-file clerk/interpreter, but soon became general secretary of the Soviet NOC, and eventually head of UMSS. Similarly, Sports Committee translator A. F. Ivushkina advanced to become head of the International Sports Organizations section of UMSS.

But Sports Committee leaders could not rely solely on interpreters to promote Soviet goals; they needed representatives with strong diplomatic skills. As N. Romanov explained in 1959:

> Our representatives should not only be good specialists, but also politically mature people, who skillfully advance the proper political line in federations. . . . They must not be merely specialists in their sport, but must know how to solve problems in a way that wins support from representatives of foreign sport [for Soviet proposals]."[68]

"Politically mature" meant more than simply being a party member.[69] Rather, Soviet representatives had to be "mature" in international sports politics, able to promote Soviet proposals in international organizations, eliciting support and maintaining good relationships with the other members. To do so, Soviet representatives had to be knowledgeable and respected in their sport, understand Soviet goals, present them in a constructive manner that harmonized with the international organization's values, and show initiative and tenacity in pursuing desired outcomes. Representatives who "did not live up to their responsibilities" or "made mistakes" were "recalled from their posts" and "replaced by other comrades" who showed more initiative in advancing Soviet positions internationally.[70] The new Soviet sports administrator needed to be skilled in the art of public diplomacy.

SPECULATION, DRUNKENNESS, AND "DUBIOUS FOREIGN CONTACTS": MORAL EDUCATION IN SOVIET SPORTS

As international engagement expanded under Khrushchev, many ordinary Soviet citizens embraced the movement toward reduced tensions with the West and took advantage of the new opportunities for travel and cultural exchange it promoted. Seeing this new course as a chance to indulge their curiosity about the West, they soaked up Western cultural products and embraced expanded opportunities for travel.[71] As Anne Gorsuch and Diane Koenker have noted, in the Soviet context, "*turizm* was meant to involve work, the enhancement of one's intellectual and physical capital, not leisure."[72] For Soviet sports delegations and even the tourist delegations that began to accompany them to the Olympic Games, this "work" involved not only enhancing their moral and intellectual development through self-conscious sightseeing, but often practical considerations as well. Becoming familiar with Western training methods and obtaining the latest sporting technical equipment became important functions of sports delegations. Demonstrating the successes of the Soviet way of life through one's behavior abroad also marked a significant vocational function of sports-related travel under Khrushchev.

Because many Soviet citizens were new to international travel, UMSS workers and delegation leaders strove to ensure that their delegations gave the right impression abroad. Soviet tourist bureaus expressed anxiety over the appearance of Soviet tourists, fearing that their unfashionable clothes and uncouth behavior would make them (and Soviet society by implication) objects of ridicule abroad.[73] For this reason, tourists needed to be educated in proper manners and customs of dress appropriate to international travel. The same held true for Soviet sports representatives. Not only athletes and trainers, but higher level administrators and especially translators had to appear cultured and sophisticated in order to mix well in international circles. According to Pesliak, cadres sent abroad must "represent disciplined and cultured sportsmen . . . who may rightly represent our Soviet state abroad."[74] This goal was realized at the Winter Games in 1960 where Soviet athletes "conducted themselves with discipline, tact and self-control," and trainers and athletes "established good comradely contact with foreign athletes and trainers."[75]

Hospitality, often in the form of sharing a bottle of vodka and tins of caviar, cultivated authority when mixing with sporting dignitaries. Many proposals for sports delegations included souvenirs to impress foreign representatives.[76] At the same time, these strategies came into conflict when athletes and officials drew criticism from their coworkers and superiors for unsanctioned drinking parties (*vypivki*), or for taking part in the "exchange of souvenirs" rather than of mutual understanding.[77] For example in March 1953, the Sports Committee fired Petr Sobolev and Vladimir Chubarov along with another International Relations Department employee for organizing a drinking bout at a Moscow hotel hosting a Hungarian sports delegation and billing it to the Hungarian delegation.[78] Similarly, A. Krivtsov's report on Soviet participation in the 1953 world speed skating championships in Helsinki noted the "failings and great lack of experience," "lack of tact in conversations with foreigners," and "superfluous garrulity" of the secretary of the Soviet delegation, Vorob'ev.[79]

The awakening of consumerism in the Soviet Union during the Khrushchev years also meant that trips abroad provided opportunities to obtain coveted foreign goods and cultural products, and sports delegations were no exception. The consumer drive and lagging resources to satisfy the Soviet consumer caused tension as delegation leaders, the KGB, the Central Committee, and the Sports Committee strove to combat black market trading and "speculation" among athletes (as well as trainers and Sports Committee personnel) traveling abroad. International sports delegation members routinely took items that could be bought cheaply in the Soviet Union, such as watches and cameras, to sell abroad. Athletes also brought back to the USSR hard-to-find items such as tape recorders, electrical appliances, and ladies' stockings to sell on the black market.[80] The state tourist company, Intourist, shared concerns over such "speculation" not only because of the negative impressions that under-the-table trading could impart to foreign visitors but also because of the hard currency revenues this illegal trade would divert from the official tourist business.[81] For example, a group of water polo players smuggled in forty pair of women's shoes, and another athlete about three hundred raincoats.[82] A high-profile, international scandal erupted when Soviet track and field athlete Nina Ponomareva was arrested and tried for shoplifting during a trip to London.[83]

In the view of the KGB and Agitprop, responsibility for such behavior belonged to the trainers and Sports Committee administrators charged with the proper "moral" and "political" education of athletes. Noting that athletes "spend long periods at training camps and competitions in other cities, torn away from their collectives," a KGB report from 1963 implied that this isolation from the collective encouraged anti-social behavior among the athletes.[84] Similarly, Agitprop workers grumbled that several athletes engaged in "drunkenness," "money grubbing," "speculation," and "greediness," reflecting "improper moral and political education."[85] Soviet leaders connected poor behavior abroad with political unreliability as KGB informants found that Soviet athletes "accepted gifts from foreigners," "established dubious contacts with foreigners," and became "objects of enemy intelligence."[86] The suspicions of the KGB aside, it seems likely that sports delegation members saw no inherent contradiction in representing their country and taking advantage of access to Western culture. As Roth-Ey notes in regard to Soviet travelers, "It was possible to remain committed to the brand in the abstract—Soviet culture as distinctive and spiritually superior, the clear victor in the historic battle (in the long run, but still)—while also taking other personal pleasures in the here and now."[87] Soviet athletes could bring home the gold as well as pantyhose without developing a cynical attitude toward the system as a whole.

"A DIFFICULT SITUATION": THE UNRAVELING OF THE SOCIALIST BLOC IN INTERNATIONAL SPORTS

The Khrushchev period also marked a shift in priorities for Soviet sports diplomacy as cleavages in the socialist world complicated the Soviet democratization campaign. Many leaders in Eastern Europe embraced Khrushchev's new course of limited cultural thaw, peaceful coexistence, and de-Stalinization, and unrest marked the Khrushchev years in the Soviet bloc. Even before Khrushchev consolidated power, cracks in the East European bloc began to show. In June 1953, East Berlin workers staged a demonstration against the East German regime, and Soviet troops still stationed in the divided city stepped in to restore order. In response to West Germany's joining NATO in November 1954, Khrushchev formed the Warsaw Treaty Organization in May 1955. Yet after Khrushchev's rapprochement with Yugoslavia and his acceptance of Josip Broz Tito's national path to socialism, other members of the Soviet bloc began to pursue directions independent of Moscow. Almost immediately after the release abroad of Khrushchev's speech denouncing Stalin's crimes to the Twentieth Communist Party Congress, reform-minded party leaders in Poland embarked on their own "Polish road to socialism," but the newly rehabilitated Polish Communist Party leader Władysław Gomułka managed to avoid Soviet military intervention by pledging to retain one-party rule and Warsaw Pact solidarity. In Hungary in October 1956, however, student protests led to a full-scale revolution that toppled the Stalinist government and left thousands dead. After the new leader, Imre Nagy, announced his intention to withdraw from the Warsaw Pact and establish free elections, the Politburo sent Soviet troops to remove the new leadership and restore a Soviet-backed government. These events drew tremendous sympathy from many Soviet citizens for the Hungarians and discredited the Soviet leadership. The Hungarian Revolution and Soviet military response also undermined the policy of peaceful coexistence and helped to delineate the boundaries of the cultural thaw and de-Stalinization.

The 1956 Summer Games in Melbourne were known as the "friendly games," but they took place during a volatile time in international relations. Soviet representatives to the 52nd IOC Session denounced "reactionary" sports administrators from Holland, Switzerland, and Spain and "anti-Soviet organizations" for exploiting the "recent events in Hungary," using them as an excuse to boycott the Olympic Games and demand that Soviet athletes be banned from Melbourne. Meanwhile, Britain, France, and Israel became embroiled in a struggle with Egypt over access to the Suez Canal, causing Arab countries, including Egypt and Syria, to call upon the IOC to ban teams from England, Israel, and France because of their "aggressive actions" against Egypt.[88]

These crises sparked protest and debate within the IOC, but its firm belief that politics should not interfere with its work or the Olympic Games gave Soviet representatives reason to believe that their authority in the IOC would continue to grow. Fearing that boycotts could damage its reputation, the

IOC adopted a unanimous resolution expressing its "sorrow and regret" as "an organization concerned solely with sport" over the decision by "a small number of nations" to pull out of the Games for reasons "not in keeping with the Olympic ideal."[89] Despite the calls for solidarity in protesting the Soviet invasion of Hungary, the majority of IOC members sided with the Soviet representatives who decried the intrusion of politics into the Olympics. This resolution exemplifies the tactic used by Soviet representatives in the IOC of exploiting the apolitical stance of the IOC and the concern among its members over bad press in their efforts to solidify their position within the organization. It also demonstrates the great irony of the IOC's apolitical stance whereby "its leaders frequently protest against the use made by politicians of sport, while they themselves are being obliged to act politically."[90] Despite the "difficult situation" noted at the IOC session in Melbourne, Soviet and East European representatives "were able to reach decisions that would considerably strengthen their position and influence in the IOC." The election of Bulgarian representative Stoichev to the Executive Board of the IOC was of particular significance.[91]

"WHAT'S UNDEMOCRATIC ABOUT THE IOC?" REORGANIZING THE OLYMPIC MOVEMENT

After the Melbourne Games, Soviet sports representatives transformed their piecemeal approach to increasing their position internationally into a comprehensive proposal to completely overhaul the governance structure of the Olympic Movement. Posing the rhetorical question, "What is undemocratic and reactionary in the activities of the IOC?" Sports Committee head Nikolai Romanov declared that the IOC betrayed a "disloyal, and even hostile position" toward socialist countries.[92] Romanov maintained that IOC leaders continually tried to ensure "advantageous" conditions for American and other capitalist athletes competing in the Olympic Games, while excluding teams from the PRC, North Korea, and the GDR. According to Romanov, the IOC also held a "discriminatory attitude" toward various sports, developing countries, and women's events. Worst of all, in the opinion of the Soviet representatives, the IOC as an organization did not truly represent the Olympic Movement because it did not allow National Olympic Committees and International Federations to participate directly in the work of the IOC itself. Romanov blamed the members from "capitalist countries who were representatives of reactionary ruling imperialist circles" for the IOCs shortcomings.[93] Blending Marxist-Leninist rhetoric with Olympic ideology, Romanov quoted the *Olympic Charter*, which stated that the Olympic Games should "create international trust and good will and help create the best and most peaceful world," as damning evidence against the current atmosphere in the IOC which, according to him, reflected a "reactionary political line [that] prevents the strengthening and development of friendship between all countries."[94]

In April 1959, Andrianov sent the Soviet NOC's plan for reorganizing the IOC to Avery Brundage, now IOC president. Seeking to transform the IOC from a relatively small group of 64 members into a "broad representative international organization, consisting of 210–215 persons," the Soviet proposal specified that each National Olympic Committee and International Federation recognized by the IOC be given a representative in the IOC itself.[95] Soviet administrators hoped this reorganization would shift the balance of power in the IOC away from "reactionary" members. Positioning themselves as a friend to newly independent nations, Soviet representatives also hoped to expand the IOC to include new members who would support Soviet proposals.

A long-time avid and vocal proponent for maintaining the IOC's traditional makeup, Brundage did not show great enthusiasm for the Soviet proposal, stating, "this naturally must be studied most carefully by all concerned."[96] The Soviet Olympic Committee members likely anticipated that he would be hard to win over. Indeed, in further correspondence with Brundage, Andrianov emphasized the "urgent" need for change in the IOC that he argued had been "brought to the agenda by life itself."[97] In response to Soviet entreaties "to keep abreast with the times and not lag behind," Brundage warned that "adoption of [the Soviet] proposal would destroy most of the fundamental principles of the Olympic Movement" and would "disturb the IOC's independence and impartiality."[98] In other words, the Soviet proposal would deprive current members of the IOC of the opportunity to exercise their customary "care" in selecting members of "the same general type" as them.[99]

To Brundage, the traditional selection process was crucial to the IOC's autonomy as it reinforced the sense among members that they were representatives of the Olympic Movement to their countries and should not see themselves as delegates of their home nation. At its 1955 Session in Paris, the IOC had taken steps to buttress its selection process by requiring that new members make a formal declaration upon their election, to "make them aware of their responsibilities and of the obligations which they undertake in accepting the position of member of the IOC."[100] A. Siperco, the newly elected representative from Romania, became the first to join the IOC under this new system, affirming before the session his resolve "to remain free from all political, confessional or commercial influence, and to respect the fundamental principles of the Olympic Charter, as they were created and handed down by Baron Pierre de Coubertin."[101]

In promoting the IOC's traditions, Brundage often betrayed attitudes of Western cultural superiority and ethnocentric assumptions about the non-Western world. His comments at the Paris IOC meeting on the wording of Olympic Rule 25 regarding National Olympic Committees reflect a hesitancy to recognize new NOCs from non-Western nations. Arguing that the IOC needed "protection" from NOCs being organized by "outsiders" who have not been properly educated in Olympic ideals, Brundage noted, "this rule is not written for the nations which are familiar with the Olympic Movement and know very well the Olympic spirit. The rules which we are discussing are particularly intended for remote countries not experienced in Olympic affairs, such as Liberia, Rhodesia, Nicaragua, Indochina, Bolivia, and many others."[102] Before new NOCs could be recognized, Brundage advocated "send[ing] a representative of the IOC to all these countries in order to teach them the Olympic philosophy before they are recognized."[103] Brundage spoke of the "serious battle" in Cuba where the government had established a Department of Sport, placed the brother-in-law of the president of Cuba at its head and then "tried to take over the NOC." Yet, earlier in the same session, the IOC elected Prince Gholam Reza Pahlavi to its membership after being told, he "was educated in Switzerland and practices several sports. He is the President of his country's Olympic Committee, and is the brother of the Shah of Iran." While the circumstances in Cuba reflected a growing phenomenon of NOCs "organized by outsiders who often have no accurate knowledge of the Olympic Movement," Prince Pahlavi's royal pedigree coupled with his European education reassured IOC members that he was like them and therefore could be trusted as an ambassador of Olympism to Iran.[104] The Soviet proposal helped to heighten fears among IOC members that they were losing control of their organization to outside agitators.

Soviet administrators also promoted women's participation in sport as part of their overall strategy to "democratize" the IOC and the Olympic Games. In December 1959, the Soviet NOC included promotion of women's sports as a key task in their revised bylaws. They also linked these efforts to the "decisive" protest against racial, political, and other forms of discrimination in sport and for the "protection of peace."[105] In meetings with sports leaders from socialist countries, Soviet sports administrators called the promotion of women's sport a "fundamental question" facing the Olympic Movement. During the 1950s and 1960s, a number of IOC members expressed concern that the Olympic Games were growing too large and involved and sought to reduce the number of sports on the program, as well as the number of athletes competing, to make the Games more manageable for the host cities. Soviet representatives saw this movement for "reduction" of the Games as a thinly veiled attempt to limit participation of socialist and developing nations and block women from competing. In fact, Brundage had proposed eliminating all female competitors from the Olympics in 1952.[106] Rather than reducing the program, Soviet sports leaders wanted to see the Games continue to grow, and they framed their opposition within Olympic idealistic language. Nikolai Romanov complained to socialist sports leaders, "the IOC reveals a discriminatory attitude toward various sports, toward female youth." He also highlighted the role of socialist nations in promoting women's sports, noting that "Before the entrance into the Olympic Movement of countries of the socialist camp, the IOC never concerned itself with [such] questions."[107] The Soviet Union did have a strong history of promoting sport among women, and the addition of women's sports gave socialist countries an advantage in the medal count.[108] At the same meeting, Pesliak called upon socialist representatives to work for "presenting to women's competitions their proper place in the Olympic Games that they should occupy due to the enormous development of sport among women."[109] In presenting their proposal to overhaul the IOC, Soviet administrators defended their actions as an attempt to counteract "persistent and obstinate attempts . . . to hinder wide participation of women in the Olympic Games."[110]

Between the submission of their proposal and its eventual appearance on the agenda for the IOC session in June 1961, Soviet administrators spent the intervening time drumming up international support.[111] "[C]onsidering Brundage's negative attitude," Soviet representatives particularly focused on convincing the NOCs and IFs to agitate for a greater role for their organizations in the business of the IOC, as the Soviet proposal stipulated.[112] In their campaign, Soviet officials enlisted their socialist counterparts to "establish wide contacts with NOCs of various countries" and conduct work with leaders of international federations to get their backing for Soviet proposals.[113] At the IOC meetings in Athens in 1961, the Soviet delegation emphasized the need for IFs and NOCs, "those organizations who are really doing all the development of sport and organization of the Olympics," to be given wide representation in the IOC instead of being treated like "poor relatives."[114]

Despite the efforts of Soviet and East European representatives to International Federations, when push came to shove, the IFs refused to back the Soviet reorganization proposal because it would have given the NOCs more voting strength. The practice of effecting change through personal networks played much more to the IFs' favor in a small setting than in a large body, made up of hundreds of national representatives compared to the mere dozens of IF representatives. When it was finally put to a vote in the IOC, the Soviet proposal failed with only seven votes in favor and thirty-five against.[115]

The failure of their proposal forced Soviet sports officials to reassess their campaign to "democratize" international sports. Concluding that to insist upon their reorganization plan would antagonize "the majority of members of the IOC," Sports Committee workers suggested that the Soviet Union pursue a new path of "gradual democratization of the IOC."[116] Soviet sports leaders redirected their efforts toward the active promotion of candidatures from socialist and developing countries and toward increasing the influence of IFs and NOCs by other means.

"FRIENDLY MATCHES" AND "ENEMY ELEMENTS": GROWING CLEAVAGES IN THE SOCIALIST BLOC

By the 1960s Soviet administrators noted in international sports a broad breakdown of the socialist consensus that they had cultivated in the postwar decade. At a meeting of the Presidium of the Soviet Olympic Committee in October 1960, sports leaders complained of a lack of cooperation from other socialist representatives. In their report on the 57th IOC Session in Rome, the Soviet representatives documented "occasions of conflicting actions with representatives from fraternal [socialist] sports organizations."[117] Similarly, M. M. Gramov expressed dissatisfaction that socialist representatives attending IF meetings in Rome were not "active" enough in endorsing Soviet proposals at the Rome meetings. In fact, Soviet representatives to the International Amateur Athletics Federation (IAAF), the International Amateur Swimming Federation (FINA), the International Federation of Amateur Wrestling (FILA), and the International Amateur Basketball Association (AIBA) all noted a lack of support from socialist representatives for Soviet proposals to the organizations.[118]

Also by the early 1960s, bilateral sports ties with socialist countries were becoming scenes of popular outlets of anti-Soviet feelings. Markku Jokisipila considers how the Olympic Games became an arena for struggle between East and West during the Cold War, and how the prominent defeats of the Soviet hockey team in international play compromised the authority of the Soviet Union while increasing the authority of the Czechoslovak team after the Prague Spring, as well as the United States in their "Miracle on Ice" in 1980 in Lake Placid. Similarly, Jorg Ganzenmuller discusses how international meets between Czechoslovakia and the Soviet Union in hockey became the scenes of political protest, drawing into question the authority of the Soviet Union in the Eastern Bloc and providing an avenue for Czechoslovakia to promote its internal authority in opposition to the Soviet leadership, as well as its external authority through expression of independence from the socialist bloc.[119] In a report prepared for the meeting of sports leaders of socialist countries in October 1961, the UMSS listed numerous occasions where sports matches between Soviet and other socialist teams were "used for kindling nationalist and chauvinistic feelings among the [host country] population."[120] For example, according to the report, "so-called fans" in the GDR and Poland yelled "fascist" slogans such as "Russian swine," "Ivan go home!," and "beat the Russians."[121] Other examples of "hooliganish" outbursts included spectators in Bulgaria and Poland throwing bottles and stones at, yelling at, and sometimes physically assaulting Soviet athletes. The document also cited incidents in the PRC and North Korea, where "unqualified" and "non-objective" judges robbed Soviet teams of victory, and other occasions where "undisciplined behavior" by Romanian, North Korean, and Bulgarian athletes sent Soviet soccer players home with grave and serious injuries.[122]

Soviet sports leaders believed that their socialist colleagues were not doing enough to anticipate and prevent anti-Soviet demonstrations and feared that allowing such events to continue would damage Soviet prestige internationally. Reporting that "Sometimes our friends, whether voluntarily or involuntarily, now and then allow actions that seek to compromise Soviet athletes and show the superiority of the athletes of their country," they enjoined their socialist comrades to educate their athletes in the "spirit of internationalism, friendship, and comradeship" and prevent matches from taking place that could possibly lead to anti-Soviet outbursts.[123] Soviet officials also blamed the local press where such occurrences took place for becoming "mouth-pieces" for "enemy elements."[124] Suggesting several measures for preventing anti-Soviet manifestations from taking place in the future, Soviet sports leaders appealed to their socialist counterparts to do everything they could to prevent sporting matches from becoming vehicles for nationalist and anti-Soviet sentiments.

In addition to calling on other socialist sports leaders to exercise more control over sports meets with Soviet teams in their countries, Soviet administrators tried to control the volatile international situation by decreasing sports exchanges within the socialist bloc. The UMSS recommended reducing or eliminating meets in various sports with some socialist countries, especially team sports such as football, hockey, basketball, and volleyball. Their report also called for abolishing international competitions in the socialist bloc in boxing and wrestling altogether.[125] Soviet organizers had curtailed socialist sports ties before. At a meeting of socialist sports leaders in 1959, N. Romanov reminded delegates that they had cancelled certain sports events during "Soviet friendship month," because holding the events "promoted not friendship, but something else entirely."[126] In the 1940s and early 1950s, sports ties with socialist countries had been a key part of building a solid pro-Soviet bloc internationally; by the end of the 1950s, they had become a liability.

On top of all this, the continued failure to achieve recognition by the IOC and various IFs of the GDR and Peoples' Republic of China, coupled with attempts by those countries to challenge the Soviet Union's preeminence in the socialist bloc, put additional pressure on Soviet sports administrators to maintain Soviet authority in international sports. In a handwritten report dated December 1962, head of the International Relations section of the Sports Committee A. S. Chikin put forward a new strategy with regard to East Germany. He challenged the current approach of boycotting competitions where GDR athletes were "discriminated" against as "not expedient," because capitalist countries could use their absence as a pretext for excluding Soviet and other socialist athletes from other meets. Understanding that boycotts would also risk negative articles in the Western press, isolation from leading circles within international sports organizations, and even expensive economic sanctions from various IFs, Chikin suggested that the Soviet Union compete even in countries where GDR athletes could not obtain visas, while registering formal protests against what they saw as discriminatory actions on the part of the host country.[127]

In order to successfully expand the Soviet-endorsed Olympic Movement, sports bureaucrats working abroad had to balance pressures from their socialist comrades with the demands of international sports organizations. This balancing act can be seen clearly in the case of Soviet relations with the People's Republic of China. Andrianov found the Chinese sports representatives especially intransigent on the question of whether to recognize the Olympic Committee from the PRC, an issue commonly referred to in IOC parlance as the problem of the "two Chinas." The IOC had recognized the Olympic committee of Taiwan under the name of the Republic of China, and PRC delegates objected to the IOC recognizing a state they considered to be part of China. Chinese authorities at the time prioritized building a vanguard communist society over participation in Western sport, and the PRC made Taiwan's expulsion from the IOC a prerequisite for PRC membership.[128] Andrianov counseled Chinese IOC member Dong Shouyi not to oppose the "two Chinas" approach at the 1955 IOC session in Paris, warning him, "We socialist nations occupy a very small minority, if you provoke something it will be bad for us."[129] Andrianov thought the Chinese comrades made the situation unnecessarily complicated for all socialist countries, because of their stubborn refusal to play by the IOC rules and adapt to the political culture of the IOC in order to promote a Soviet-led socialist agenda. Following a few years of heated debate between Dong and Brundage, in which Brundage derided the Chinese IOC member for bringing up "political questions" at IOC sessions and Dong accused Brundage of being "a faithful minion of the US imperialists bent on creating two Chinas," Dong resigned from the

IOC and China withdrew from eleven IFs, effectively disassociating itself from the Olympic Movement as a whole for the next twenty years.[130] After this episode, Soviet representatives pushed for the IOC and IFs to renew their recognition of the PRC, but without the cooperation of their Chinese comrades.

Because many International Federations had rules in place forbidding members to hold competitions with non-members, the failure to achieve recognition of the PRC by various IFs placed the Soviet Union in a tough situation. Romanov urged the socialist bloc to achieve changes to federation rules that would allow for uninhibited matches between socialist countries and Communist China, but without much success.[131] Under pressure from IFs such as the International Swimming Federation (FINA) and threats of economic sanctions and disqualifications from key events such as world and European championships, Soviet sports administrators began to regard ties with an increasingly stubborn China as a liability to Soviet prestige and authority in international sports. The Sports Committee tried to convince the Central Committee that maintaining solidarity with their sports comrades in China would risk exclusion from FINA, denying Soviet athletes opportunities to compete internationally in swimming (a sport U.S. athletes continued to dominate) and damaging the Soviet position internationally.[132]

As he did in the case of the GDR, A. S. Chikin assessed the situation and recommended changes in policy regarding competitions with China. This entailed prioritizing contradictory directives from the Central Committee: to maintain close sports ties with socialist countries, to expand the Soviet presence in Asia through sports leadership, to increase the authority of the Soviet Union's representatives in International Federations, and to ensure every opportunity for Soviet athletes to win more medals. Chikin proposed to limit sports ties with the PRC only to minor sports and to stop holding meets with Chinese athletes "in those sports where we have the opportunity to win large international competitions and demonstrate the advantages of Soviet culture and socialist construction."[133] Chikin argued that Soviet representatives had to be "delicate" in their negotiations with the Chinese sports leaders, recognizing the need for caution and tact in dealing with them.[134] Chikin obviously hoped that, by holding limited competitions with China, the Soviet Union could maintain friendly sports ties with the PRC without risking sanctions, and the accompanying loss of Soviet prestige within international sports organizations. Despite the increasingly bitter political struggle with the PRC over who would be the leader of the socialist world in Asia, Soviet sports representatives had worked too long and too hard to establish their authoritative presence in the IFs to let China's recalcitrance rob them of the degree of influence they have achieved in international sport.

A "VERY EMBARRASSING POSITION":
INDONESIA AND GANEFO

Tensions rose within the socialist bloc at a time when the focus of the Cold War shifted south, and the United States and Soviet Union increasingly sought support from the newly emerging states of Asia and Africa. As anti-colonial movements in Asia, Africa, the Middle East, and Latin America heated up, former colonies resisted European influence in those regions, and both superpowers saw an opportunity to promote their own system while undermining their Cold War opponent.[135] Cultural diplomacy became a key avenue for both sides to increase their influence in these regions, and sports were seen as a particularly fruitful avenue for exercising "soft power" in the developing world. As Kenneth Osgood notes, "the [US] Information Agency capitalized on this natural interest in sports to spread positive messages about life in the United States."[136] Similarly, Soviet officials promoted sports exchanges to demonstrate the successes of the socialist system of sports and to show Soviet support for progress in newly independent nations. As newly independent leaders sought to build their new nations into modern economic powers, recognized and respected internationally, participation in the Olympic Games and other major sports events became an important status symbol, and many leaders sought support and material aid to build their sports systems.[137] Soviet sports administrators in turn saw an opportunity to capitalize on anti-imperialist and anti-Western sentiments in developing countries and portray itself as a loyal friend to newly independent nations. However, support for the anti-colonial movement could put Soviet representatives at odds with the international sports movement, and some independence leaders pursued their own agendas that could compromise Soviet efforts to build authority in international sports.[138] Therefore, Soviet representatives had to walk a fine line to maintain Soviet authority in both Western sports circles and among emerging nations.

Indonesia under President Sukarno's leadership posed such a challenge to Soviet goals in Asia. In the fall of 1962, when the Indonesian government refused visas to athletes from Taiwan and Israel to compete in the fourth Asian Games in Jakarta, several countries threatened to boycott those games and the IOC withdrew its backing of them. Despite Andrianov's efforts to get the "Indonesian question" taken off the agenda, the IOC Executive Board voted five to one to revoke recognition of the Indonesian NOC indefinitely.[139] In late 1962, Indonesia also organized the Games of the New Emerging Forces (GANEFO) as a forum for newly developing socialist nations to compete with one another. In his speech at the organizing conference for GANEFO, Sukarno declared that the IOC was "an instrument of imperialism and colonialism, and the Olympic Games were an arena of political discrimination against new emerging forces."[140] Soviet sports leaders could not back out of the GANEFO Games, which they saw as growing out of their campaign to "democratize" the IOC and IFs from within, but they also wanted to ensure that competing in these rival games would not prevent them from participating fully in world championships and the Olympic Games. Soviet representatives took steps to make sure that the documents of GANEFO stated that the event would correspond to Olympic ideals and principles. Also, rather than risk sanctions from the IOC or IFs, the Sports Committee recommended to send only teams "not connected with the IOC or IFs."[141] Chairman of the Central Soviet Iurii Mashin acknowledged that Indonesia had no intention of "complicating the position" of Soviet representatives in the IOC and IFs, but Soviet representatives needed to work to get Indonesia back into the Olympic Movement as to avoid "a schism in the international sports movement."[142]

As controversy mounted surrounding the GANEFO Games, Andrianov and the Central Soviet proposed a number of measures to the Central Committee for ensuring that the GANEFO Games would not harm Soviet prestige. Warning Agitprop that Avery Brundage was attempting to press for wide sanctions against socialist and developing countries participating in GANEFO, Mashin argued that Soviet representatives had an "opportunity to exert serious influence" on IOC members' attitudes toward GANEFO by convincing them that the rules of GANEFO demonstrated their belief in Olympic ideals."[143] He called for Soviet and socialist representatives to international sports organizations to act in concert to prevent "reactionary elements" from securing sanctions on any countries participating in the GANEFO Games. He also argued the need to publish articles in the Soviet youth and sports press "characterizing the GANEFO Games as a major international sports and cultural event, bringing great success and supplementing the efforts of the IOC and existing international sports organizations to spread and develop physical education and sports in all countries, especially in the young states of Africa and Asia."[144] Far from a rival organization to the IOC, Soviet authorities perceived and promoted GANEFO as a complementary organization and criticized "reactionary elements" within the IOC for trying to "artificially aggravate the situation around GANEFO" that threatened to divide the international sports movement.[145]

Andrianov defended the success of the fourth Asian Games to Brundage, denouncing the Executive Board's decision to suspend the Indonesian NOC. Andrianov proclaimed that the reason for the "tense atmosphere" was "not political interference from the outside but a hasty decision of the Executive Board itself."[146] Shifting the guilt from the Indonesian authorities, to whom the Soviet Union had been sending money and weapons to build up its influence in the Far East, Andrianov blamed the IOC's Executive Board for not upholding Olympic ideals.[147] The question of sanctions against Indonesia gave Andrianov a chance to further solidify his authority within the IOC, as Brundage and other members of the Executive Board asked him to step in and offer "assistance" and deliver a solution that could be acceptable to both sides.[148] During their correspondence over the Asian Games, Brundage offered both acknowledgement of, and a challenge to, Andrianov's claim as a promoter of Olympism, replying, "It is unfortunate that the Russian sportsmen who were responsible for the fine facilities provided for the Games did not teach the Indonesians some of the basic principles of international Olympic sport."[149] Three months later, however, Brundage apologized for the press coverage of the decision on Indonesia that had placed Andrianov in a "very embarrassing position" and expressed his confidence that "the USSR is in a strong position to control the situation, which is largely inspired by China."[150] As a member of the EB, Andrianov furthered his image as an influential figure in the Olympic Movement, upholding Olympic ideals, and deflecting attention away from Soviet foreign policy endeavors.

In dealing with the GANEFO situation, Soviet administrators put themselves squarely in support of the IOC and the established IFs. In the directives proposed for K. A. Akhmetov's delegation to the GANEFO executive board, Mashin made the number one objective "to create peaceful, friendly and professional conditions" and prevent discussions "of a divisive character."[151] Yet Soviet administrators also recognized the need to couch their position on GANEFO within the goals of the Soviet leadership, within the anti-colonial and anti-imperial rhetoric that held increasing sway on developing countries of Africa and Asia, and also within the stated ideals of the Olympic Movement. As Mashin wrote,

> Insofar as the international sports movement is a means of strengthening friendship and mutual understanding between youth of the world, a means of struggle for world peace and world coexistence that corresponds to the spirit of the Bandung Conference and Olympic ideals, countries and organizations joining GANEFO should campaign for the unity of the international sports movement.[152]

Promoting the incorporation of GANEFO into the mainstream sports movement, Soviet administrators attempted to demonstrate solidarity with the newly emerging states of Asia and Africa, to combat increasing Chinese influence over those regions, and to retain the authority and influence of Soviet and socialist nations within the IOC and International Federations. Mashin also proposed that Soviet representatives to GANEFO make an effort to "raise the international significance" of the GANEFO Games by working with IFs to gain recognition of world records set at the games, to improve the quality of judging, and to increase the overall sporting level of the competitions.[153] Such an effort on the part of Soviet representatives not only served Soviet propaganda goals, but also the IOC goal of promoting Olympic concepts of international sport by spreading knowledge of the rules and practices of international sports competitions.

"TO FRIENDSHIP!" DEMOCRATIZATION AND "SOFT POWER" IN AFRICA

While Soviet administrators found it difficult to maintain their dominant position in socialist sports circles and in Asia, where China and Indonesia vied for influence, they were able to achieve a degree of success in promoting the Soviet Union as a friend of the newly independent countries of Africa. In a 1959 article on sports exchanges entitled "Za Druzhbu!" (To Friendship!), the vice president of the National Olympic Committee of the USSR, Mikhail Pesliak, announced the first Soviet sports delegation to Africa. Ukrainian soccer players had traveled to Egypt, Sudan and Ethiopia, becoming in Pesliak's words the "first explorers in our [Soviet] sports journey into the depths of Africa, to countries who have great sympathy for the Soviet Union."[154] Despite the IOC's insistence on sport remaining outside politics, Soviet sports administrators exploited the political potential of sports exchanges, organizing competitions, sending coaches and trainers, offering scholarships for coaches and educators to train in the Soviet Union, and providing sports equipment and expertise in building sports facilities.[155] Certain members of the IOC Executive Board, especially Avery Brundage, worried that expanding the Olympic Movement in Africa would bring into the Movement new countries "with only a vague notion of sports matters and of what Olympism means."[156] However, gaining IOC recognition for newly independent countries of Asia and Africa also constituted a core aspect of the Soviet led initiative to "democratize" international sports and the IOC. As Sports Committee Chairman Nikolai Romanov noted, "open[ing] wide the door [of the Olympics] to the athletes of free countries of Africa," would bolster Soviet efforts to counteract the "political interests of the Americans and other imperialist circles."[157]

Soviet IOC members continued their push to expand the Olympic movement at the 59th IOC Session, held in Moscow in 1962. Despite the failure of most of their proposals at the Moscow session, Andrianov was elected to the Executive Board, and Soviet representatives convinced the IOC to make expanding the Olympic Movement to new states of Asia and Africa a priority, as well as passing a Soviet proposal to ensure geographic representation

on the IOC Executive Board (Figure 2.1).[158] As a member of the EB, Andrianov served as a leading voice within the IOC for expanding the Olympic
Movement in Africa and combatting racial discrimination in African sport.
Andrianov used his status as an Executive Board member to help the vice
president of the South African Non-Racial Olympic Committee (SANROC)
be accepted into the Executive Board meeting to inform the members of
the racial discrimination taking place in South Africa.[159] Through the help
of Andrianov, the question of barring South Africa from the 1964 Games
was brought before the IOC session in 1963 in Baden-Baden and a strongly
worded resolution was adopted at that session warning South Africa that they
would be banned from the Olympic Games unless the South African government changed the policy of racial discrimination in sport by 31 December
1963.[160]

Figure 2.1.   Meeting of the IOC Executive Board, Lausanne, 1974, featuring Konstantin
Andrianov (standing, third from right). Andrianov joined the executive board in 1962
and served as vice president of the IOC from 1966 to 1970. The make-up of the board
in 1974 demonstrates the geographical representation on the board that Andrianov
secured in 1959. Courtesy International Olympic Committee.

By the mid-1960s, Soviet sports diplomacy in Africa was beginning to show some success. Instrumental in the formation of a special commission of the IOC to provide sports aid to Africa, Andrianov noted the leading role taken by Soviet sports organizations in sending trainers and teams, sports inventory, and training literature to African countries.[161] For example, in planning for the third Spartakiad in 1963, the Central Soviet proposed to invite a larger number of sports personnel from the developing world compared to previous Spartakiads in 1956 and 1959, and to pay part of the travel expenses for "weakly developed" countries that requested such assistance.[162] By the 1964 Summer Games in Tokyo, Soviet officials noted that the number of NOCs from Africa and Asia had expanded from three African and eighteen Asian in 1952 to twenty-two and twenty-six respectively in 1964.[163] Yet expanding IOC membership of socialist countries and "young states of Asia and Africa" remained a key priority since there were only eight IOC members from socialist countries, five from Africa, and seven from Asia.[164]

CONCLUSION

As the IOC came to terms with Soviet participation, it redefined the purpose and priorities of the Olympic Games in an emerging Cold War context. The old way of doing things, and the gentlemen's club mentality of the IOC, appeared more and more outdated in the face of the Soviet Union's apparently progressive and aggressive movements to open the Olympics to more and more countries. By co-opting the language of Olympism and making "strengthening friendship" the central feature of Olympic ideology, the Soviet Olympic Committee members demonstrated that it would no longer be business as usual in the IOC or the IFs. Rather, Soviet representatives would be an active force within the Olympic Movement, furthering their influence by becoming the strongest, most vocal proponents of their newly redefined Olympic ideals. Early successes in expanding the representation of Soviet and East European representatives in international sports organizations inspired the Soviet NOC in 1959 to put forth a radical proposal for reorganizing the IOC by greatly expanding its membership and making its Executive Board more geographically representative. This proposal ultimately failed to gain enough support to pass, but it did help convince the IOC that changes needed to be made if it was to maintain its importance as the leader of amateur sports and its legitimacy as an organization committed to spreading peace and friendship among nations. In this area, the goals of international sport and Soviet external politics matched up nicely, but the Sports Committee workers needed support in the IFs and the IOC to accomplish the tasks put before them, appealing to other socialist countries as well as capitalist countries, businessmen, and noncommunist or even anticommunist sports leaders. They attempted to organize a bloc sufficiently strong to get proposals passed while maintaining the appearance that their actions and alliances were in keeping with the overall vision of the international sports movement. To accomplish this, Soviet representatives promoted spreading peace and friendship as the core value of international sports, painted themselves as the true proponents of that vision, and sought to deflect the blows launched at them by gaining personal "authority." Internally, it was the Soviet Olympic Committee and Sports Committee officials who masterminded this multifaceted push to level the playing field for socialist countries within the IOC.

There is no doubt that Soviet sports administrators hoped to expand Soviet influence throughout the world through their involvement in the Olympic Movement. Yet, when Soviet sports bureaucrats complained that the IOC and many IFs were led by conservative blocs, they had a point: there was in fact a prevailing prejudice against representatives from Eastern Europe, against female participation, and toward athletes from the newly independent countries of Africa, Asia, and Latin America. Worries over the size of the Olympic program masked paternal attitudes toward women whose bodies might be damaged by too intensive competition, and toward athletes from fledgling nations who would not understand the principles of the Olympic Movement without being educated by men of "the same general type" as the original European IOC membership.[165] When Soviet officials pushed to expand women's participation and extend sports aid to developing nations, they couched these efforts in the language of Olympism. In this way, what they exported was not a model of socialist sport, but a Soviet adaptation of modern sport, wrapped in the evolving ideals of the Olympic Movement, giving everyone the right to participate in sports and encouraging friendship between nations. Their efforts helped transform the Olympic Games into a truly global movement even as they brought Soviet sport closer in line with mainstream Western sports.

Under Khrushchev, the men responsible for maintaining sports relations also helped redefine their roles within the Soviet sports bureaucracy and determined the skills required of the men and women chosen to participate in sporting delegations abroad. Increased attention to international sports ties after the death of Stalin heightened the need for qualified administrators to organize and lead international delegations. While the Stalinist leadership had looked for political reliability above all, Stalin's successors valued international experience, knowledge of foreign languages and international sports regulations, ties with foreigners, and the ability to cultivate personal connections across cultures. In the new atmosphere of peaceful coexistence, these qualifications became equally as important as ideological purity and patriotism for delegation members, because these skills helped to advance the Soviet position. In turn, travel abroad brought Soviet athletes, trainers, interpreters, and sports bureaucrats further into contact with a variety of foreign contexts. Whereas Stalin's people fought against "cosmopolitans" during its cautious forays into international sports, the ideal representative of the Soviet Union under Khrushchev was in many ways a true "cosmopolitan": someone educated, cultured, and knowledgeable about the world.

This changing role of sports administrators illustrates the potential for bureaucrats to gain respect and influence as valued "experts" in the post-Stalin era. International representatives were the eyes and ears of the Soviet leadership. Through their participation in international sports congresses, Soviet representatives became specialists in their particular organizations' internal politics and proposed to their superiors in the Sports Committee the best way to safeguard Soviet interests in those organizations. Sports Committee leaders then incorporated these recommendations into the plans they submitted to the Central Committee for approval. The Soviet leadership's reliance on these administrators for both information and policy recommendations, combined with their successes in advancing Soviet interests in international sports organizations, demonstrates the state bureaucracy's capacity for influencing decision-making and priority-setting, both within the Soviet Union and in the international organizations in which they participated.

NOTES

1. Letter from Chairman of the Council of Ministers of the Soviet Union to Participants in the XVII Olympic Games, 22 August 1960, GARF, f. 9570, op. 2, d. 3504, l. 1.

2. See Robert E. Rinehart, "'Fists Flew and Blood Flowed': Symbolic Resistance and the International Response in Hungarian Water Polo at the Melbourne Olympics, 1956," *Journal of Sport History* 23.2 (1996): 120–39.

3. Gorsuch and Koenker, eds., *Turizm*; Donald J. Raleigh, *Soviet Baby Boomers*; and Susan E. Reid, "Cold War in the Kitchen."

4. Nanci Adler, *Keeping Faith with the Party: Communist Believers Return from the Gulag* (Bloomington: Indiana University Press, 2012); Miriam Dobson, *Khrushchev's Cold Summer: Gulag Returnees, Crime, and the Fate of Reform after Stalin* (Ithaca, NY: Cornell University Press, 2009).

5. Polly Jones, *Dilemmas of De-Stalinization*, 14. See also Zubkova, "The Rivalry with Malenkov," in William Taubman, ed., Nikita Khrushchev (New Haven: Yale University Press, 2000), 83.

6. Robert Hornsby, *Protest, Reform and Repression in Khrushchev's Soviet Union*, New Studies in European History (Cambridge: Cambridge University Press, 2015).

7. Sergei Khrushchev, "The Military-Industrial Complex," 244, 252–53.

8. Samuel H. Baron, *Bloody Saturday in the Soviet Union: Novocherkassk, 1962* (Stanford: Stanford University Press, 2001); Vladimir Kozlov, *Mass Uprisings in the USSR: Protest and Rebellion in the Post-Stalin Years*, The New Russian History Series (Armonk, NY: ME Sharpe, 2002).

9. Hope M. Harrison, *Driving the Soviets up the Wall: Soviet-East German Relations, 1953–1961*, Princeton Studies in International History and Politics (Princeton: Princeton University Press, 2005).

10. Oleg Troyanovsky, "The Making of Soviet Foreign Policy," in Taubman, *Nikita Khrushchev,* 217. See also Zubok, *Failed Empire*, 150.

11. Mark Kramer, "The Soviet Union and the 1956 Crises in Hungary and Poland: Reassessments and New Findings," *Journal of Contemporary History* 33.2 (1998): 163–214. On East Berlin protests, see Hope Harrison, *Driving the Soviets*, 34–36.

12. See Odd Arne Westad, *The Global Cold War: Third World Interventions and the Making of Our Times* (Cambridge: Cambridge University Press, 2007), 160–63.

13. Geoffrey Cowan and Nicholas J. Cull, "Preface: Public Diplomacy in a Changing World," Annals, *AAPSS* 616 (March 2008), 6. See also Eytan Gilboa, "Searching for a Theory of Public Diplomacy," Annals, *AAPSS* 616 (March 2008), 55.

14. Joseph S. Nye Jr., "Public Diplomacy and Soft Power," Annals, *AAPSS* 616 (March 2008), 94.

15. Riordan and Peppard, 9.

16. Hoberman, *Olympic Crisis*, 6–7.

17. Nicholas J. Cull, "Public Diplomacy: Taxonomies and Histories," Annals, *AAPSS* 616 (March 2008), 45.

18. See Hixon, *Parting the Curtain*; Richmond, *Cultural Exchange and the Cold War*; and Caute, *The Dancer Defects*.

19. Tomoff, *Virtuosi Abroad*, 14; Peteri, "Sites of Convergence," 5; Keys, *Globalizing Sport*, 160, "Soviet Sport," 416, and "The Soviet Union, Cultural Exchange and the 1956 Olympic Games," 133.

20. Gorlizki and Khlevniuk, *Cold Peace*, 166–68.

21. Mikhailov to Malenkov, 6 January 1953, RGANI, f. 5, op. 16, d. 649, l. 19 and P. Romanov and F. Mulikov to N. A. Mikhailov, 9 January 1953, ibid., ll. 61–63.

22. Order of the Ministry of Health No. 740, 8 September 1953, "On the Organization of the Soviet of the Ministry of Health for Physical Culture and Sport," GARF, f. 7576, op. 1, d. 951, l. 13. This structure lasted less than a year, and the Sports Committee was reinstated in February 1954, see Riordan, *Sport in Soviet Society*, 168.

23. Pesliak's educational and professional background is unclear, but he was already involved with Olympic sport, having been part of the Soviet delegation to the 1952 Games in Helsinki as a vice chairman of the Sports Committee. See N. N. Romanov to G. M. Malenkov, 30 April 1952, RGASPI f. 17, op. 132, d. 571, ll. 113–16.

24. Draft Appendix on Commissions of the USSR NOC for the Plenary Meeting of the USSR NOC, 26 August 1955, GARF, f. 7576, op. 30, d. 464, l. 26.

25. Draft Decree of the Plenum of the USSR NOC, 9 December 1955, GARF, f. 7576, op. 30, d. 464, ll. 15–16.

26. Ibid., l. 19.

27. Ibid., l. 18.

28. Work Plan of the Sports Committee, 14 January–10 September 1956, GARF, f. 7576, op. 1, d. 1135, ll. 11–12.

29. Report of Soviet Delegation to XXVI Congress of the International Skating Union /ISU/, June 1955, GARF, f. 7576, op. 2, d. 1045, l. 37.

30. Report of Soviet Delegation to International Fencing Congress (FIE) in Italy, May 1955, GARF, f. 7576, op. 2, d. 1045, l. 34.

31. Ibid.

32. Report of Soviet Delegation to Executive Committee of International Football Federation in Brussels, 17–18 September 1955, GARF, f. 7576, op. 2, d. 1045, l. 84.

33. Tomoff, *Virtuosi Abroad*, 17, 81.

34. Report of Participation of Soviet Representatives in the Work of Leadership Organs and Congresses of IFs in Melbourne, November–December 1956, GARF, f. 7576, op. 2, d. 1160, l. 285.

35. Draft Decree of the Plenum of the USSR NOC, 9 December 1955, GARF, f. 7576, op. 30, d. 464, l. 17.

36. Tomoff, *Virtuosi Abroad*, 112.

37. Brundage to Andrianov, 2 September 1954, ABC Box 50.

38. Draft Decree of the Plenum of the USSR NOC, 9 December 1955, GARF, f. 7576, op. 30, d. 464, l. 17.

39. Report of Participation of Soviet Representatives in Work of Leadership Organs and Congresses of IFs in Melbourne, November–December 1956, GARF, f. 7576, op. 2, d. 1160, l. 267.

40. Decree of the USSR NOC On Preparation and Holding of the Third International Friendly Sports Games of Youth 1957, GARF, f. 7576, op. 30, d. 464, l. 46.

41. See Richmond, *Cultural Exchange and the Cold War*, 11–13.

42. Minutes of the Plenum of the Central Soviet of the Union of Sports Organizations and Societies, 7 July 1961, GARF, f. 9570, op. 1, d. 83, l. 111.

43. "Za mir i druzhbu," *Fizkul'tura i sport,* May 1955, p. 2.

44. "SSSR prinimaet turistov," *Fizkul'tura i sport,* February 1956, pp. 20–21.

45. "Za Druzhbu!" *Fizkul'tura i sport*, April 1959, p. 6.

46. Walter Hixon calls "the 1958 cultural agreement was one of the most successful initiatives in the history of American Cold War diplomacy," arguing that it undermined Communist Party authority in the long run, Hixon, *Parting the Curtain*, 227. Kiril Tomoff's assessment of the agreement is more nuanced, recognizing the role of Soviet institutional leaders in parting the curtain in ways that achieved short term soviet influence and long term integration of the Soviet bloc into a globalized order. Tomoff, *Virtuosi Abroad,* 14.

47. Joseph M. Turrini, "'It Was Communism versus the Free World': The USA-USSR Dual Track Meet Series and the Development of Track and Field in the United Sates, 1958–85," *Journal of Sport History* 28.3 (2001): 428.

48. Elena Zubkova, "The Rivalry with Malenkov," 83. Sergei Khrushchev, "The Military-Industrial Complex," 42.

49. See for example, George W. Breslauer, "Khrushchev Reconsidered," *Problems of Communism* 10 (1976): 23–25.

50. Tarschys, "Management by Duplication," 44.

51. Khrushchev, *Stroitel'stvo kommunizma* III, p. 170, quoted in Breslauer, "Khrushchev Reconsidered," 25.

52. N. Romanov to Central Committee, 16 May 1963, RGANI, f. 5, op. 55, d. 11, ll. 107–8.

53. Minutes of the Plenum of the USSR NOC, 7 January 1960, GARF, f. 9570, op. 2, d. 3482, ll. 63–64.

54. The only Soviet NOC meeting minutes I found in the archive were from this period.

55. Minutes of the Plenum of the USSR NOC, 7 January 1960, GARF, f. 9570, op. 2, d. 3482, l. 4.

56. Ibid., ll., 14, 33.

57. Ibid., 35. The phrase "uninteresting (*neinteresno*)" is evocative. Elena Zubkova notes in *Russia after the War* that Komsomol membership declined in the postwar years, because they found such work "boring and uninteresting," 111. Similarly, Alexei Yurchak notes that Komsomol youth in the 1970s regarded official party discourse as "uninteresting," and looked for fulfillment through other activities outside of their formal positions, *Everything Was Forever*, 132.

58. Ibid., 62.

59. Minutes of the Plenum of the Central Soviet of the Union of Sports Organizations and Societies, 7 July 1961, GARF, f. 9570, op. 1, d. 83, l. 111.

60. Ibid., l. 111–12.

61. Draft Decree of the Plenum of the USSR NOC, 9 December 1955, GARF, f. 7576, op. 30, d. 464, l. 19.

62. Report by B. Seregin to K. Andrianov, 1955, GARF, f. 7576, op. 2, d. 1036, l. 207.

63. See for example, Report of Soviet Delegation to Meeting of Executive Commission of International Gymnastics Federation, 29 March–1 April 1956, GARF, f. 7576, op. 2, d. 1160, l. 98.

64. Report on Participation of Soviet Representatives in IX Session of the Conference of Delegates of National Basketball Federations of Europe and the Mediterranean, GARF, f. 9570, op. 1, d. 1103, ll. 65–66.

65. Report by N. V. Semashko and interpreter on the FIBA Congress, 15 and 21 October 1964, GARF, f. 9570, op. 1, d. 1103, l. 94.

66. Report of Work with the Sports Delegation from GDR during the 1954 Sports Parade, 27 July 1954, GARF, f. 7576, op. 2, d. 926, l. 118.

67. Report of Meetings with Czechoslovak Representatives during the 1954 Sports Parade, 28 July 1954, GARF, f. 7576, op. 2, d. 926, l. 107.

68. Agenda and Minutes of Meeting of Representatives of Sports Organizations of Socialist Countries, Moscow, 12 March 1959, GARF, f. 9570, op. 1, d. 446, ll. 3, 27.

69. For example, during preparations for the 1964 Summer Games in Tokyo, only fifty of the eight-four Soviet members of international sports organizations belonged to the Communist Party. Oral Report of Central Soviet of Sports Organizations and Societies on Preparation of Soviet Athletes for XVIII Olympic Games in Tokyo, June 1964, GARF, f. 9570, op. 1, d. 254, l. 35.

70. Report on Participation of Soviet Sports Organizations in work of International Sports Associations, 20 August 1962, GARF, f. 9570, op. 1, d. 827, l. 16.

71. See Gorsuch and Koenker, *Turizm* and Raleigh, *Soviet Baby Boomers.*

72. Gorsuch and Koenker, *Turizm*, 3.

73. Anne E. Gorsuch, "Time Travelers: Soviet Tourists to Eastern Europe," in Gorsuch and Koenker, *Turizm*, 222–23.

74. Minutes of the Plenum of the Central Soviet of the Union of Sports Organizations and Societies, 7 July 1961, GARF, f. 9570, op. 1, d. 83, l. 114.

75. Report of participation of Soviet athletes in VIII Winter Games in Squaw Valley, 1960, GARF, f. 9570, op. 1, d. 40, l. 65.

76. Nikonov to Central Committee, 22 January 1963, RGANI f. 5, op. 55, d. 12, l. 26.

77. Minutes of the Plenum of the Central Soviet of the Union of Sports Organizations and Societies, 7 July 1961, GARF, f. 9570, op. 1, d. 83, l. 116.

78. Agenda for Meeting of the Vice-Chairmen of the All-Union Committee for Physical Culture and Sport, GARF, f. 7576, op. 1, d. 952, l. 25. Despite this incident, both men had been reinstated by 1954.

79. A. Krivtsov to the Central Committee, P. K. Romanov, 31 May1953, RGANI, f. 5, op. 16, d. 649, l. 128.

80. RGANI f. 5, op. 60, d. 36, l. 45 cited in Prozumenshchikov, *Bol'shoi sport,* 38. Gorsuch also talks about Soviet citizens bringing personal items to sell abroad and lists watches and cameras as the most prominent items. Gorsuch, "Time Travelers," 219. One may wonder why foreign consumers would buy Soviet-made items, but perhaps the prospect of a cheap watch outweighed any concerns over its quality. Westerners might have bought such items as curiosities. Gorsuch suggests that these items were more readily available in the Soviet Union than other items, so an enterprising Soviet traveler could smuggle out a fairly large number of cameras or watches and use the proceeds to bring popular but hard to get items like women's stockings and radios back to sell on the black market.

81. Shawn Salmon, "Marketing Socialism: Inturist in the Late 1950s and Early 1960s," in Gorsuch and Koenker, *Turizm*, 187.

82. RGANI, f. 5, op. 60, d. 36, l. 45 cited in Prozumenshchikov, *Bol'shoi sport,* 38.

83. Peter Beck, "Britain and the Cold War's 'Cultural Olympics': Responding to the Political Drive of Soviet Sport," 1945–58, *Contemporary British History* 19.2 (2005): 180.

84. V. Semichastnyi to Central Committee, 27 April 1963, RGANI, f. 5, op. 55, d. 11, ll. 122–23.

85. Udal'stov and I. Zubkov to Central Committee, April 1963, RGANI, f. 5, op. 55, d. 11, ll. 115–20.

86. V. Semichastnyi to Central Committee, 27 April 1963, RGANI, f. 5, op. 55, d. 11, ll. 122–23.

87. Roth-Ey *Moscow Prime Time*, 20.

88. Ibid., ll. 262–63.

89. Meeting Minutes of the 52nd IOC Session, Melbourne, 19–21 November and 4 December, 1956, IOC Archives, Lausanne, Switzerland.

90. Christopher Hill, *Olympic Politics*, 33.

91. Report of Participation of Soviet Representatives in the work Leadership Organs and Congresses of IFs in Melbourne, November-December 1956, GARF, f. 7576, op. 2, d. 1160, l. 263.

92. Agenda and Minutes of meeting of Representatives of Sports Organizations of Socialist Countries, Moscow, 10–11 March 1959, GARF, f. 9570, op. 1, d. 445, l. 18.

93. Ibid., l. 21

94. Ibid., l. 22.

95. Andrianov to Brundage, 29 April, 1959, copy to Otto Mayer, IOC Archives/ NOCs USSR Correspondence 1951–1966, Olympic Studies Center, Lausanne, Switzerland.

96. Brundage to USSR NOC, 9 May 1959, IOC Archives/ NOCs USSR Correspondence 1951–1966, Olympic Studies Center, Lausanne, Switzerland.

97. Andrianov to Brundage, 12 December 1959, ABC Box 50.

98. The USSR NOC to Brundage, April 1959, ABC Box 149. Brundage to Andrianov, 2 January 1960, ABC Box 50 and Report to the Members of the IOC, the International Federations and the Olympic Committees on the proposal of the Olympic Committee of the USSR for a reorganization of the International Olympic Committee, IOC Archives/Konstantin Andrianov Biography and Correspondence 1951–84.

99. Brundage to members of the IOC, 30 January 1954, ABC Box 70.

100. Meeting Minutes of the 50th IOC Session, Paris, June 1955, IOC Archives.

101. Ibid.

102. Ibid.

103. Ibid.

104. Ibid.

105. Agenda for Meeting of the Presidium of the Central Soviet of the Union of Sports Societies and Organizations of the USSR, 1 December 1959, GARF, f. 9570, op. 2, d. 3481, l. 13.

106. Minutes from IOC Session in Mexico (Russian Translation), GARF, f. 7576, op. 2, d. 825, l. 37. At the 1953 IOC Session in Mexico City, the organization voted unanimously *not* to exclude women from the Games, but Brundage added the qualification that "women competitors should only be accepted in sports appropriate to them." Minutes from the 48th IOC Session (English), Mexico City, April 1953, IOC Archives.

107. Agenda and Minutes of the Meeting of Representatives of Sports Organizations of Socialist Countries in Moscow, 10–11 March 1959, GARF, f. 9570, op. 1, d. 445, l. 20.

108. For more on women and Soviet sport, see Christina Kiaer, "The Swimming Vtorova Sisters: The Representation and Experience of Sport in the 1930s," in Nikolaus Katzer et al., eds., *Euphoria and Exhaustion*, 90; Pat Simpson, "Parading Myths: imaging New Soviet Woman on Fizkul'turnik's Day, July 1944," *Russian Review* 63.2 (2004): 204–5; Riordan, "Rise, Fall, and Rebirth," 190, 192; and Alison Rowley, "Sport in the Service of the State: Images of Physical Culture and Soviet Women, 1917–1941," *International Journal of the History of Sport*, 23.8 (2006):

1326–29. The emphasis on women's sports also spread to Eastern Europe under So- viet influence. See, for example, Nameeta Mathur, "Women and Physical Culture in Modern Poland," (Ph.D. diss., Eberly College of Arts and Sciences at West Virginia University, 2001).

109. Ibid., l. 143.

110. USSR Olympic Committee to Avery Brundage, March 1961, ABC Box 149.

111. Agenda of Meeting of the Executive Commission of the IOC, San Francisco, 12 February 1960, IOC Archives, Lausanne, Switzerland.

112. Meeting of the Presidium of the USSR NOC, 28 January 1960, GARF, f. 9570, op. 2, d. 3483, l. 71.

113. Material from the Meeting of Representatives of Leading Organs of Sports Organizations of Socialist Countries, 25–30 October 1961, Budapest, GARF, f. 9570, op. 1, d. 559, l. 42.

114. Theses for Presentation at Meeting of EB of the IOC with IFs, Athens, June 1961, GARF, f. 9570, op. 1, d. 689, ll. 43–44. Presentation of the Soviet Delegation to the Meeting of the EB of the IOC with NOCs, Athens, 17 June 1961, GARF, f. 9570, op. 1, d. 689, ll. 32–42.

115. Meeting Minutes of the 58th IOC Session, 19–21 June 1961, IOC Archives, Lausanne, Switzerland.

116. Proposal on the Future Activities of Sports Organizations of the USSR in the IOC, GARF, f. 9570, op. 1, d. 689, l. 74. It is not clear who wrote this report or for whom, but considering the content and its location among other materials related to the 59th IOC Session in Athens, it is reasonable to assume that the report was written by workers in the International Sports Relations Section of the Sports Committee and that the intended audience was the Sports Committee leadership and probably the Central Committee.

117. Draft Report, On Results of Participation of Representatives of Soviet Sports Organizations in the 57th Session of the IOC and Congresses of International Sports Unions, Rome, 7 October 1960, GARF, f. 9570, op. 2, d. 3483, l. 10.

118. Minutes of the Meeting of the Presidium of the Olympic Committee of the USSR, 7 October 1960, ibid., ll. 1–3.

119. Lu Seegers, Review of Braun, Jutta; Teichler, Hans Joachim, *Sportstadt Berlin im Kalten Krieg: Prestigekämpfe und Systemwettstreit* and Malz, Arie; Ste- fan Rohdewald, and Stefan Wiederkehr, *Sport zwischen Ost und West: Beiträge zur Sportgeschichte Osteuropas im 19. und 20. Jahrhundert*, H-Soz-u-Kult, H-Net Reviews, September, 2007, http://www.h-net.org/reviews/showrev.php?id=34272.

120. Report on Serious Occurrences at Sports Competitions in Socialist Countries, 1961, GARF, f. 9570, op. 1, d. 688, l. 161.

121. Ibid., l. 162.

122. Ibid., l. 163.

123. Ibid., l. 162.

124. Ibid., ll. 163–64.

125. Ibid., l. 165.

126. Agenda and Minutes of Meeting of Representatives of Sports Organizations of Socialist Countries, Moscow, 12 March 1959, GARF, f. 9570, op. 1, d. 446, l. 38.

127. Report on International Sports Relations by A. S. Chikin, December 1962, GARF, f. 9570, op. 1, d. 827, l. 40.

128. For more on the role of sports in the PRC, see Susan Brownell, *Building the Body for China: Sports in the Moral Order of the Peoples Republic* (Chicago: University of Chicago Press, 1995) and Xu Guoqi, *Olympic Dreams: China and Sports, 1895–2008* (Cambridge and London: Harvard University Press, 2008).

129. Susan Brownell, "'Sport and Politics don't mix': China's Relationship with the IOC During the Cold War," in *East Plays West*, 259–60. For more on Chinese attitudes toward international sports, see Fan Hong and Lu Zhouxiang, "Politics First, Competition Second: Sport and China's Foreign Diplomacy in the 1960s and 70s," in Dichter and Johns, eds., *Diplomatic Games*, 385–407.

130. Ibid., 263.

131. Agenda and Minutes of the Meeting of Representatives of Sports Organizations of Socialist Countries, Moscow, 12 March 1959, GARF, f. 9570, op. 1, d. 446, ll. 28–30.

132. Minutes of the Meeting of the Presidium of the Olympic Committee of the USSR, 7 October 1960, GARF, f. 9570, op. 2, d. 3483, ll. 4–5.

133. Report on International Sports Relations by A.S. Chikin, December 1962, GARF, f. 9570, op. 1, d. 827, l. 38.

134. Ibid., l. 40.

135. The most complete exploration of Cold War intervention in the developing world is Odd Arne Westad, *The Global Cold War*. For more on Soviet policies in the developing world see Zubok, *A Failed Empire*, chapters 7 and 8; Sergey Mazov, *A Distant Front in the Cold War: The USSR in West Africa and the Congo, 1956–64*, James H. Hershberg, ed., *Cold War International History Project* (Stanford, CA: Stanford University Press, 2010); Alessandro Iandolo, "The Rise and Fall of the 'Soviet Model of Development' in West Africa, 1957–64," *Cold War History* 12.4 (2012): 683–704; and Roger E. Kanet, "The Superpower Quest for Empire: The Cold War and Soviet Support for 'Wars of National Liberation," *Cold War History* 6.3 (2006): 331–52.

136. Kenneth Osgood, *Total Cold War: Eisenhower's Secret Propaganda Battle at Home and Abroad* (Lawrence: University Press of Kansas, 2006), 263. On US cultural diplomacy, see also Wilson P. Dizard, Jr., *Inventing Public Diplomacy: The Story of the U.S. Information Agency* (Boulder and London: Lynne Rienner, 2004). For more on US sport diplomacy, see Rider, *Cold War Games* and Hunt "American Sport Policy."

137. See for example, Peter Alegi, *African Soccerscapes: How a Continent Changed the World's Game* (Athens: Ohio University Press, 2010) and Benjamin Talton, "1960s Africa in Historical Perspective: An Introduction," *Journal of Black Studies* 43 (2012): 7.

138. Witherspoon, *Before the Eyes of the World: Mexico and the 1968 Olympic Games* (Dekalb, IL: Northern Illinois University Press, 2008), Chris Bollsmann, "Mexico 1968 and South Africa 2010: Sombreros and Vuvuzelas and the Legitimisation of Global Sporting Events," *Bulletin of Latin American Research* 29 (2010): 93–106; Robert Huish, "Punching above Its Weight: Cuba's Use of Sport for South-

South Cooperation," *Third World Quarterly* 32.3 (2011): 417–33; Cesar Torres, "Peronism, International Sport, and Diplomacy," 151–82; Antonio Sotomayor, "The Cold War Games of a Colonial Latin American Nation: San Juan, Puerto Rico, 1966," 217–49 and Fan Hong and Lu Zhouxiang, "Politics First, Competition Second," in Dichter and Johns, eds., *Diplomatic Games*.

139. Report of the EB IOC meeting and meeting of the EB with IFs, 7–8 February 1963, RGANI, f. 5, op. 55, d. 11, l. 57.

140. Report on Participation in the International Conference on the Preparation and Holding of GANEFO Games, May 1963, ibid., l. 133.

141. Iu. Mashin to Central Committee, 13 May 1963, ibid., l. 128.

142. Ibid., l. 130.

143. Iu. Mashin to Central Committee, 13 December 1963, RGANI, f. 5, op. 55, d. 11, l. 193.

144. Ibid., l. 194.

145. Ibid.

146. Andrianov to Brundage, 10 April 10 1963, ABC Box 50.

147. Adam Ulam, *Expansion and Coexistence: Soviet Foreign Policy, 1917–73*, 2nd edition (New York: Praeger, 1974), 709. See also Westad, *Global Cold War*, 129.

148. Report of Soviet Representatives to Meetings of the EB IOC and EB with IFs in Lausanne, June 1963, RGANI, f. 5, op. 55, d. 11, l. 164.

149. Brundage to Andrianov, 16 May 1963, ABC Box 50.

150. Brundage to Andrianov, 31 August 1963, ABC Box 50. China indeed sought to use GANEFO for its own public diplomacy goals. See Fan Hong and Lu Zhouxiang, "Politics First, Competition Second," 390–96.

151. Directive Instructions for Soviet Representatives to the meeting of the Executive Board of GANEFO, 7 August 1964, ibid., l. 73.

152. Ibid. Held 18–24 April 1955 in Bandung, Indonesia, the Bandung Conference was a large-scale meeting of African and Asian states, many newly independent, that had as its stated aim opposition to colonialism and neocolonialism in all its forms. While the conference's condemnation included the Soviet Union's treatment of Eastern Europe and Central Asia, Soviet administrators apparently endorsed the overall anti-colonial sentiment of the conference no doubt in order to win support among newly independent states in the developing world.

153. Ibid.

154. *Fizkul'tura i sport*, April 1959, 7.

155. See, for example, Report of Gifts sent to Africa, 1960–61, GARF f. 9570, op. 1, d. 1673, l. 8 and Ambassador to Libya Notes from Meeting with the chairman and secretary of the Sports Festival Commission, 17 December 1962, GARF f. 9570, op. 1, d. 1097, ll. 12–13.

156. Minutes of the IOC Executive Board Meeting, Lausanne, February 1963, IOC Archives.

157. Report on Participation of Soviet Sports Organisations in work of International Sports Associations, 20 August 1962, GARF, f. 9570, op. 1, d. 827, l. 40.

158. Report on Participation of Soviet Sports Organizations in work of International Sports Associations, 20 August 1962, GARF, f. 9570, op. 1, d. 827, ll. 20–26.

159. Report of Soviet Representatives to Meetings of the EB IOC and EB with IFs in Lausanne, June 1963, RGANI, f. 5, op. 55, d. 11, l. 168. SANROC was formed in response to warnings from the IOC that South Africa would be barred from competing in the 1964 Olympic Games if measures were not taken to eliminate racial discrimination in South African sports. For more on the anti-apartheid movement in sport and the exclusion of South Africa see Douglas Booth, *The Race Game: Sport and Politics in South Africa* (London and Portland, OR: Frank Cass Publishers, 1998).

160. Minutes of the 60th IOC Session, 16–20 October 1963, Baden-Baden, Germany, IOC Archives.

161. Report of Soviet Representatives to Meetings of the EB IOC and EB with Ifs in Lausanne, June 1963, RGANI, f. 5, op. 55, d. 11, l. 167. In 1971, the Committee for International Olympic Aid was eventually combined with the International Institute for the Development of NOCs to form the Commission for Olympic Solidarity. See "Olympic Solidarity: Creation and Development," Olympic.org: Official Website of the Olympic Movement, http://www.olympic.org/Documents/Reports/EN/en_report_1072.pdf.

162. Iu. Mashin to Central Committee, 9 May 1963, RGANI, f. 5, op. 55, d. 12, l. 112–13.

163. Oral Report of Central Soviet of Sports Organizations and Societies on Preparation of Soviet Athletes for XVIII Olympic Games in Tokyo, June 1964, GARF, f. 9570, op. 1, d. 254, l. 13.

164. Ibid., l. 35.

165. Brundage to members of the IOC, 30 January 1954, ABC Box 70.

Chapter Three

Getting Things Done

Soviet Bureaucrats' Expanding Role in the IOC and Moscow's Bid to Host the Games

In May 1970, Konstantin Andrianov addressed the IOC members gathered in Amsterdam to choose the host city for the 1976 Olympic Summer Games. Andrianov insisted that many of the IOC members who had visited the USSR over the year had queried, "when will Moscow become an Olympic City?"[1] In fact, Andrianov and other administrators in the Soviet Sports Committee had also been asking that very question since the mid-1950s. After repeatedly requesting that the Central Committee approve an Olympic bid, Sports Committee officials had finally received permission to submit Moscow's candidacy. Now Andrianov could assure his IOC colleagues, "we are inviting the Olympic Games to the City of Moscow," and the Soviet Union moved one step closer to hosting the Olympics.[2] Unfortunately, permission came too late in 1970, and the IOC voted for Montreal to host the 1976 Olympiad. However, merely submitting a bid represented a significant achievement for Andrianov and the Sports Committee. It required not only substantial efforts by Soviet bureaucrats but also a change of priorities from the Soviet leadership and a shift in international politics.

Nikita Khrushchev's colleagues ousted him in October 1964. As testament to the changes that he and his fellow Politburo members had enacted, he was not arrested or publicly denounced and executed. Instead, they quietly voted him out, sending him into internal exile, where he lived out his years peacefully, working on his memoirs. Leonid Il'ich Brezhnev replaced Khrushchev as General Secretary of the Communist Party, and Aleksei Nikolaevich Kosygin became Chairman of the Council of Ministers. In the mid-1960s, after Khrushchev's disorienting domestic reforms and international nuclear brinkmanship, Brezhnev offered a degree of peace and security. The establishment of détente with the West resulted in arms control agreements, expanded trade and cultural exchange between the United States and the USSR, and the signing of the Helsinki Final Act, recognizing the postwar European boundaries and committing both countries to recognize human rights. Yet this period also saw the implementation of the Brezhnev Doctrine after the 1968 invasion of Czechoslovakia: asserting the right to intervene wherever socialist regimes were threatened, Warsaw Pact countries used their military might to abort the Czechoslovakian reform program. At the same time, the KGB cracked down on the growing dissident movement at home.

In trying to comprehend these ambiguities, scholars have suggested a number of theories on how the Soviet Union was governed under Brezhnev. Many scholars have characterized Brezhnev as a broker between competing interests, trying to build consensus and compromise.[3] Other scholars postulated that the capitalist and socialist systems were both moving toward each other as both systems struggled to balance social welfare with economic production in the modern industrialized world. Pointing to rising levels of urbanization, education, and professionalization, proponents of this convergence theory saw an increasingly "modern" society taking shape in the Soviet Union.[4] Edwin Bacon links the search for compromise, characteristic of Brezhnev's time in power, with the idea of a "social contract" between state and society, whereby the regime built consensus and stability through increased consumer spending in exchange for silence among Soviet citizens over civil and political freedoms.[5] Other scholars have noted that Brezhnev's version of peace papered over growing cleavages in Soviet society and silenced productive dialogue as it quashed dissent and reinstituted bureaucratic obstacles and control.[6] Samuel Baron contends that renewed populist policies instituted under Brezhnev to placate the population with artificially high wages and price decreases helped curb social volatility, but Vladimir Kozlov counters that the conservative shift under Brezhnev also sowed the seeds of apathy and disillusionment among the Soviet population.[7] Other scholars have noted that the economic and social stability of the Brezhnev years masked structural and cultural problems that would eventually lead to the Soviet collapse.[8]

Lending credence to the idea that Brezhnev's leadership ushered in a period of reactionary and conservative entrenchment, Brezhnev instituted a number of measures to reverse what he and others saw as disruptive and ill-conceived reforms of his predecessor. After Brezhnev assumed his position as General Secretary, a *Pravda* editorial from 17 October 1964 blamed the need for political change on Khrushchev's "harebrained schemes." Responding especially to pressure from state and party bureaucrats, Brezhnev recentralized government bureaus and established a "stability of cadres" policy that guaranteed job security for many in administrative posts.[9] As Brezhnev's tenure in office wore on, these cadres aged in office, contributing to the stagnation of the Soviet bureaucracy, both imagined and real. The reliance on consensus building and privileging of technical expertise that went along with this policy, however, provided an opportunity for mid-level administrators to act without as much interference from the Central Committee, although they still had to acquire support from the party leadership.

Brezhnev's tenure also marked a turning point in another scheme, pursued since at least 1954 by Sports Committee administrators: to host the Olympic Games in Moscow—perhaps not harebrained, but certainly ambitious. Sports bureaucrats had long promoted the importance of Olympic competition to the spread of peace and mutual understanding, and détente provided a further impetus for their campaign to show the friendly side of Soviet power. Yet Moscow's candidacy did not materialize until after repeated calls from the Sports Committee and the Soviet NOC. Brezhnev long dreamed of hosting the Olympic Games in the Soviet capital, and his accession to power meant a Moscow Olympiad could be realized.[10] Pushing the Central Committee into bidding for the Olympic Games and demonstrating flexibility and skillfulness in drumming up support for Moscow's bid among the international sports community, the Sports Committee took advantage of the change in leadership to realize a project it too found important.

"WE CONSIDER IT PREMATURE": THE SPORTS COMMITTEE'S PUSH TO HOST THE OLYMPIC GAMES

Early attempts to advance Moscow to host the Olympic Games met with reluctance and delay from the Communist Party leadership. Soviet sports administrators first sought permission to host the Olympic Games under Khrushchev in 1956.[11] The Central Committee, however, put off its decision until 1958 when the Sports Committee again asked for permission to bid for the 1964 Games. Doubting the USSR's readiness to host the Games, and not wishing to invite athletes from countries with which the USSR had no diplomatic ties, the Central Committee decided it was "inexpedient" to submit Moscow's candidacy at that time.[12] The timing of the requests was also politically inauspicious, the first coming on the heels of the Soviet invasion of Hungary and the Suez Canal crisis, and the second at a time when the party leadership tried to force the Western powers to the negotiating table by provoking a crisis over West Berlin.[13]

Not to be deterred, Soviet sports administrators continued to build support within the IOC for a Moscow Olympiad even as they followed the Central Committee's instructions to promote Tokyo's bid for the 1964 Games. At the same time, the Sports Committee drafted a proposal to radically alter the organization of the IOC.[14] The timing of this push to "democratize" the IOC, coupled with repeated requests to submit a bid to host the Olympic Games, strongly suggests that the former was geared at least in part toward making conditions in the IOC more favorable to Moscow winning a chance to host the Games. In 1959, N. Romanov assured representatives of sports organizations from socialist countries that even though the Soviet NOC had wanted a Moscow bid for the 1964 Games, supporting Tokyo instead could not only help the USSR build friendly relationships in Asia, but could in turn help Moscow secure the bid for the 1968 Games.[15] Anticipating permission to submit Moscow's candidacy for the 1968 Games, the Sports Committee prepared an article for *Sovetskii sport* explaining Moscow's qualifications to host the Games and suggesting that the 1968 Games could be organized in the Soviet Union. In approving this text for publication, the Central Committee deleted reference to the 1968 Games, noting "we consider it premature to make such an announcement at this time."[16] At the same time, however, Agitprop indicated that 1968 remained a possibility. Noting the IOC's "unwritten rule" to hold the Games alternatively in a European city and non-European city, Agitprop officials concluded that, since the 1960 Games were held in Rome, the 1964 Games should be held outside of Europe because "holding . . . the 1964 Games in another European city would exclude . . . Moscow as the host for staging the Olympiad in 1968."[17]

Further evidence that Soviet sports administrators aimed to host the 1968 Games comes from their role in determining the location of the 1962 and 1963 IOC sessions. Soviet representatives sought to host the 1962 IOC session in Moscow in order to secure Moscow as the host city for the 1968 Olympic Games.[18] When Moscow beat out Nairobi as host of the 1962 Session, R. S. Alexander of the Kenyan Olympic Committee wrote to the USSR OC asking Moscow to surrender the 1962 IOC session in favor of Nairobi "as a gesture to demonstrate [their] interest in [Africa].[19] Shortly after receiving confirmation from IOC Chancellor Otto Mayer that the host city for 1968 would be chosen at the 1963 IOC session, Soviet administrators decided to seek permission from the Central Committee to agree to the Kenyan NOC's request.[20] Andrianov wrote to Brundage proposing to surrender the hosting of the 1962 IOC session to Nairobi as a way "to draw sportsmen from countries of Africa and Asia into the world Olympic Movement."[21] Soviet sports administrators saw the request by the Kenyan NOC as an opportunity to both support the development of Olympic sport in Africa and to gain the home field advantage by hosting the IOC session where the fate of the 1968 Games would be decided.

When IOC members resisted the attempt to switch the sessions, Soviet administrators supported Nairobi's bid for the 1963 IOC session instead, and the IOC voted to accept Nairobi to host the 1963 Session in the third round of voting.[22] Putting a positive spin on this result, Pesliak suggested that the

IOC voted to keep the 1962 session in Moscow and award the 1963 session to Nairobi precisely because it wanted to see Moscow selected as the host city for the 1968 Games. Because the selection for the host city was to be made in 1963, Pesliak observed "that decision must be made in a country that is not a contender for organization of the 1968 Olympiad."[23]

Despite the obvious interest within the Sports Committee and some favorable attitudes from the Central Committee, Moscow never put together a bid for the 1968 Games, presumably because the Central Committee withheld its permission. In another curious turn of events, the IOC did not hold its 1963 session in Nairobi as planned. Concerned that the Nairobi government would deny entry into the country to representatives of South Africa due to its Apartheid system, Avery Brundage even threatened to expel Kenya from the Olympic Movement.[24] Kenyan ministers conceded to allow a multiracial South African delegation to attend the session, but the IOC Executive Board had already agreed to move the session to Baden-Baden.[25] Ultimately, the IOC met in Baden-Baden, the Kenyan NOC retained IOC recognition, and Mexico City won the right to host the 1968 Olympiad in the third round of voting.[26]

Even though the drive to host the Olympic Games appears to have stalled in the early 1960s, the Central Soviet used the IOC session in 1962 to further advance the authority of the Soviet Union in international sports circles. Hosting IOC members in the Soviet Union had been an effective tool for generating good feeling about the USSR in 1947, when the Sports Committee had invited Lord Burghley to attend the second postwar Physical Culture Day Parade, and again in 1954, when Avery Brundage attended the festival and became enamored of the superb organization of the synchronized gymnastics displays he witnessed.[27] The 1962 IOC session provided an opportunity for Soviet sports administrators to show off their organizational skills and Soviet sports facilities to all IOC members as well as to those representatives to International Federations. The UMSS headed by Pesliak and the OC USSR chaired by Andrianov carried out most of the planning for the session, but the Moscow City Soviet arranged housing, transportation, and cultural events for the foreign guests.[28] To impress their visitors, the Central Soviet arranged for souvenirs to be given to all the foreign participants, a concert at the Kremlin theatre, and a performance of *Swan Lake* at the Bolshoi.[29] Participants were also invited to take part in excursions around Moscow and in a three-day trip to Leningrad.[30] In addition, vice chairman of the Central Soviet L.S. Khomenkov headed a commission responsible for organizing a sports festival to coincide with the 59th IOC Session, replete with a formal welcome of the IOC members with children to give them flowers.[31]

Meetings of foreign sports dignitaries with Soviet and party leaders constituted another important opportunity for the Soviet sports administrators to boost their credentials among IOC members. The plan for the session included a visit by IOC members to Leonid Brezhnev (then Chairman of the Presidium of the Supreme Soviet), a reception for the members of the IOC Executive Board at the Council of Ministers, and a luncheon for three hundred session participants, diplomats, and others.[32] Following the IOC session in Moscow, the Central Soviet also arranged a meeting between Avery Brundage and Nikita Khrushchev.

Soviet administrators saw the meeting between Khrushchev and Brundage as a chance to win over Brundage, whom they had always considered a prime opponent in the IOC. Andrianov and Pesliak, both present at the meeting, must have coached Khrushchev in what subjects would most appeal to Brundage, because Khrushchev opened the meeting recounting how he played soccer in the 1910s while living among miners.[33] Then Khrushchev and Brundage exchanged stories about how they both hurt their arms playing sports at an early age, Khrushchev while playing soccer, and Brundage at a track and field competition in St. Petersburg in 1912.[34] These similarities provided a useful common ground between the leader of the Soviet Union and the IOC president. Brundage doubted Khrushchev's assertion that "Our physical culture leaders, as I understand, respect you and note your objectivity." When Brundage noted that he had been labeled at various times "a Nazi, fascist, capitalist, imperialist, and communist," Khrushchev reassured him, "we do not consider you a fascist."[35] Despite this tense exchange, Brundage and Khrushchev found many points of agreement on the philosophy of sport, acknowledging that physical culture helped to teach discipline in young people and that sport was of universal value in "the harmonious development of the person."[36] Brundage also praised his "Soviet friends" for the success of the IOC session in Moscow, the "great results" by Soviet gymnasts in the Olympic Games, and for the "decorum" and "discipline" of Soviet athletes.[37] Khrushchev further assured Brundage that "we support the Olympic Movement in every way and consider it our duty to lend aid to the development of sport in the country."[38]

The 59th IOC Session in Moscow also made it possible for Leonid Brezhnev to assert his personal support for the Olympic Games and their role in spreading peace and friendship among nations. In his welcome address at the session's opening ceremony, Brezhnev expressed appreciation to the IOC for selecting Moscow to host the meeting in "recognition of the contribution made by our country's athletes and their organizations to the international Olympic Movement."[39] The Olympic goal of bringing together the peoples of the world in peaceful interaction through sport, Brezhnev argued, was also the foundation of Soviet foreign policy, and he emphasized that "the Olympic Games enjoys the greatest appreciation and support in the Soviet Union." He ended his speech by wishing the IOC future success in "the wonderful cause of putting the Olympic ideals into practice, in the organization of the Olympic Games, and in their transformation into mass displays of friendship and of joyful, peace-loving youth of the whole world, free of any discrimination."[40]

The meeting with Khrushchev and the speech by Brezhnev must be seen as attempts by Soviet sports administrators to help pave the way for an eventual Moscow Olympiad, by demonstrating to the IOC, and to Brundage personally, that the entire Soviet leadership was committed to the cause of Olympism. In both cases, the Soviet leaders highlighted the affinity between Olympism and the Marxist-Leninist philosophy of sport. They insisted upon the Soviet Union's great contributions to the Olympic Movement and the enthusiastic support that the Games enjoyed throughout the country. Finally, both Khrushchev and Brezhnev used the opportunity to emphasize the peaceful nature of Soviet foreign policy and how, in that way, the USSR and the IOC were fellow travelers in the goal of building friendship and mutual understanding between nations. Though neither referred specifically to a possible Moscow Olympiad, what better way to cement the relationship between the USSR and the International Olympic Committee than to stage the Olympic Games in the Soviet capital?

Even if hosting the Games was not a top priority of the Central Committee at this time, the Central Soviet continued to push for a Moscow Olympiad. In December 1965 Mashin again requested that the Central Committee consider putting forth Moscow as a candidate for hosting the 1972 Summer Games. The petition emphasized the "authority of the Soviet Union and Soviet sports abroad and also the experience in staging large-scale international sports competitions in the USSR."[41] The Central Soviet also sought to allay apprehensions within the Politburo that hosting the Games might harm Soviet foreign relations. Four countries caused particular concern: Taiwan, whose National Olympic Committee had been recognized by the IOC, and whose athletes therefore would have to be invited to participate; the People's Republic of China (PRC), which could not be invited given its exclusion from the IOC in 1958; and the African countries of Rhodesia and South Africa. The request noted that South Africa and Rhodesia would likely be banned from the Olympics in the future due to their racist sports policies.[42] However, by citing the authority of the Soviet Union and its experience in hosting important competitions in the past as the two chief reasons for a Moscow candidacy, Mashin and the Central Soviet downplayed the significance of political considerations in comparison to the potential propaganda success of staging the Olympics in Moscow.

The Central Soviet and the National Olympic Committee took the initiative in requesting permission to host the Games, but the Moscow City Soviet of Workers' Deputies would need to submit the official request to the IOC, since the IOC chose host *cities* for the Games and not host countries. The Central

Soviet drafted supporting letters from V.F. Promyslov, head of the Executive Committee of the Moscow City Soviet, and the Soviet National Olympic Committee. The sports administrators' knew the city selection process and how bids should be framed, assuring Brundage that Moscow had the necessary sports facilities and experience hosting international competitions, and expressing Moscow's desire to "make our contribution in the Olympic Movement."[43] The OC USSR supported the proposal, declaring that it "would be pleased to welcome the IOC members as their honored guests," and promising that the Games would be held "in correspondence with the IOC Charter and to the full satisfaction of the IOC."[44] These letters made four key points of interest to the IOC: that IOC members would be given their rightful honored role in the Games' ceremonies, that the Games would be staged according to IOC rules, that the bid was being made out of a sincere desire to contribute to the noble goals of the Olympic Movement, and that Moscow had the logistical capacity to host the Games. The letter also portrayed proper deference to the IOC, humbly asking the IOC members "to entrust Moscow with the staging of such an illustrious international sports event as the Olympic Games in our time."[45]

Despite the careful drafting and planning, the Central Committee demonstrated unwillingness in 1965 to throw its weight behind the Central Soviet's desire to host the Olympic Games. In denying the request to bid for the 1972 Games, the Central Committee asserted that the question "called for additional and more detailed study."[46] Some members of the Central Committee later regretted their hesitation when they saw the list of candidate cities: Madrid in Franco's fascist Spain, Munich in the capitalist Federal Republic of Germany, Detroit Michigan in the United States, and Montreal in Quebec province, Canada. The Central Soviet proposed supporting Montreal, but expressed fears that the North American location would advantage U.S. athletes.[47] During discussion of which city Soviet IOC members should support, N.A. Shelepin wondered why Moscow could not put forth its candidacy, but Mashin informed him that it was too late to submit a bid.[48] Ultimately the Central Committee instructed Andrianov and A. Romanov to vote for a European city first, then Madrid over Munich to placate their GDR comrades.[49] At the 1966 IOC Session in Rome, Munich won the right to hold the 1972 Summer Games by the narrowest margin of one vote on the second ballot.[50]

"AN ANTI-SOVIET CHALLENGE": INTERNATIONAL TENSIONS, OLYMPIC FAILURES, AND DOMESTIC DISSENT

Despite the enthusiasm of the Central Soviet to bring the Olympic Games to Moscow, the period after 1964 was a volatile one both domestically and internationally, and events both inside and outside the world of sports may have contributed to the hesitancy of the Central Committee to approve a bid to host the Games in 1972. Inside the Soviet Union, the leadership eroded the brief period of intellectual and cultural thaw initiated by Khrushchev's anti-Stalinist campaign. The public denouncement and trial in 1966 of writers Andrei Sinyavsky and Yuli Daniel, sentenced to hard labor for publishing "anti-Soviet" material abroad, marked the beginning of the Soviet dissident movement and the Brezhnev regime's attempts to silence this growing, disaffected stratum of the intelligentsia.[51] Meanwhile, developments in the Middle East exacerbated Soviet anti-Israeli policies, as Soviet Arab client states engaged in a combined attack on the state of Israel in the Six-Day War of 1967. As part of the fall-out from this brief engagement, Soviet authorities increased their support of Egypt and grew increasingly suspicious of Jewish dissidents at home.[52]

Soviet foreign policy in the late 1960s also hampered the Central Soviet's efforts to host the Games. In Czechoslovakia, when Alexander Dubcek led his Prague Spring reform movement to introduce "socialism with a human face," Warsaw Pact countries invaded, led by the USSR. The military intervention temporarily damaged the image of the Soviet Union abroad, fueling anti-Soviet sentiments both inside the Soviet Union and among its socialist allies, and threatening to further undermine the efforts of Soviet sports representatives to build a socialist bloc within the IOC and other international sports organizations.[53] In September 1968, the Czechoslovak member of the IOC, F. Kroutil, appealed to Andrianov and A. Romanov as fellow IOC members and colleagues to convince the Soviet government to end the occupation. Kroutil cautioned that such intervention could be detrimental to the image and authority of socialist countries, questioning, "How will your sportsmen and athletes of other socialist countries that take part in the occupation of our country be received at the Olympic Games?"[54] When the European NOCs met in France that same month, the Italian representatives proposed the adoption of a resolution condemning the invasion.[55]

Soviet representatives L. Kazanskii and V. Savvin exhibited political savvy as they sought to control a potentially volatile situation. They held a series of bilateral meetings with French, Czechoslovak, and Italian representatives, urging them not to discuss the events in Czechoslovakia. Kazanskii and Savvin also enlisted the aid of their Czechoslovak colleague Kroutil to convince other countries not to make an issue of the invasion, despite his personal opposition to the Soviet military intervention. As a result of Soviet efforts, the resolution was not discussed and "all attempts to use [the events in Czechoslovakia] against the Soviet Union sports organizations or socialist countries" were thwarted.[56] Kazanskii and Savvin recommended that the results of the European NOC meetings be reported to the Soviet representatives attending the IF congresses during the Mexico Games, "bringing to their attention the importance of realizing their directives, exhibiting flexibility and skill, and using their personal contacts with foreign leaders to prevent reactionary elements" from exploiting the invasion "to mount an anti-Soviet challenge."[57] In stressing the need for flexibility, Kazanskii and Savvin highlighted key attributes that the most successful Soviet sports representatives had demonstrated over the years. Unable to change the Soviet government's military policies, sports administrators could only try to mitigate the damage that the invasion posed to Soviet prestige.

Nevertheless, fallout from the events in Prague played out in the sporting arena. As tensions rose in Czechoslovakia during the late 1960s, several incidents of Czechoslovak spectators shouting and throwing objects at Soviet teams, brawls between Czechoslovak and Soviet players, and other exhibitions of anti-Soviet feeling occurred at sporting matches between the two countries.[58] After tying with a Soviet gymnast on the floor exercise and losing out to another Soviet on the beam during the Mexico City Games, Czechoslovakian Olympic gymnast Vera Caslavska gave a silent protest to the events in Prague, bowing her head and looking to the side, refusing to watch the Flag of the USSR rise while its national anthem played.[59] Caslavska, a vocal supporter of the Prague Spring, was not allowed to travel abroad after her protest by the Czechoslovak sports authorities.

Other international developments might also have influenced the Central Committee to delay a Moscow Olympic bid. Tensions between the Soviet Union and the Peoples' Republic of China had been growing throughout the 1960s, erupting into border clashes between March and August 1969. The year 1968 witnessed an upsurge of youth unrest around the world, and student protests in Mexico ten days before the start of the Summer Games in Mexico City threatened to mar the Olympic festival. On 2 October, the Mexican police and military broke up student demonstrations in the Tlatelolco Plaza of Mexico City by shooting at the unarmed crowd, possibly killing as many as 300.[60] The IOC Executive Board discussed the demonstrations at their Mexico City meeting held during the Games. Once the Organizing Committee had obtained assurances from the Mexican government that the Games "could be staged peacefully without any danger for athletes and spectators," the EB agreed that the Games would go on as planned.[61] The events in Mexico City exposed the IOC's belief in the separation of sport and politics as increasingly naïve if not downright hypocritical. By the end of the Games the brutal authoritarian government of Mexico received no sanction while the African American athletes Tommie Smith and John Carlos were stripped of their medals and sent home for their silent protest against racial discrimination in sport.[62]

More significant for Soviet sports than the Tlatelolco massacre or the Black Power salute, the 1968 Mexico City Games marked the first time since

1952 that the Soviet Union came in second to the United States in both the medal count and the unofficial team point total at the Summer Games. The Soviet delegation to the 1968 Winter Games in Grenoble also came in second, behind Norway. After the Winter Games concluded, sports officials blamed the unsuccessful performances on the lack of facilities and equipment, poor oversight of preparing of the national teams, and a lack of personal commitment by athletes and their trainers. The Presidium disciplined a number of trainers and sport federation officials, preventing some from working with the national teams in the future.[63]

The 1968 defeats convinced the Central Committee to reassert control over the sports administration. The head of the propaganda department, V. Stepakov, expressed "considerable anxiety" about preparations of the Soviet team for the Mexico City Games, noting a number of "mistakes" and "deficiencies" in training athletes, poor methods and lack of discipline among trainers and athletes, poorly equipped training facilities, and "weak control by the Central Soviet over the work of trainers and athletes."[64] Concerned that winning the Sumer Games was impossible under current circumstances, the Central Committee placed the former head of the Komsomol, Sergei Pavlovich Pavlov, in charge, enjoining the Central Soviet to "mobilize all of its resources" to improve the discipline, organization, and "responsibility" of athletes and trainers in the final stage of preparing for the Games.[65] Pavlov came to the sports administration with considerable credentials. He was first secretary of the Komsomol and deputy to the Russian and USSR Supreme Soviets, where he served as a member of the Foreign Affairs Commission, leading delegations to Austria, Guinea, Cuba, Finland, Bulgaria, and East Germany between 1959 and 1963. Pavlov even studied at the Moscow Institute of Physical Culture from 1950 to 1952, giving him training in sports administration.[66] In October 1968, during the Mexico City Games, Soviet leaders disbanded the unwieldy and less effective Central Soviet of the Union of Sports Organizations and Societies. After the Soviet team lost to the United States as feared, Sergei Pavlov led a meeting of the newly reconstituted Sports Committee to discuss why. While the previous meeting had involved only the top leadership of the Central Soviet, members of the propaganda department of the Central Committee, representatives of the Council of Ministers and of the secretariat of the Central Soviet of Trade Unions attended this one. Also, each speaker signed the minutes of the meeting at the beginning or end of his presentation.[67] This was a novel control measure, no doubt instituted to instill a sense of personal responsibility among Sports Committee and sports federation administrators for the development of top-class athletes in their respective sports.

While sports leaders agonized over the embarrassment of losing to the United States in Mexico City, the KGB warned the Central Committee about other disturbing developments at the Games. In an October 1968 report, Iurii Andropov, then vice chairman of the KGB, described the presence of "active nationalistic propaganda among athletes, tourists, and journalists of Jewish nationality" instigated when the American and Israeli embassies, together with the Jewish community in Mexico, had invited a number of Soviet Jews to a special reception.[68] He drew attention to the circulation of "Zionist literature" among the Soviet delegation, and to Baltic émigrés who attempted to lure the Estonian men's choir members into defecting. Andropov also observed that "provocative literature" about the Czechoslovakian invasion had been circulated, but he stressed that relations between the Czechoslovak and Soviet delegations "continue to normalize."[69] Increased agitation among the Soviet delegation, coupled with the growing dissident movement and continued social unrest at home, help to account for the Central Committee's reluctance to host the Olympic Games.

"PERHAPS ON ANOTHER OCCASION": MOSCOW'S FAILED BID FOR THE 1976 GAMES

After three false starts, the Sports Committee finally secured the backing of the Central Committee to submit Moscow as a candidate for the XXI Olympic Games in 1976. The Sports Committee personnel, the Soviet Olympic Committee, and Soviet IOC members made every effort to win the right for Moscow to host the 1976 Games, working all their international connections, schmoozing with powerful individuals in the sporting world, and sending battalions of sports officials all over the world to cultivate support for Moscow.

In September 1969 the Central Committee resolved to submit Moscow's candidacy for the 1976 Olympic Games, and the Sports Committee and Soviet Olympic Committee wasted no time in putting together a number of commissions and a full plan of measures for promoting Moscow's candidacy. Andrianov again worked with V. F. Promyslov to notify the IOC of Moscow's bid and to oversee the drafting and presentation of it at the IOC session in 1970.[70] The Sports Committee decided that Andrianov would supervise an effort to promote Moscow's candidacy among socialist countries, developing countries, capitalist countries, Scandinavian countries, International Federations, and IOC members. An international commission would oversee propaganda surrounding the bid and travel to a number of countries and international sporting events to campaign for Moscow's bid. A commission for construction and material supplies and a commission for sports facilities would presumably take responsibility for much of the content of the official bid, which would necessarily include a breakdown of available sports facilities, planned construction projects, and testimonials by various sports federations, confirming that Moscow was able to stage the Games according to IF standards for each sport. Though led by Sports Committee personnel, all three commissions included representatives from numerous other Soviet agencies and departments, including the Moscow City Soviet, TASS, the Chief Administration of Sports Production (Glavsportprom), Profsoiuz, and leaders of Soviet sports federations.[71]

Once they had given official notice of their intentions, the bid commissions set to work to ensure the IOC would select Moscow. In the lead-up to the 1970 IOC session in Amsterdam, where the host city for 1976 would be chosen, Andrianov and Pavlov met with their East European counterparts to orchestrate a united front and "clarify a plan of action" for the session.[72] The networks of contacts and associates that each socialist IOC member had been cultivating for the past three decades were now mobilized in the joint goal of securing enough votes for Moscow to win the right to host the 1976 Olympic Summer Games. For example, Manfred Ewald of the East German NOC proposed inviting a group of journalists from capitalist and developing countries to "show the achievement of the USSR in sport," to improve public opinion toward Moscow. He also believed that the Soviet press needed to publish material highlighting the "modernizing of communications and information systems in connection with the Olympic Games."[73]

At a meeting in Lausanne in February 1970, Soviet sports administrators sounded out the European NOCs and IOC members about their opinion of the Moscow bid for the 1976 Games. Brundage expressed sympathy toward Moscow's candidacy, noting that during his first-hand visit to the USSR, Moscow had proven its ability to guarantee "good organization of the Games." According to Andrianov, the Marquis d'Exeter (formerly Lord Burghley), despite being anti-communist, regarded Moscow's hosting the Games as "an important victory of the Olympic Movement" because it would bring a number of athletes, journalists, and tourists to the USSR.[74] Promises of support also came from IOC members from France, Ireland, Switzerland, and Italy, including future IOC presidents Lord Killanin and Juan Antonio Samaranch. Even West Germany apparently favored Moscow's hosting the Games. Willi Daume, the West German NOC president, told Soviet representatives in private meetings and in "strictest confidence" that he had met with Brandt and secured the West German chancellor's permission to vote for Moscow.[75] In the report on the meetings, Andrianov underscored the importance of personal contacts and private meetings in Moscow's campaign to win the right to host the 1976 Olympic games. Outside of formal meetings, according to Andrianov, his delegation held "personal negotiations" with thirty-three IOC members, of whom twenty-three promised to support

Moscow. Even though many IOC members considered Moscow's proposal too late, as Los Angeles and Montreal had spent two years "working" among IOC members, Andrianov assured his comrades that many members thought Moscow had a "serious chance" to win the bid.[76]

Andrianov and company also used these meetings to generate support among non-European IOC members. Soviet representatives to international sports organizations had made a concerted effort to develop sports ties with countries of the developing world, and Andrianov personally had done a lot of work in developing the Olympic Solidarity program, which provided funds for building sports facilities and supporting physical education programs, especially in Africa. The Mexico IOC member pledged his support for Moscow, thanking the Soviet representatives for their help in securing the Games for Mexico City in 1968. The Nigerian IOC member called on all African countries to back Moscow in recognition of Soviet help to Africa. V. Ali of Pakistan also promised to endorse Moscow's bid.[77] These efforts to make friends in the developing world paid off in Soviet efforts to secure the 1976 Olympic Games for Moscow.

Two months before the Amsterdam meeting, Soviet representatives ramped up their campaign to win the bid for 1976. In March 1970, the Secretariat of the Central Committee approved a "Plan of Informational-Propagandistic Measures for Nominating Moscow to Host the XXI Summer Olympic Games." This plan included tasks for several departments, including the MID, the Central Committee, the Komsomol, and several newspaper editorial boards.[78] The same month, Pavlov and Andrianov officiated at a meeting of IOC members from East European socialist countries, where Andrianov laid out the tasks for socialist representatives at the Amsterdam session. At the meeting, Czechoslovak, Polish, and East German IOC members reported that U.S. and Canadian representatives intimated that they were more concerned about their Denver and Vancouver bids for the Winter Games than their candidacies of Los Angeles and Montreal. According to their socialist comrades, Moscow's bid depended a great deal on appearing prepared, including demonstrating adequate sports facilities, tourist accommodations, transport, political guarantees, economic assurances, and souvenirs for IOC members.[79]

Foreign press reports served as an important barometer of international opinion, and Soviet administrators used them to inform their goals and strategies. The international press identified problems in Moscow that tourists and journalists encountered at recent sports events. Foreign journalists at the 1970 figure skating championships reported trouble getting telephone connections and complained that they could not find an open restaurant to dine in after the competitions. Andrianov warned that "our opponents use any of our mistakes or errors to show that the Games in Moscow would be worse than in a Western city," insisting that "counter propaganda" must dispel such negative reports. Meanwhile the Sports Committee worked to eliminate technical problems and improve the quality of communications and services for foreign visitors, especially members of the media.[80] They also kept track of Western press coverage of the bid, which often listed Moscow as the favorite to win the right to host the 1976 Games.[81]

In some ways the bid document itself reads like any standard article on Soviet sports, providing a laundry list of the many "successes" of Soviet sports, but it also reflects the sheer enormity of the coordination necessary to bring the Olympics to Moscow, as well as the many individual efforts required to make a successful bid. The bid pamphlet opened by attesting to the investment and support for the Games by the Moscow City Soviet, the USSR NOC, and the Supreme Soviet of the USSR, all of which guaranteed that "the Games of the XXI Olympiad would be conducted in full accordance with the lofty principles of the Olympic Movement and according to the rules and regulations of the International Olympic Committee."[82] The pamphlet enumerated the reasons Moscow should get the bid, highlighting Russian and Soviet contributions to the Olympic Movement.[83] The bid concludes with lists of all the sports facilities already available for Olympic competition and of the construction plans for additional sports facilities, as well as the Olympic Village, with guarantees by the Soviet sports federations for all twenty-one Olympic sports, promising to fulfill the standards of their respective international federations. These guarantees were in some ways formulaic, but each one incorporated specific information and details pertinent to its sport that reflected the concerns of each international federation. These detailed reports from the USSR sports federations demonstrate the depth of knowledgeable administrators in the Soviet sports world and give a sense of the organizational capacity needed to stage the Olympics in Moscow.

Finally, a delegation travelled to Amsterdam to present Moscow's candidacy to the IOC session in May 1970. The group brought a film, an exhibit on Soviet sports, models of sporting arenas, books, and an album entitled "Moscow—1976," all designed to show Moscow in its best light.[84] Promyslov, Pavlov, and Andrianov all gave speeches supporting Moscow's bid. Declaring "the sincere desire of the entire population of our city to welcome the participants to this major sports festival of our times," Promyslov's speech emphasized the excellent amenities Moscow could offer. From its "modern, well-appointed hotels," restaurants, cafes, and parks, to its "132-kilometer-long Metro," Moscow provided modern conveniences as well as the cultural offerings of Moscow's theaters, concert halls, and museums that would be available for the recreation of the IOC and Olympic athletes.[85] In addition to many existing sports facilities as well as new sports venues, Promyslov assured IOC members a modern system for tabulating results, a special Press Center to accommodate the media, and an Olympic Village at Moscow's Iz-mailova Park with an adjacent Institute of Physical Culture, replete with sports training facilities for the Olympic competitors.

In his speech, Sports Committee Chairman Sergei Pavlov highlighted the Soviet Union's contributions to international sports and Moscow's experience in hosting large sports competitions over the years. Noting that the Soviet Union belonged to 50 international sports federations and maintained sporting relations with 72 countries around the world, Pavlov reported that 2,000 Soviet athletes had competed in the Olympic Summer and Winter Games, with 83 of them setting Olympic records and 130 Muscovites among them winning gold.[86] Pavlov also listed the many European and World championships that had been staged in Moscow in recent years. In addition to these events, Pavlov pointed out that Moscow hosted the quadrennial Tournament of Peoples of the USSR with 10,000.competitors.

Konstantin Andrianov made the final speech proposing Moscow's readiness to host the XXI Games in 1976, emphasizing the role of the Olympic Games, and of Moscow's potential as host city to encourage the wide, mass participation in sport and the further spreading of the Olympic ideal throughout the world. He highlighted the "broad development" of sport in the USSR, which made it accessible to "everyone—from children to people of old age."[87] Andrianov reminded the IOC members of their personal visits to the Soviet Union where they experienced first-hand the staging of mass sports competitions like the Tournament of the Peoples of the USSR, appealing to their personal memories as testament to Moscow's ability to host the Games. Promising that a Moscow Olympiad would "make a considerable contribution to the promotion and consolidation of the International Olympic Movement," Andrianov insisted that there were no "political, economic, or sport reasons to prevent the success of the Games in Moscow."[88]

All three speakers insisted upon Moscow's intention to organize the Games in full compliance with Olympic rules and in full spirit of Olympic ideals and values. Promyslov promised that the Games, if awarded to Moscow, would be held in "full conformity with the rules and statutes of the International Olympic Committee."[89] Andrianov also stressed Moscow's intention "to strictly observe the requirements of the Olympic Charter of the IOC," emphasizing the ability of a Moscow Olympiad to contribute to the "development of Olympic ideas throughout the world" and to "facilitate a fresh upsurge of sport."[90] Pavlov's speech also promised to advance Olympic ideals, "to facilitate the comprehensive development of man, and the strengthening of friendship and peace through sport."[91] If the IOC were "to act fairly and farsightedly" and allow Moscow to host the Games, Pavlov continued, it would "open a fresh page in the history of the Olympics," by entrusting them to an East European nation for the first time. Pavlov concluded that, in return, all sporting organizations of the Soviet Union would "spare no effort to see that the Games in Moscow facilitate the further advancement of the sports movement and become a bright festival of sport, peace, and friendship."[92] These speeches were meant to reassure skeptics among the IOC members who might doubt Soviet aims and fear Soviet organizers' intention to stage a socialist sports festival with disregard for IOC traditions. While giving these assurances, however, the Soviet representatives stressed the aspects of Olympic philosophy that coincided with Marxist-Leninist ideas of mass sports participation, promotion of physical education for all, and peace and friendship between nations. These speeches continued a core strategy of Soviet sports representatives since the 1940s to couch their proposals within Olympic philosophy and language, painting the USSR as a key promoter of Olympism. Because promoting peace and friendship was a key component of peaceful coexistence and détente, Moscow's bid to host the Olympic Games could be seen as the culmination of a process of melding Soviet and Olympic ideals.

Despite the careful planning and tireless efforts of Soviet sports administrators, Moscow lost the bid to host the 1976 Games to Montreal by a vote of forty-one to twenty-eight.[93] Like the lead up to the Soviet Union's first Olympic Games in 1952, the bid for 1976 displayed *shturmovshchina*: a frantic, last-minute production spurt. In his *Bol'shoi sport*, Prozumenshchikov argues that such an approach was characteristic of "Moscow, where the bureaucratic machine always worked sluggishly and clumsily."[94] However, once given permission by the Central Committee, the Sports Committee bureaucratic machine worked quickly and relatively effectively. Largely as a result of the delayed decision of the Central Committee, Soviet organizers had barely six months to plan and carry out their campaign. Presumably, given more time to work among the IOC membership, the Soviet bid committee could have won the vote. Indeed, important IOC members remained favorably disposed to Moscow's hosting future Games. In a May 1970 letter to Promyslov, Brundage voiced his hope that "the intense Olympic spirit" of the Soviet Union would not be diminished and that "perhaps on another occasion it will be possible to stage the Games in Moscow."[95]

The Sports Committee responded to the failed bid by deflecting blame onto the IOC itself, while still maintaining the hope of a successful bid in the future. Denouncing the conservative and "bourgeois" proclivities of many members of the IOC, twenty-two of whom were royalty, Soviet officials called out "certain businessmen" whose "behind-the-scenes scheming" they blamed for Moscow's failed bid. The Sports Committee also chastised

Andrianov and Aleksei Romanov for being too trusting, believing the "hypo-critical, untrustworthy" Avery Brundage.[96] The Sports Committee also pro-posed publishing a series of articles in *Sovetskii sport* and the weekly Soviet newspaper *Literaturnaia gazeta* denouncing the IOC's attitude and renewing calls for its immediate reorganization along more "democratic" lines, but the Central Committee declined to launch an attack against the composition of the IOC.[97] Sergei Pavlov slammed the IOC for its politically motivated deci-sion and argued that the IOC Charter needed to be revised. Promyslov, on the other hand, noted that Moscow should not be discounted from bidding for a future Olympic Games.[98]

"THE USSR ONCE AGAIN INVITES THE OLYMPIC GAMES": THE CAMPAIGN FOR 1980

Over a year after losing the bid to host the 1976 Olympics and three years be-fore the selection would be made, Soviet administrators submitted Moscow's candidacy for the Games of the XXII Olympiad. Expressing "the genuine desire of the population our country's capital to organize the Olympic Games and prompted by the desire to make a worthy contribution to developing the modern Olympic Movement," V. Promyslov, chairman of the Executive Committee of the Moscow City Soviet promised to spare no effort in mak-ing the Games a success.[99] As before, Promyslov assured Brundage that all participants, officials, delegations, and representatives of IFs, international press, radio and television would be given free entry visas to the USSR. He also promised that the Games in Moscow would be held "in complete conformity with the Olympic Charter."[100] Konstantin Andrianov followed up Promyslov's invitation with assurances from the Soviet NOC that Moscow was well-qualified to host the Games.[101]

Once a decision had been made to put forward Moscow's candidacy for 1980, the Soviet press wasted no time in publicizing it. An article appeared in the October edition of *Sport in the USSR* announcing the upcoming bid and indicating that a number of "eminent leaders of international sport" had already pledged their support to Moscow. The article expressed a sense of betrayal at Moscow's not having been chosen to host 1976, but insisted that the USSR was determined to rise above Cold War politics and "behind the scenes scheming" and again bid for the Olympic Games despite its earlier failure. Highlighting that Moscow wanted to host the Games in order to ful-fill its role in the spreading of peace, friendship, and mutual understanding through sport, the article announced that "the capital of the USSR once again invites the Olympic Games."[102]

After the failed bid in 1970, important changes took place in the IOC that directly reinforced the efforts of Soviet administrators to secure the 1980 Games. At its session in September 1971 in Luxembourg, the IOC elected Vitalii Georgievich Smirnov to join its ranks following the retirement of A. O. Romanov (Figure 3.1).[103] By replacing the sixty-seven year old Romanov with thirty-six year old Smirnov, the Soviet leadership and the Sports Committee injected new blood into the bid for 1980. Smirnov also graduated from the State Academy of Physical Culture and Sport, so he brought a degree of professional sporting expertise that would garner respect from the IOC as well as benefit the Sports Committee. Earlier that year, Smirnov replaced Igor Kazanskii on the program commission of the IOC, giving the Soviet Union a more active voice on that commission.[104] He likewise was chosen to head working groups of socialist representatives under the name of "Olympic Games 1972" for both the Sapporo Winter Games and the Munich Summer Games.[105] Moreover, at the Munich session of the IOC in August 1972, Lord Killanin, an Irish nobleman who had served as vice president of the IOC since 1968, replaced Avery Brundage as president.[106] Soviet sports leaders also wanted to ensure that Vitalii Smirnov would take Andrianov's place on the executive board, and Killanin was receptive to the idea.[107]

By 1971, the international situation had also shifted in favor of a Moscow Olympiad. The new chancellor of West Germany, Willy Brandt, had ushered in his policy of improved relations with East Germany known as *Ostpolitik* in 1970. Following Brandt's lead, Leonid Brezhnev and Richard Nixon began to pursue détente between the two superpowers. The two leaders held their first summit in May 1972 and began work to limit their nuclear arsenals with the first Stategic Arms Limitation Treaty (SALT I) that same year. *Ostpolitik* and détente provided the necessary background for Soviet sports leaders to forge a close working relationship with their West German colleagues. As hosts of the 1972 Summer Games, the Munich organizers would prove to be a crucial source of information and experience for the Moscow Organizing Committee. Also, the president of the Munich Organizing Committee (Orgcom) and the West German NOC, Willi Daume, held a great deal of sway within the IOC, therefore cultivating close ties with him that could help Moscow win the selection process.

Increasingly difficult relations with their comrades in East Germany served to push Soviet administrators closer to their West German colleagues. A Sports Committee report on international relations in early 1969 complained that the GDR seemed to be holding back on agreements for sports exchanges with the USSR, fulfilling only 50 percent of the plan for technical exchange.[108] Pavlov also complained that GDR representatives took unilateral action on sports issues and at times went against the agreed-upon position.[109]

Figure 3.1.   Vitaly Smirnov replaced the aging Aleksei Romanov as the second Soviet IOC member in 1971. He then replaced Andrianov on the Executive Board in 1974 and became vice president of the IOC in 1978. Courtesy International Olympic Committee.

GDR representatives even suggested that socialist countries refuse to participate in the cultural program and youth camps of the Munich Games after the
socialist countries decided to join in "to exert more active influence on the
population of the FRG."[110] As hosts of the 1972 Games and potential hosts
for 1980, the FRG and USSR sports leaders recognized their mutual interest
in working together. Soviet organizers had nothing to gain from disrupting
the Munich Games, and the actions of GDR representatives threatened to undermine the socialist cooperation that was crucial to putting forth a successful
bid for the 1980 Games.[111]

Learning from their past mistakes, Soviet administrators began their 1980
bid early, leaving plenty of time to generate support for Moscow among
NOCs, IFs, and IOC members. In pushing their bid for the 1980 Games,
Soviet administrators utilized the full spectrum of tactics they had perfected
during their twenty years of active participation in the Olympic Movement.
Soviet IOC members and IF representatives formed a permanent commission of socialist sports leaders to further coordinate their activities bolstering
Moscow's candidacy.[112] The bid committee organized "individual work"
with IOC members and IF leaders, enlisting the aid of Soviet diplomatic
staff abroad to distribute information and to arrange meetings with important
sports figures.[113]

Soviet representatives participated even more vigorously in the kind of
"behind-the-scenes scheming" they felt had been so successfully utilized
by their opponents during the 1976 campaign. Every IF meeting and every
international sports event became a venue for assessing the opinions of foreign sports leaders and securing promises of support from IOC members. At
the meeting of the Bureau of FINA in Singapore in November 1971, Z. P.
Firsov held meetings with Singaporeans to ask for their support in "creating
favorable public opinion toward Moscow among Asian countries." They held
similar meetings with a number of FINA personalities, including representatives from Mexico, West Germany, Peru, Yugoslavia, and Canada. All those
with whom they met, according to Firsov, "proclaimed with certainty that this
time, justice would win out" and the IOC would select Moscow to host the
Games.[114] Similarly, at the International Canoeing Federation (ICF) meeting
in May 1974 in Madrid, V. N. Lukatin confirmed that the Bureau of the ICF
voted unanimously to support Moscow.[115] According to a Sports Committee
decree, on the eve of the Vienna session where the host city for 1980 was
chosen, most IOC members and all twenty-one International Federations
governing Olympic sports had intimated their support for Moscow.[116]

To garner support for Moscow's bid for the 1980 Games, Soviet administrators invited prominent members of the IOC and other international sports
organizations to the Soviet Union to see first-hand what Moscow had to

offer.[117] From 1972 through 1974, fifty members of the IOC visited the USSR, including Lord Killanin, all the executive board members, and presidents and/ or technical experts from the federations of all the Olympic sports.[118] Hosting major sports competitions also allowed sports administrators to show off their organizational abilities to influential international guests. In addition to "the usual events," Pavlov insisted that competitions required "special propaganda measures" to give "the proper social and political resonance."[119] IOC and IF members were accustomed to being wined and dined by prospective host cities, and the Soviet organizers knew they had do this in order to win over the leaders of international sport to the Moscow bid.[120]

"SPORTS, PEACE, AND FRIENDSHIP": THE 1973 WORLD STUDENT GAMES

As part of their campaign to win the 1980 Olympic Games, Soviet sports organizers invited the International Federation of University Sports (FISU) to stage the Universiad-73 World Student Summer Games in Moscow. By offering to hold these games the year before the Vienna IOC session, where the 1980 host city would be selected, Soviet sports administrators hoped to impress the IOC with their ability to stage a large-scale international sports festival. In his report to the IOC Executive Board on preparations for the Universiad, Andrianov emphasized the size of the competition, with ten sports on the program, an estimated 4,300 athletes, officials, coaches, and judges, and potentially 10,000 tourists who wanted to attend the event. Andrianov praised Moscow's housing facilities, including the Moscow State University dorms for participants, and the Metropol, National, and Ukraine hotels available for honored guests and accredited journalists. He also promised that over five hundred guides with facility in thirty languages would be on hand to aid guests of the Universiad. Andrianov assured the EB that the "best sports facilities," such as Lenin Stadium, the Soviet Army Club Palace of Sport, and the Brothers Znamensky Sports Center, and the press center had all the necessary modern communications technology required by the one thousand journalists expected.[121] Asserting that the FISU expected the Universiad-73 to "be the greatest event of the international student sports movement," Andrianov bragged that the Organizing Committee was making every effort to hold the games at the "highest technical level, in full compliance with the rules of the International Sports Federations and in the true spirit of the FISU regulations."[122] The language Andrianov used to promote the Universiad mirrors in many ways the statements of Soviet officials regarding Moscow's Olympic bid, and the motto chosen for the student games, "Sports, Peace, and Friendship," summed up the central tenant of Soviet Olympic propaganda since the 1950s.

Despite Andrianov's promotion of the event, some members of the IOC still doubted Moscow's ability to host a major sporting event, and this gave the Universiad added significance in proving them wrong. Killanin admitted that questions over telecommunications capabilities could hurt Moscow's chances. Even though he believed that Moscow's hosting the 1980 Games was a foregone conclusion, Killanin warned Andrianov of "enemies" who will use "any weakness on your part as propaganda against Moscow."[123] For these reasons, Soviet officials attempted to control reporting of the Universiad and win over the international press in support of Moscow's bid. Because foreign journalists complained about the facilities and services available in Moscow, the 1980 Moscow bid committee appealed directly to journalists, inviting them to Moscow where they could experience Moscow hospitality directly. Soviet sports organizations hosted a large group of foreign journalists in Moscow before the IOC session in Vienna in order to give them a good impression of Moscow's readiness to host the Games.[124] Reporting on the success of the event, Pavlov remarked that many had been opposed to Moscow's candidacy but "changed the tone of their coverage after the visit."[125] He credited the success of this propaganda action in helping ensure "objective and full publication on the pages of foreign press the Olympic capabilities of Moscow" in the lead up to the IOC session in Vienna.[126] Ian Woodridge, a Kiev-based journalist for the British newspaper the *Daily Mail*, reported that Moscow bestowed VIP treatment on twenty-three sports writers from around the world on their June 1974 trip to the Soviet Union in hopes that they would write favorably in support of Moscow's Olympic bid.[127]

Despite these precautions, the Universiad had the unanticipated consequence of inciting negative press and accusations of discrimination against Israeli citizens during the event. The IOC office received substantial, apparently coordinated, correspondence decrying the treatment of Israelis at the Moscow Universiad, complaining that Jewish ticket holders were refused seating, that Israeli journalists were denied entry, and that the Israeli team had been catcalled during the opening ceremonies. Killanin and IOC director, Monique Berlioux dutifully forwarded all such correspondence to Andrianov for his information and response.[128] Maintaining that his lack of information made it difficult for him to respond to questions about the Jewish/Israeli situation at the Universiad, Killanin pleaded with Andrianov to discuss the matter with Pavlov and Smirnov and "brief" him on it at their upcoming meeting in Paris.[129] Killanin requested that Andrianov investigate these breaches of protocol and alleged acts of discrimination, but he apparently received no response from the Soviet Olympic authorities.

The reports of anti-Semitism during the 1973 Universiad came at a turbulent time in the Cold-War Middle East relations. During the 1972 Summer Games in Munich, members of the Palestinian terrorist organization Black September kidnapped and killed eleven members of the Israeli Olympic delegation.[130] Hosting the Universiad less than a year after the Munich massacre of Israeli athletes no doubt placed Soviet organizers under increased scrutiny. Furthermore, the Soviet Union had cut off diplomatic ties with Israel after the Six-Day War in 1967, and continued to support Israel's Arab neighbors, including the Palestinian Liberation Organization (PLO) which had connections to the Black September group. Furthermore, repression of dissidents in the Soviet Union, many of them Jewish, increased criticism in the West of Soviet attitudes toward human rights. Historically, Jews occupied a complex and problematic space in Soviet society. Many sought to emigrate in the wake of the Six-Day War, and the Soviet leadership was under increasing pressure to allow Jews to leave the Soviet Union.[131] All of these factors likely heightened the reaction to the 1973 Universiad and threatened to undermine the Soviet bid to host the 1980 Games.

Given the timing, the Soviet organizers worked with the IOC to try to mitigate the damage of the reports, defend the Universiad, and promote Moscow's readiness to host the Olympic Games. To counter stories "slandering" the 1973 Universiad, Smirnov sent translations of the journal *Sport in the USSR* to be reprinted in IOC publications and other Soviet publications for the IOC library and recommended articles from the international press that provided "objective" evaluations of the event.[132] Expressing gratitude for Smirnov's cooperation, Berlioux withheld negative articles about the event from the "Press Analysis of the University Games."[133] Andrianov answered criticism of the Universiad and World Student Games at the IOC Executive Board meeting in September and October 1973. Andrianov claimed that the sports competitions had been a success and that they were held in "strict accordance with Olympic Rules." He noted that all participants were allowed entry, including Israeli and South Korean teams, and that the athlete village had been closed to the press due to increased security measures inspired by the tragic events at the Munich Olympiad in 1972. Andrianov denied reports that Israeli journalists had been denied entry, and claimed that the men in question were not members of the press and "had not followed the normal channels." Customs restrictions brought up by Willi Daume were, according to Andrianov, instituted to prevent arms smuggling. Andrianov also explained the presence of Yassir Arafat at the Universiad, assuring Executive Board members that he had been invited by the Soviet government and not by the Soviet NOC or the FISU.[134] In responding to the concerns raised by incidents at the Universiad, Andrianov and other Soviet sports administrators had few good options. The presence of Israeli athletes in the Soviet Union sparked a variety of responses and touched upon long-standing social, cultural, and political tensions within the country that no amount of bureaucratic activity could overcome. Attempting to counterbalance the bad press generated by the event, Soviet representatives continued to assure the IOC and the public that, if Moscow were to win the bid to host the 1980 Games, "every athlete or spectator that wishes to come" to the Moscow Games would be granted entry, and afforded all the privileges due to recognized National Olympic Committees.[135]

THE "FINAL STAGE" OF THE CAMPAIGN:
THE 1974 VIENNA IOC SESSION

Soviet representatives no doubt approached the 1974 Vienna IOC session with caution, as they could not afford a repeat of the 1970 Session in Amsterdam. In early October 1974, the Sports Committee issued a special decree summarizing the measures taken by Sports Committee personnel, the Moscow City Soviet, and other Soviet agencies and departments to secure the Games for Moscow and issuing instructions for the campaign's "final stage." As in 1970, the Sports Committee published a number of propaganda brochures, assembled exhibitions, and produced a film to supplement the bid presentation in Vienna.[136] The Sports Committee and Moscow City Soviet had also petitioned Gosplan to include sports facilities and other capital construction projects in the next five-year plan, in case Moscow won the right to host the Games (see Figure 3.2).[137] Asserting that the session would entail a "difficult struggle" for the right to host the 1980 Games, the decree noted that the team from Los Angeles had a "major propaganda campaign" of their own and had the means to resort to "bribery and buying of votes."[138] Given the "importance of properly managing work with IOC members, IF leaders and representatives of the press," the Sports Committee sent a delegation of twenty-one to Vienna for the session, led by Pavlov, Promyslov, Smirnov, Andrianov, and the head of the Tallinn City Soviet, with secret directives for their work during the session.[139]

One issue that continued to raise doubts about a Moscow Olympics was whether athletes, officials, tourists, and journalists would be allowed freedom of movement within the USSR during the Games. When the IOC Executive Board discussed this point at their February 1974 meeting, Andrianov suggested removing the reference to "freedom of movement" from the "Questionnaire for candidate cities staging the Games." Maintaining that it was beyond the capacity of the Organizing Committee to guarantee freedom of movement

Figure 3.2.   Soviet representatives emphasized their existing sports facilities and plans for enhancing them as part of their bid to host the Games. The picture shows a model of the Minor Arena of the Central Lenin Stadium, 1975. Courtesy International Olympic Committee.

throughout the host country, Andrianov insisted that the questionnaire should cover the freedom of entry and movement within Olympic areas for "all accredited persons." President Killanin mused that this was only a problem for the Soviet Union, but agreed that "people should not be allowed to wander through a country uninhibited." The Executive Board agreed to remove the words "and movement" from that question on the official questionnaire.[140] In his speech introducing Los Angeles's bid, Mayor Thomas Bradley noted that the city could "guarantee free movement not only within the city but within the whole of the United States for all participants, officials, press, etc."[141] Bradley's mention of "free movement" indicates that despite the assurances of Soviet press reports and Soviet sports administrators, there were lingering doubts among IOC members on that score that the LA bid committee hoped to exploit.

In the official minutes of the Soviet delegates, there is no mention of promising freedom of movement. Instead, the minutes note Promyslov's assurances that all the necessary financial backing was available, and Andrianov's promise that Moscow had first-class sports facilities and would offer the athletes "warm hospitality."[142] When the floor was opened up for questions, members asked about currency exchange facilities, housing for journalists, and the availability of international newspapers for visitors and athletes staying in the Olympic Village and hotels. All these issues relate to the Soviet Union's status as a closed society and reflect anxiety among IOC members over how it might impact the Olympic Games. The Soviet delegation reassured the IOC member- ship that a Moscow Olympiad would be staged in accordance with all the rules and traditions they had become accustomed to in Games past.

When the floor was opened to questions and comments from the IF represen- tatives, the ground work that Soviet representatives had been laying in building support for their candidacy paid off. The IFs present expressed confidence that Moscow would provide excellent facilities and venues for their respective events. Only two federations, archery and weightlifting, expressed reluctance to give their approval of Moscow's facilities, but Pavlov assured that an archery stadium would be built and that plans for an eight-thousand seat hall for the weightlifting competitions would be provided as soon as possible.[143] Aside from these two examples, all other IFs stated either that Moscow had the nec- essary facilities or that they were satisfied with Moscow's plans for renovating existing facilities or constructing new ones. This near-unanimous support of Moscow from the IFs must be seen as the result of the Sports Committee's long-term strategy, articulated first in the late 1940s, to cultivate authority for Soviet and socialist representatives within international sports organizations.

On 23 October 1974, the IOC membership selected Moscow to host the Games of the XXII Olympiad. Before a vote was taken, Killanin reminded the members present of the "importance of the decision which they were going to make" and expressed his hope that they would vote "according to which city would best serve Olympism."[144] In the end Moscow won the voting, with thirty-nine votes to Los Angeles' twenty. The majority of IOC members apparently believed that Moscow had answered all doubts and should be given a chance to demonstrate its ability to serve the Movement. Furthermore, Moscow had been promoting a Moscow Olympics for nearly six years and, having barely lost out in 1970, many in the IOC considered it "Moscow's time" to host the Games.

CONCLUSION

At the inaugural meeting of the newly appointed Organizing Committee for the Games of the XXII Olympiad, Orgcom President Ignatii Novikov attrib- uted Moscow's successful bid to the "enormous authority of the Soviet Union" and the respect for Soviet sports successes in the international community. He also praised the "Leninist Central Committee" of the Communist Party, and the leadership of "Leonid Il'ich" [Brezhnev] and his "program of peace" that he announced at the Twenty-fourth Congress of the Communist Party in 1974.[145] While the dominance of Soviet athletes certainly played a role, it is more accurate to say that Moscow won the 1980 bid thanks to the efforts of a legion of bureaucrats who had spent the last twenty years cultivating a network of sports leaders to become sympathetic to the Soviet Union, propagandizing the successes of Soviet sports, schmoozing with important and influential sports figures, and building authority within the IOC and the wide array of International Federations.

Novikov was correct, however, to give credit to Brezhnev. Until he came to power, the Sports Committee's repeated calls to host the Olympic Games in Moscow went unheeded. Brezhnev took a personal interest in sport and had long dreamed of hosting the Games in the Soviet Union. Also, without détente with the West initiated by the General Secretary, Moscow might never have been given the opportunity to stage the Games. The bid for 1980 came at a high point in East-West relations, and this provided the critical backdrop for Moscow's campaign to win support. Furthermore, Brezhnev's "stability of cadres" policy left Sports Committee bureaucrats free to pursue their plans. Having managed to outlive Stalin and outlast Khrushchev, sports administrators maintained their sense of direction and purpose until a more sympathetic leadership emerged. Brezhnev's coming to power brought a more flexible foreign and domestic policy less ambivalent toward international sports relations, paving the way for the idea of a Moscow Olympiad to become a reality.

NOTES

1. Speech by K. Andrianov, ABC Box 194.

2. Ibid.

3. Edwin Bacon, "Reconsidering Brezhnev," in *Brezhnev Reconsidered*, Edwin Bacon and Mark Sandle, ed., (New York: Palgrave, 2002), 16. See also H.G. Skilling and F. Griffiths, eds., *Interest Groups in Soviet Politics* (Princeton: Princeton University Press, 1971) and George Breslauer, *Khrushchev and Brezhnev as Leaders: Building Authority in Soviet Politics* (London and Boston: Allen and Unwin, 1982).

4. Bacon, "Reconsidering Brezhnev," 17. See also Ian D. Thatcher, "Brezhnev as Leader," 33 in the same volume.

5. Bacon, "Reconsidering Brezhnev," 17.

6. See, for example, Paul R. Josephson, *New Atlantis Revisited: Akademgorodok, The Siberian City of Science* (Princeton: Princeton University Press, 1997).

7. Samuel H. Baron, *Bloody Saturday in the Soviet Union: Novocherkassk, 1962* (Stanford: Stanford University Press, 2001); Vladimir Kozlov, *Mass Uprisings in the USSR: Protest and Rebellion in the Post-Stalin Years*, The New Russian History Series (Armonk, NY: M. E. Sharpe, 2002).

8. In his *Armageddon Averted*, Kotkin argues that rising oil prices and a production boom in Siberian oil allowed the regime to put off painful economic restructuring while placating the populace with relatively high living standards but when the oil bubble burst in the 1980s, the system was unsalvageable. See *Armageddon Averted*, pp. 16–18. Alexei Yurchak demonstrates that the stability of the Brezhnev years exposed 'inherent paradoxes of late socialism" and led to alienation and disillusionment with the Soviet project among the youth. Yurchak, *Everything Was Forever, Until It Was No More: The Last Soviet Generation* (Princeton, NJ: Princeton University Press, 2005), pp. 15–18.

9. Edwin Bacon points out that the "stability of cadres" policy had limits and that Brezhnev did not hesitate to remove any challengers to his own position. Bacon, "Reconsidering Brezhnev," 11.

10. Prozumenshchikov, *Bol'shoi sport*, 199 and T. Iu. Konova, M. Iu. Prozumenshchikov, *Piat' Kolets:Pod Kremlevskimi Zvezdami, Dokumental'naia khronika Olimpiady-80 v Moskve*, Mezhdunarodnyi fond "Demokratiia" (Fond Aleksandra N. Iakovleva), 2011, 15.

11. Prozumenshchikov, *Bol'shoi sport*, 19 (RGANI, f. 4, op. 16, d. 29, l. 115–16).

12. Ibid., 193.

13. Zubok, *Failed Empire*, 132.

14. See chapter 2. See also Parks, "Nothing but Trouble."

15. Agendas and Minutes of the Meetings of Representatives of Sports Organizations of Socialist Countries in Moscow, 10–11 March 1959, GARF, f. 9570, op. 1, d. 445, ll. 85–86.

16. Prozumenshchikov, *Bol'shoi sport*, 193 (RGANI, f. 5, op. 47, d. 322, l. 71). See also *Sovetskii sport*, 17 May 1959.

17. Ibid.

18. Prozumenshchikov, *Bol'shoi sport*, 195.

19. R.S. Alexander to President of the USSR NOC, 7 April 1961, ABC Box 149.

20. IOC to USSROC, telegram, 5 May 1961, ABC Box 149 and Agenda No. 11, Meeting of the Commission for the Study of Current Questions of the Central Soviet of the Union of Sports Organizations and Societies, 11 May 1961, GARF f. 9570, op. 1, d. 94, l. 108.

21. Andrianov to Brundage, n.d., 1961, ABC Box 50.

22. Recommendations on the Future Activities of Sports Organizations of the USSR in the IOC, n.d., GARF, f. 9570, op. 1, d. 689, ll. 83–84 and Minutes of the 58th IOC Session at Athens, 19–21 June 1961, IOC Archives.

23. Minutes of the V Plenum of the Central Soviet of the Union of Sports Organizations and Societies, 7 July 1961, GARF, f. 9570, op. 1, d. 83, l. 140.

24. Christopher Hill, *Olympic Politics*, 207.

25. Ibid. It is not entirely clear why the meeting was moved. As late as the June 1963 meeting of the IOC Executive Board, the IOC still planned to meet in Nairobi and wanted to use the session as an opportunity to meet with African sports leaders regarding the development of Olympic sport in Africa. See Minutes of the Meeting of the Executive Board of the IOC, 5 June 1963, IOC Archives.

26. Minutes of the 60th IOC Session in Baden-Baden, 16–20 October 1963, IOC Archives.

27. See chapter 1.

28. Record of the Meeting of the Presidium of the Central Soviet, 12 April, 1962, GARF, f. 9570, op. 1, d. 120, ll. 47–48.

29. Ibid., 48.

30. Ibid.

31. Decree of the Presidium of the Central Soviet, 12 May 1962, GARF, f. 9570, op. 1, d. 132, ll. 76, 78.

32. Record of the Meeting of the Presidium of the Central Soviet, 12 April, 1962, GARF f. 9570, op. 1, d. 120, ll. 47–48.

33. Notes of Meeting of N. S. Khrushchev with the President of the IOC Brundage, 12 June, 1962, GARF, f. 9570, op. 1, d. 822, l. 1.

34. Ibid.

35. Ibid., l. 3

36. Ibid., ll. 5, 6. See also Chatziefstathiou, "Ideology of Olympism," 26–27.

37. Ibid., l. 2–5, 8.

38. Ibid., l. 6.

39. "Moscow Session: Speech by Mr. Brezhnev, Chairman of the Presidium of the Supreme Soviet of the USSR," *Olympic Review* 81 (1963): 41.

40. Ibid.

41. Mashin to Central Committee, 8 December 1965, RGANI, f. 5, op. 33, d. 228, l. 147.

42. Ibid.

43. Draft letter from Moscow Executive Committee to Avery Brundage, 8 December 1965, ibid., ll. 150–51.

44. Draft letter from the OC USSR to Brundage, 8 December 1965, ibid., l. 152.

45. Ibid.

46. Iakovlev and Zubkov to the Central Committee, 27 December 1965, ibid., l. 154.

47. Central Council of the Union of USSR Sports Societies and Organizations Report on the 64th Session of the International Olympic Committee, 1 April 1966, History and Public Policy Program Digital Archive, RGANI f.4, op. 20, d. 2, l. 82. Obtained for CWIHP by Mikhail Prozumenshikov and translated by Gary Goldberg, http://digitalarchive.wilsoncenter.org/document/122934.

48. Concerning the Instructions to the Soviet Representatives at the 64th Session of the International Olympic Committee, April 1966, History and Public Policy Program Digital Archive, RGANI f.4, op. 44, d. 1, l. 57. Obtained for CWIHP by Mikhail Prozumenshikov and translated by Gary Goldberg, http://digitalarchive.wilsoncenter.org/document/122937.

49. Decree of the Secretariat of the CC of the Communist Party of the Soviet Union, Instructions to the Soviet Representatives of the 64th Session of the International Olympic Committee in April 1966, 2 April 1966, History and Public Policy Program Digital Archive, RGANI f.4, op. 20, d. 2, ll. 80–81. Obtained for CWIHP by Mikhail Prozumenshikov and translated by Gary Goldberg, http://digitalarchive.wilsoncenter.org/document/122933.

50. Minutes of the 64th IOC Session, Rome, April 1966, IOC Archives. The vote was 31 to 30.

51. See for example, Simon Huxtable, "The Life and Death of Brezhnev's Thaw: The Changing Values of Soviet Journalism after Khrushchev, 1964–68," in Fainberg and Kalinovsky eds., *Reconsidering Stagnation*, 21–42.

52. Westad, *Global Cold War*, 198–199. Zubok, *Failed Empire*, 199–200, 234–37. Under pressure from the United States, Soviet authorities began to ease restrictions on Jewish immigration in the early 1970s. Zubok, 231.

53. Prozumenshchikov, "Sports as a Mirror of Eastern Europe's Crises," *Russian Studies in History* 49.2 (2010): 51–93.

54. Mashin to Central Committee, 3 September 1968, RGANI, f. 5, op. 60, d. 36, ll. 52–55.

55. Report of Meeting of NOCs of Europe, September 1968, France, Ibid., l. 64.

56. Ibid.

57. Ibid., ll. 69–70.

58. Prozumenshchikov, "Sports as a Mirror," 71–73.

59. William Grimes, "Vera Caslavska, Gymnast Who Faced Off with Soviets, Dies at 74," *New York Times*, 31 August 2016, http://www.nytimes.com/2016/09/01/sports/olympics/vera-caslavska-gymnast-soviets-czechoslovakia-dead.html?_r=0.

60. Witherspoon, *Eyes of the World*, 104–5.

61. Minutes of the EB IOC Session, 30 September–6 October, 1968, Mexico City, IOC Archives.

62. For a thorough analysis of the complicated politics surrounding the Mexico City Games, see Witherspoon, *Before the Eyes of the World*.

63. Minutes of the Meeting of the Presidium of the Central Soviet of the Union of Sports Organizations and Societies on the Results of Participation of Soviet Athletes in the Winter Olympic Games, 28 March 1968, GARF, f. 9570, op. 2, d. 3579, ll. 1–115.

64. V. Stepakov to Central Committee, 30 May 1968, RGANI, f. 5, op. 60, d. 36, l. 10.

65. Ibid., l. 11.

66. Riordan, *Sport in Soviet Society*, 405.

67. Minutes of the Meeting of Leading Physical Culture Workers of the Country on the Results of Participation of Soviet Athletes in 1968 OG and Tasks for Development of Mass Sport and Raising of Sports Mastery, 2–4 April 1969, GARF, f. 7576, op. 31, d. 41, ll. 1–310.

68. KGB to Central Committee, 28 October 1968, RGANI, f. 5, op. 60, d. 36, l. 158.

69. Ibid.

70. Konstantin Andrianov to Avery Brundage, telegram, 26 November 1969, ABC Box 194. See also Prozumenshchikov, *Bol'shoi sport*, 198–201.

71. Plan for Promoting the Candidacy of Moscow for Organization of the Games of the XXI Olympiad 1976, GARF, f. 7576, op. 31, d. 11, ll. 111–17.

72. Pavlov to the Central Committee, 9 March 1970, RGANI, f. 5, op. 62, d. 48, ll. 23–24.

73. Ibid., l. 24.

74. Report on Results of the Meeting of NOCs of Europe and the EB IOC, 5 March 1970, RGANI, f. 5, op. 62, d. 48, ll. 27–29. See also Prozumenshchikov, *Bol'shoi sport*, 198–201.

75. Ibid.

76. Ibid. See also Prozumenshchikov, *Bol'shoi sport*, 198–201.

77. RGANI, f. 5, op. 62, d. 48, l. 28. See also Prozumenshchikov, *Bol'shoi sport*, 198–201.

78. Prozumenshchikov, *Bol'shoi sport*, 198–201.

79. Pavlov to Central Committee, 20 March 1970, RGANI, f. 5, op. 62, d. 48, l. 32.

80. Report on Several Results of Participating in the Work of the Meeting of NOCs of Europe and the EB IOC, 5 March 1970, Ibid., l. 29. See also Prozumenshchikov, *Bol'shoi sport*, 198–201.

81. Pavlov to Central Committee, 8 April 1970, ibid., l. 36.

82. "Moscow—Candidate for the Games of the XXI Olympiad in 1976," ABC Box 194.

83. Ibid.

84. Prozumenshchikov, *Bol'shoi sport*, 198–201. See also Plan of Measures in Connection with Raising the Candidacy of Moscow for Organization of the Games of the XXI Olympiad 1976, GARF, f. 7576, op. 31, d. 11, ll. 114–17.

85. Speech by V. Promyslov, ABC Box 194.

86. Speech by S. Pavlov, ABC box 194.

87. Speech by K. Andrianov, ABC Box 194.

88. Ibid.

89. Speech by V. Promyslov, ABC Box 194.

90. Speech by K. Andrianov, ABC Box 194.

91. Speech by S. Pavlov, ABC box 194.

92. Ibid.

93. Minutes of the 70th Session of the IOC in Amsterdam, 12–16 May 1970, IOC Archives.

94. Prozumenshchikov, *Bol'shoi sport*, 198–201.

95. Avery Brundage to V. Promyslov, 30 May 1970, ABC Box 194.

96. RGANI, f. 4, op. 20, d. 699, l. 193, quoted in Prozumenshchikov, *Bol'shoi sport*, 198–201. Not having access to this particular *fond,* I had to rely on Prozumenshchikov's account of the fallout from the failed bid. I assume from established practice, that this comes from a meeting of the Sports Committee leadership, but I cannot speculate on who in particular expressed these views since I have not read the original document.

97. RGANI, f. 4, op. 20, d. 699, l. 193, quoted in Prozumenshchikov, *Bol'shoi sport*, 198–201.

98. "IOC Charter Criticism," *Times*, 21 May 1970, ABC Box 194.

99. V. Promyslov to Avery Brundage, 19 November 1971, ABC Box 195.

100. Ibid.

101. K. Andrianov to Avery Brundage, 22 November 1971, ABC Box 195.

102. "Moscow Invites the Olympic Games," *Sport in the USSR*, October 1971, translation in ABC Box 149.

103. Minutes of the 71st Session of the IOC, Luxembourg, September 1971, IOC Archives.

104. M. Berlioux to K. Andrianov, 14 March 1971, IOC Archives/ Konstantin Andrianov Biography and Correspondence 1951–84, Olympic Studies Center, Lausanne, Switzerland.

105. Decree of the Collegium of the Sports Committee, 29 October 1971, GARF, f. 7576, op. 31, d. 751, l. 33.

106. Minutes of the 73rd IOC Session at Munich, August and September 1972, IOC Archives.

107. V. Ivonin to Central Committee, 12 July 1974, RGANI, f. 5, op. 67, d. 130, l. 5.

108. Report of International Sports Relations of the Sports Committee for the First Quarter 1969, RGANI, f. 5, op. 61, d. 45, l. 140.

109. Pavlov to Central Committee, 19 January 1971, RGANI, f. 5, op. 63, d. 102, l. 11.

110. Report on the Meeting of Representatives of Central Committees of Filial Parties of Socialist Countries, 30 November 1970, RGANI, f. 5, op. 62, d. 48, l. 185. See also Prozumenshchikov, *Bol'shoi sport*, 184.

111. For more on relations between the FRG, the GDR, and the Soviet Union, see Evelyn Mertin, "Steadfast Friendship and Brotherly Help: The Distinctive Soviet-East German Sport Relationship within the Socialist Bloc," in *Diplomatic Games*, 53–84 and *Deutsch-sowjetische Sportbeziehungen im "Kalten Krieg"* (Sankt Augustin, Germany: Academia Verlag, 2009).

112. Decree of the Sport Committee, On Preparations for the IOC Session in Connection with Raising the Candidacy of Moscow for the XXII Olympic Games in 1980, 9 October 1974, GARF, f. 7576, op. 31, d. 1942, l. 101.

113. Ibid.

114. Report On Work Of Representative of the USSR Z. P. Firsov and translator B. I. Fomenko at Meeting of Bureau of FINA, 17–20 November 1971, GARF, f. 7576, op. 31, d. 1035, l. 165.

115. Report of Participation of V. N. Lukatin in the Meeting of the Bureau of the International Canoeing Federation, 10–13 May 1974, Madrid, GARF, f. 7576, op. 31, d. 2262, ll. 82–83.

116. Decree of the Sport Committee, On Preparations for the IOC Session in Connection with Raising the Candidacy of Moscow for the XXII Olympic Games in 1980, 9 October 1974, GARF, f. 7576, op. 31, d. 1942, l. 102.

117. Prozumenshchikov, *Bol'shoi sport*, 203. Prozumenshchikov makes a point of "noblemen" that were invited to visit Moscow, including Lord Killanin, the Duke of Edinburgh, and Franz Joseph II of Liechtenstein.

118. Decree of the Sport Committee, On Preparations for the IOC Session in Connection with Raising the Candidacy of Moscow for the XXII Olympic Games in 1980, 9 October 1974, GARF, f. 7576, op. 31, d. 1942, ll. 101–2.

119. Pavlov to Central Committee, 12 April 1974, RGANI, f. 5, op. 66, d. 157, ll. 35–36.

120. For more on candidate city bidding practices see Heather L. Dichter, "Corruption in the 1960s?: Rethinking the Origins of Unethical Olympic Bidding Tactics," *International Journal of the History of Sport* 33. 6–7 (2016): 666–682, DOI: 10.1080/09523367.2016.1195374.

121. Minutes of the IOC Executive Board at Lausanne, June 1973, IOC Archives.

122. Ibid.

123. Report of Meetings of EB of IOC and Tripartite Commission for Olympic Congress in Lausanne, June 1973, GARF, f. 7576, op. 31, d. 1854, ll. 51–52.

124. Prozumenshchikov, *Bol'shoi sport*, 204.

125. Pavlov to Central Committee, August 1974, RGANI, f. 5, op. 67, d. 130, l. 8.

126. Ibid., l. 11.

127. M. Berlioux to K. Andrianov, 2 September 1974, NOCs USSR Correspondence 1967–1973, IOC Archives.

128. See M. Berlioux to K. Andrianov, 1 April 1974; M. Berlioux to K. Andrianov, 22 July 1974; and M. Berlioux to K. Andrianov, 14 August 1974, ibid.

129. M. Killanin to K. Andrianov, 28 March 1974, ibid.

130. For more on the Munich tragedy, see David Clay Large, *Munich 1972: Tragedy, Terror, and Triumph at the Olympic Games* (Lanham, MD: Rowman and Littlefield, 2012) and Kay Schiller and Christopher Young, "The End of the Games: Germany, the Middle East, and the Terrorist Attack," in *The 1972 Munich Olympics and the Making of Modern Germany* (Los Angeles: University of California Press, 2010), 187–219.

131. For more on the history of Jews in the Soviet Union, see See also Benjamin Pinkus, *The Jews of the Soviet Union: A History of a National Minority* (Cambridge, New York, and Melbourne: Cambridge University Press, 1988).

132. V. Smirnov to M. Berlioux, 3 October 1973. NOCs USSR Correspondence 1967–1973, IOC Archives.

133. M. Berlioux to V. Smirnov, 2 November 1973. NOCs USSR Correspondence 1967–1973, IOC Archives.

134. Minutes of the Executive Board of the IOC, Varna, Bulgaria, September-October 1973, IOC Archives.

135. M. Berlioux to K. Andrianov, 2 September 1974, NOCs USSR Correspondence 1967–1973, IOC Archives.

136. Decree of the Sport Committee, On Preparations for the IOC Session in Connection with Raising the Candidacy of Moscow for the XXII Olympic Games in 1980, 9 October 1974, GARF, f. 7576, op. 31, d. 1942, ll. 102–103.

137. Ibid., l. 103.

138. Ibid.

139. Ibid., ll. 103–5. The decree did not include the directives, so I can only speculate about their contents.

140. Minutes of the Executive Board of the IOC, Lausanne, February 1974, IOC Archives.

141. Minutes of the 75th IOC Session, Vienna, 21–24 October 1974, IOC Archives.

142. Ibid.

143. Ibid.

144. Ibid.

145. Minutes of the First Meeting of the Organizing Committee, 7 March 1975, GARF, f. 9610, op. 1, d. 3, l. 21.

Chapter Four

"An Exemplary Communist City"

Preparing Moscow for the 1980 Olympic Games

At the inaugural meeting of the Organizing Committee for the Games of the XXII Olympiad (Orgcom), President Ignatii Novikov recounted the history of the Olympics from ancient Greece to the modern Olympic Movement, highlighting the great role the Soviet Union had played in transforming the Games from a "personal possession of privileged society" into "popular, mass, public events" while spreading the Olympics to other countries.[1] Novikov insisted that the Games provided an opportunity for the host city to display its achievements in the social, cultural, and spiritual realms, as well as its scientific and technological development and "the country's economic potential."[2] According to Novikov, the 1980 Games would help realize Soviet directives to "transform Moscow into an exemplary communist city," but in order to demonstrate to the world the greatness of the Soviet system and way of life, the Games had to meet the highest possible standards.[3]

To successfully host the 1980 Summer Games in Moscow, Soviet organizers not only needed to evaluate the technical requirements for over 200 different sporting events, construct and renovate dozens of sports facilities, and modernize their hospitality and telecommunications infrastructure, but also to coordinate this work among dozens of departments and officials throughout the party-state apparatus. The Sports Committee had a proven record of being able to put on a well-choreographed athletic display, but the enormity of the task before the Moscow Olympic organizers was something wholly different. As a closed society, accustomed to tightly controlling the movement of people, Soviet authorities would have to decide how to handle the millions of visitors coming to Moscow, both from abroad and from other parts of the country. Relatively few Soviet citizens had the opportunity to travel abroad, so of the thousands of hotel and restaurant staffers and other service personnel required for the Games, few could draw upon firsthand knowledge of

what this work entailed in order to live up to Western standards. Even domestic tourism was not well developed in the Soviet Union, so a robust hospitality infrastructure would have to be built from the ground up. The closed
economy meant that Soviet state-owned banks would have to work out how
to provide currency exchange services for the sudden influx of foreigners, not
to mention the millions of rubles worth of foreign currency needed to pay for
imported equipment and foreign contracts. These realities represented significant challenges to hosting the Olympic Games in Brezhnev's Soviet Union.

The Olympic project complicates the persistent binaries surrounding the
concept of "stagnation" in the Brezhnev period— public versus private, iner-
tia versus change, motivation versus disaffection, backward versus modern.[4]
By the late 1970s, the stagnation of the Soviet economy had become palpable,
and two decades of engagement with the world had revealed substantial dis-
parities between life in the West and the frustrating realities of "developed
socialism."[5] A boom in oil and gas revenues meant that the state could continue to improve living standards without restructuring the archaic industrial
infrastructure, raising expectations that the system was less and less able to
fulfill.[6] Ordinary Soviet citizens employed various strategies including *blat*
(connections), stocking up on goods when they became available, riding
"sausage trains" to Moscow to by meat, and patronizing unofficial markets
to get what they needed, often *na levo* (using illegal or semi-legal methods).[7]
Christopher Ward argues that the failure of the Baikal-Amur Mainline (BAM)
project mirrored Soviet society as a whole under Brezhnev, revealing the disconnect between the "propaganda trope of the railway as an economic and
social panacea" and the realities of poor organization, ecological damage, and
"great human and material cost," resulting in loss of faith in the system.[8] Yet
scholarship on the period of late socialism demonstrates that alongside stagnation, inflexibility, and degeneration, the Brezhnev years offered room for
energy, commitment, and creativity. Ward and others acknowledge that the
concept of Brezhnev-era stagnation, first theorized during Mikhail Sergeevich Gorbachev's reform program, does not adequately capture the changes
that took place during the Brezhnev years.[9] Dina Fainberg and Artemy M.
Kalinovsky argue "that the period as a whole was [not] characterized by ram-
pant cynicism and decline of faith in the socialist creed"; instead they insist
that socialist ideology continued to have the power to inspire and mobilize
the populace.[10] Even though many were losing interest in the public sphere
and sought fulfillment outside of official life, this did not imply wholescale
rejection of the system or its underpinning ideology. Instead, Christine Evans
demonstrates that Central Television staff could see themselves as experi-
menters and innovators, adapting to changing political environments, without
fundamentally challenging the overall political or economic system.[11] Simi-

larly, Aleksei Yurchak argues that "many of the fundamental values, ideals, and realities of socialism were of genuine importance" even as many people reinterpreted those values in unexpected ways.[12] Kristin Roth-Ey also demonstrates that cultural producers and consumers could "remain committed to the brand in the abstract" even as they "provided people with experiences and ways of being in the world unconnected to broader political projects of any kind."[13] Like Yurchak, she sees ambiguity and paradox in late Socialist cultural construction, revealing, "the remarkable resiliency of the Soviet system and its ultimate vulnerability, fragility, and collapse."[14]

Looking back, the party-state functionaries often are assigned the blame for the inefficiencies, corruption, disorganization, repression, and obstacles that plagued the Soviet system and made life difficult for ordinary people. Highlighting examples of informalism in Russian and Soviet administration, including duplication, *blat*, *shturmovshchina*, and "the *tolkach* (the illegal 'facilitator' and 'solver' of problems and glitches)," Karl Ryavec describes the overall pattern of administration in imperial Russia and the Soviet Union as "highly informalistic, personalistic, and with a tendency toward corrupt and self-aggrandizing behavior by bureaucrats."[15] Some studies have characterized the Soviet bureaucrats as self-interested careerists, trading their loyalty to the regime for a car, a large apartment, and access to goods (both luxuries and staples), enriching themselves at the expense of society, protecting their positions and possessions, and serving as an impediment to any attempts from above or below for meaningful reform.[16] Like most Soviet citizens, aparatchiks desired "simply stability" and the "social package" of a comfortable professional life free from political crisis.[17] Yet, these bureaucrats, as Stephen F. Cohen notes, never constituted a monolithic, organized political force, but rather were a diverse group "divided internally by privilege, occupation, education, generation, geographic location, and political attitudes."[18] This diversity was the result of a long-term process of specialization and professionalization within the state and party bureaucracy and Brezhnev's "stability of cadres" which valued technical skills and expertise and provided job security. Lifetime tenure certainly allowed for apathy, obstructionism, and corruption, but it also provided the experienced cadres necessary to make the 1980 Summer Olympics in Moscow succeed.

Hosting the 1980 Olympiad in Brezhnev's Soviet Union illustrates these paradoxes of late socialism. Soviet sports administrators faced significant obstacles to organizing the Games. The inefficiencies of the lumbering command economy caused construction delays as builders waited for supplies and equipment. Moreover, the Soviet system often manifested its shortcomings in competing with the West. Desiring to showcase the superiority of the unique socialist modernity of the Soviet way of life, organizers imported the latest in Western sports equipment and high-tech tools. Having promised Olympic guests free movement throughout Moscow and the country, Soviet authorities relocated Muscovites outside the city, cleansed the streets of vagrants and homeless, and increased the presence of security officers to protect the freedom of movement for foreign visitors. In order to prove the outstanding organizational capabilities of the first socialist civilization, Soviet administrators employed *blat, shturmovshchina, tolkaches*, and all the other informal tactics and strategies necessary to cut through bureaucratic obstacles and accomplish their task. The Moscow Organizing Committee recognized the difficulties and shortcomings of the system and took the necessary measures to overcome them to make hosting the Games possible.

THE ORGCOM'S "COLOSSAL" TASK

Despite his stress on the benefits of hosting the Games, Novikov spoke candidly about the "colossal" task facing the Orgcom.[19] According to Novikov, ninety-eight facilities needed to be built or renovated for the Games, seventy-eight of those in Moscow alone.[20] Of that number, the Organizing Committee would be responsible for constructing or refurbishing twenty-five sports grounds, including fourteen indoor arenas. Moscow already had sites for twelve sports, but several of those needed reconstruction or renovation. To meet IOC and IF standards, they would have to build six sports halls, two closed swimming pools, a cycling track, an equestrian sports complex, and the base for sailing competitions in Tallinn.[21] Even existing sports facilities lacked the seating capacity to accommodate the number of spectators expected at Olympic events or hoped for by the IFs. The Orgcom planned to renovate the Grand Arena at Luzhniki to increase its seating capacity to 100,000, and the Minor Arena would need to hold 15,000. The improvements on the complex would cost an estimated 25 million rubles.[22] In addition to the Luzhniki complex, the Orgcom estimated they would need to construct seven major sports halls, accommodating 44,000 spectators at an estimated cost of 71 million rubles.[23]

The Orgcom would have to arrange housing, medical, transport, and cultural services, and security for up to 23,000 participants—including 10,000 athletes, trainers and officials, 850 IOC members, IF representatives, foreign guests and judges, and about 3,000 delegates participating in various sports congresses—as well as 6,000–7,000 foreign journalists and an estimated one million tourists coming to Moscow for the Games.[24] An Olympic Village was needed to accommodate 12,000 participants in Moscow and another for 600 in Tallinn. Both cities needed new hotels and dormitories for tourists and guests. In 1975, Moscow's facilities offered a total of 42,000 beds and Tallinn's only 2,000.[25] The Orgcom would also have to organize an international sports camp of up to 3,000 people for twenty to thirty days and transportation to and from the USSR for participants, guests, and foreign tourists.[26]

In addition to facilities, The Orgcom would need personnel to act as everything from chauffeurs to guides, security workers, and translators. Students, the military, the police, and volunteers were identified as recruitment targets, with the main qualifications defined as loyalty, knowledge of foreign languages, education, and physical attributes.[27] An estimated 97,000 students and workers from various ministries and departments were recruited as service personnel and needed to be trained in foreign languages, service and public relations as well as political education.[28] Topics of instruction included seminars on the Communist Party, the Olympic Movement, the historical, revolutionary and architectural monuments of Moscow, the national characteristics of visitors' home countries, and of course Marxism-Leninism.[29]

The Orgcom also had to oversee television, radio, telephone, teletype, post and other means of communication with all continents and countries. This entailed the establishment of a state of the art Automated Control System, ACS-Olympiad, that would serve as a computerized information hub for everything from competition results to press accreditation, participant registration, and even the Orgcom payroll.[30] The Orgcom would have to organize the torch relay through various European countries from Greece to Moscow and prepare cultural programs, exhibitions, and other performances for participants and guests. On top of this, it also had to organize a series of meetings and congresses for the IOC, IFs, and NOCs. The estimated 6,400 million rubles required to host the Games, of which only 4,400 were provided for in the existing five-year economic plan, would come from Soviet citizens, selling of merchandising rights, television rights, and foreign donors. The Orgcom would be responsible for coordinating merchandising rights with the IOC as well as foreign firms and National Olympic Committees.[31]

OLYMPIAD-80: THE ORGANIZING COMMITTEE OF THE 1980 OLYMPIC GAMES IN MOSCOW

Before any of the work could start, Soviet organizers had to create an entirely new bureaucratic entity to oversee these undertakings and ensure their successful completion. Securing the bid to host the 1980 Olympic Games inspired another reorganization of the sports administration. Whereas previous reorganizations had little effect on the Sports Committee leadership or the international sports relations department, setting up the Olympiad-80 Organizing Committee fundamentally changed the daily operations of the

Sports Committee and marked the beginning of a qualitatively different kind of endeavor from any that the Sports Committee workers and leaders had undertaken before. In addition to Sports Committee personnel, the Organizing Committee included workers and administrators from a wide variety of Soviet and party bureaus, organs, and agencies.

In many ways, the committee represented a new kind of organization in the Soviet Union. According to IOC rules, the Orgcom had to possess juridical status, so while the Soviet NOC could simply gloss over its imaginary independence from the government, the Orgcom had to acquire real legal status as an independent body.[32] This did not impact the Orgcom's authority to oversee Games preparation, however, because it still had the full backing of the Central Committee and the Council of Ministers. In fact, the Orgcom's juridical status did not preclude it from being a department of the state. According to Soviet law, the most important criteria for being a juridical entity was economic accountability, relying on independent financial assets rather than state coffers.[33] The Orgcom certainly depended in part on state funding, but its juridical status gave it the freedom to conclude lucrative contracts with foreign firms to raise significant funds, especially in foreign currency. Novikov also highlighted the need for Orgcom members to work independently and with "initiative," because the Orgcom was an "independent public organization" not under any higher state organ. The Orgcom reported directly to the Politburo of the Central Committee.[34]

Hosting the Olympics required coordination between many different party and state bureaus, and appointing a high-level government official, Ignatii Novikov, as Orgcom head cut a layer of bureaucracy out of the hierarchy (see Figure 4.1). Very much a member of the Brezhnev generation of party leaders who came to prominence after the Revolution of 1917, Novikov's career mirrors that of Brezhnev himself. Before his appointment to the Moscow Organizing Committee, Novikov had worked his way up the party and state hierarchy. Born only a few weeks after Leonid Il'ich, Novikov also hailed from Brezhnev's home town of Kamenskoe (now Dneprodzerzhinsk). A party member since 1926, Novikov came from a working class background. Beginning his career in 1919 as a miner in Ukraine, Novikov graduated from the Dneprodzerzhinskii Metallurgical Institute in 1932, just as Brezhnev had. Working as head of the shop floor and chief power engineer at the Voroshilovsk factory, Novikov later served as director of electric stations and chief mechanic of the Chimkentskii lead factory until he became a factory director in Saratov. By 1958, Novikov had become a deputy minister of electric stations and the head of construction of electric stations in the USSR. In 1962, he became the Minister of Energy and Electrification, deputy chairman of the Council of Ministers USSR and the chairman of the State Construction Agency (Gosstroi). Novikov became a full member of the Central Committee of the Communist Party in 1961, making him a full-fledged member of the Soviet bureaucratic elite, the *nomenklatura*.

While Novikov's rank as deputy chairman of the Council of Ministers provided the Organizing Committee with a degree of authority and influence on other bureaus, Novikov delegated many of the decisions to his vice-presidents. Novikov retained direct control only over the department of cadres, while experienced administrators from the Sports Committee were chosen as vice-presidents of the Orgcom managing the departments directly responsible for staging the Games. Georgii Mikhailovich Rogul'skii—who had been overseeing the training of Olympic teams, construction of training bases, sports training technology and sports science—took charge of the Mass Production and Technical Department as well as the Material and Technical Supplies Department, making him responsible for ensuring that all sports facilities met the technical requirements for staging competitions. Vitalii Smirnov, who had been vice-chairman of the Sports Committee and an IOC member since 1971, became the vice-president in charge of the Department of Sports Methodol-

Figure 4.1. President of the Organizing Committee of the Moscow 1980 Olympic Games, Ignatii Novikov in 1980. Novikov served on the Council of Ministers of the Soviet Union before heading the Organizing Committee. His choice as president demonstrates the importance of the Games to the Soviet leadership. Courtesy International Olympic Committee.

ogy, the Facilities Department, and the Planning and Finance Department. Vladimir Ivanovich Koval', the former head of the UMSS department of the Sports Committee, oversaw the international and propaganda departments.[35]

In practical terms, this arrangement meant that many of the most pressing issues of the 1980 Games preparations fell to these three individuals. Rogul'skii and Smirnov's reports would then form the basis not only for a report to the Central Committee and the Council of Ministers, but also for instructions directing the activities of Orgcom departments and commissions.[36] Koval' had the right of first signature on agreements and contracts concluded by the Orgcom with foreign organizations and firms, giving him tremendous authority over the financing of the Games.[37] Smirnov, Rogul'skii, and Koval' authored, in communication with commission leaders, the work plan of the Orgcom apparat for its first year of operation.[38] Along with high-ranking members of the Central Committee and the Council of Ministers of the Soviet Union, the RSFSR and the Estonian SSR, Smirnov, Rogul'skii, and Koval' also served as members of the Orgcom Presidium, which directed the Orgcom's day-to-day operations. The three also served on the Orgcom Executive Committee which managed education and training of Orgcom workers; fulfillment of all Orgcom decisions; control of the activities of various ministries, agencies, institutions and organizations; and relations with the IOC and other international organizations.[39] Among the Orgcom vice-presidents, Smirnov enjoyed elevated status, and many key decisions fell to him. His purview included all interaction with IOC, IF, and NOC members; relations with sports leaders from various foreign countries; exchange of information and experience with previous organizing committees; and negotiations with foreign firms offering their services or sponsorship of various aspects of the Games. Along with Mariia L'vovna, Smirnov prepared the financial plan for Moscow and Tallinn, giving him significant responsibility.[40]

In addition to Sports Committee personnel, the Organizing Committee attracted ambitious state and party functionaries from a wide variety of Soviet and party bureaus, organs, and agencies, including Ministry of Construction of Heavy Industry, Ministry of Rural Construction, Ministry of Culture, Ministry of Instrument Making, Automation Equipment and Control Systems (Minpribor), Novosti press agency, Komsomol, Intourist, Gosplan and Profsoiuz. Of the twenty-one vice-chairmen and department heads, all were members of the Communist Party, and all boasted a higher education. Seventeen were of Russian nationality, two Ukrainian, one Jewish, and one did not have a nationality listed. Twelve of the members of the Orgcom executive were under fifty years old. Only one member, Koziulia, was over seventy. The median age was forty-five. The Orgcom thus provided an opportunity for younger, second-tier state and party administrators to move out of the shadow of their aging superiors. By 1977, the Orgcom apparat had grown to 282 people. Of those, over 70 percent held higher education degrees, eight were doctoral candidates, and 20 percent knew one or more foreign languages. The Orgcom boasted two members of the IOC, two vice-presidents and three members of executive or technical committees in International Federations. The percentage of party membership among the apparatus had also risen over 50 percent by that time. By the eve of the Games in 1980, the Orgcom numbered 945 employees.

Every task of the Orgcom had to be accomplished on the highest "organizational and ideological-political level" to serve the goals of the Soviet leadership as well as the expectations of the international sports community. One of the first tasks of the Organizing Committee was drafting the official joint Central Committee and Council of Ministers decree on the measures for preparing and staging the 1980 Olympic Games in Moscow, taking care to ensure that all relevant details found their way into the decree as well as into the Soviet five-year economic plan for 1976–1980, because doing so would give the committee leverage later on if any of the departments involved did not fulfill the tasks officially entrusted to them.[41] Novikov argued that the Orgcom needed to conduct "propaganda work" among the country's leadership "to make plain the importance and enormity of the task" before them.[42] Highlighting the personal responsibility of each member of the Orgcom to work out an individual plan and "participate actively in the resolution of all problems," Novikov made clear that no member of the Orgcom was off the hook if it was going to accomplish the "colossal" tasks before it.[43]

BUILDING A "CITY OF SPORT": CONSTRUCTION OF OLYMPIC FACILITIES

A look at the major construction projects and their estimated cost illustrates what Novikov had in mind when he spoke of the "colossal" task of hosting the Olympic Games. The centerpiece of the Olympic Games was the Grand Sports Arena at Luzhniki. The brainchild of V. P. Polikarpov, who imagined a "city of sport," the Central Stadium was designed as part of a whole complex, also replete with a smaller sports hall, swimming pool, and sports grounds. It would provide a training base for Soviet elite athletes, a staging ground for important domestic and international competitions, and a multi-use sports facility where ordinary Muscovites could engage in physical exercise.[44] Built in 1956, the Luzhniki complex housed all the Soviet Spartakiads before its reconstruction for the 1980 Olympics. The Orgcom placed primary importance on the Luzhniki complex because it would host the opening and closing ceremonies and the most popular events of the Games, including soccer finals in the Grand Arena, gymnastics in the Minor Arena, and water polo in the swimming pool.

All construction projects had to meet the demands of international prestige, budgetary constraints, and internal political power dynamics. Throughout the process, Novikov deferred to the international expertise of his Sports Committee veterans to ensure that the Games would make the necessary impression on the international community. For example, when the Moscow City Soviet balked at the cost of constructing a covered section on Lenin Stadium for VIP seating, Smirnov and others convinced Novikov that such a covered section was "a necessary technical provision" with "political significance" and that by not building a canopy over the stadium, they risked "wrecking" the most important events of the Games in the case of inclement weather.[45] Similarly, when Orgcom Vice-President Promyslov proposed to build one facility for swimming and diving events with seating for 10,000–12,000 rather than two separate facilities each seating 10,500 to cut down construction costs, another Sports Committee veteran and Orgcom Sport Department head, Vladimir Sergeevich Rodichenko, defended the necessity of having two venues in order to balance the wishes of FINA and the needs of the athletes, officials, and spectators involved.[46] In the end, the swimming and diving competitions were held in one building, but with two separate pools. The swimming arena of the Olympiski Sports Complex on Prospect Mira, included a pool for swimming competitions with seating capacity of 13,000 separated by a glass partition from the diving pool that had a 5,000-seat capacity, allowing the organizers to hold swimming and diving competitions simultaneously.[47]

LEARNING FROM PAST EXPERIENCE AND MEETING INTERNATIONAL EXPECTATIONS

Moscow organizers had to see the Games in action to fully understand what was needed to host 203 events, house and feed thousands of athletes, trainers and officials, and to accommodate and serve millions of Olympic visitors. To evaluate whether Moscow was measuring up, over the course of 1975 alone, the Orgcom sent four delegations of twenty people each to West Germany to meet with the Munich Organizing Committee and four delegations of nineteen people to Canada to observe the preparations for the Montreal Games. The Orgcom also hosted twelve specialists from Munich and Montreal to answer questions and otherwise advise the Moscow Orgcom.[48]

Members of the Munich Organizing Committee became important sources of information for the Moscow Orgcom, especially regarding the informal expectations of the international sports community not encapsulated in the official rules and regulations of the IOC and IFs. A meeting with Klaus Willing of the Munich Organizing Committee reveals the delicate and potentially expensive business of making the International Federations happy with the Games preparation. Once the IOC approves a host city, it is the IFs who are most influential in overseeing the preparation, program, and facilities for Olympic competitions. For this reason, not only did sports venues need to fulfill IF regulations, but housing and hospitality accommodations for IF personnel and international judges should meet the highest possible standards in order to "win the Olympic Games from a technical and organizational point of view."[49] Willing urged the Moscow committee to establish "personal contacts" with IF representatives and to treat IF visitors as valued guests, providing them with first-class tickets with open dates, getting the pilots to greet them on their flights, leaving gifts in their hotel rooms, and arranging private cars and drivers for the duration of their stay.[50] Willing also recommended that the Orgcom designate a specific individual to each IF member and his wife who would serve as their main contact, greeting them upon their arrival and accompanying them in all negotiations and cultural activities. Willing suggested that this would give the IF leaders a sense that there was someone they could trust in the Orgcom, while at the same time avoiding any impression that IF representatives were being monitored.[51]

Willing also cautioned that the Orgcom needed to convince Western observers that the Games would live up to European standards since public opinion in "the West" regarded the 1980 Games as a "Russian Olympiad." Since so many decisions were made in private meetings, he insisted that Orgcom personnel needed to learn foreign languages so that they could negotiate without the aid of interpreters. The Orgcom leadership had already recognized the need for their workers to be skilled in foreign languages, and the Presidium arranged for foreign language instructors to train personnel and administer exams.[52] Willing also noted that European public opinion held that it was hard to change one's itinerary in Moscow, allowing no opportunity for free movement around the city. For this reason, he encouraged the Orgcom to allow IF representatives to choose for themselves what they wanted to do. He also noted that meetings with the press and with the Moscow mayor or other government officials should be arranged, preferably at the Kremlin.[53] Similarly, Western journalists needed to be assured that they could move freely in Moscow during the Games.[54] Following Willing's recommendations, Smirnov instructed underlings to draw up a plan for working with presidents, general secretaries, technical delegates and other representatives of IFs, incorporating Willing's information about international expectations.[55]

An Orgcom delegation also traveled to Innsbruck in 1976 to observe an Olympic Winter Games in action, establish international contacts, hold meetings with foreign companies, and promote Soviet interests among the IOC and other international sports figures, especially Willi Daume of the Federal Republic of Germany. Over the years, Daume became a key advisor to the Orgcom and a close friend to Sports Committee Chairman Sergei Pavlov. At Innsbruck, Daume expressed concern over Moscow's capability to host official guests and tourists because of its lack of experience in tourist services. He recommended taking special care to make journalists happy with their housing and working conditions, to win over representatives of the press, radio, and television, because so much of world public opinion about the Games would depend on international press coverage.[56]

A delegation of thirty Orgcom workers and thirty-four specialists traveled to Montreal to observe technical aspects of the Olympic Games in 1976 and to learn from their experience. The delegation noted many complaints and shortcomings in Montreal that Moscow should avoid. Journalists had complained that their housing arrangements were too far away from the press center and most Olympic venues and that security measures restricting access to the Olympic Village had interfered with their work. Noting that Montreal residents seemed indifferent to the Olympics being held in their city, the Orgcom delegation insisted that the Moscow organizers should do more to promote the Games among Soviet citizens.[57] The Soviet delegation criticized security at the Games, asserting that the show of force of police and the army "obviously calculated for a psychological effect" dampened the atmosphere of the "sports celebration of the world's youth." The Soviet delegation also perceived that, despite the numbers of security personnel, they were often ineffective, allowing "provocative attacks and outrages" that interfered with the competitions and "discredited" the Olympic events. The Soviet observers also mused that the Montreal organizers failed to produce a "modest Games" and instead spent $250–300 million on the Games.[58]

"A TASK FOR THE PRESTIGE OF OUR WHOLE COUNTRY": BALANCING REPUTATION AND PRACTICALITY

To Novikov the construction of Olympic venues, hotels, and other facilities played a key role in promoting the right impression of Moscow and of the Soviet way of life to foreign visitors, and like Willing and Daume, he expressed concern that Moscow tourist facilities be brought up to Western standards. As he stated, "this grand-scale political event must be prepared and carried out at the highest political level, and not as publicized by several journalists and other individuals, who come, see nothing good, and somewhere or another see a drunk, photograph him and later tell the world that we have drunks lying about. For this reason, we must decisively solve construction projects first of all."[59]

The Organizing Committee had to balance the need to keep up with modern sports technology with the cost of developing Soviet-made equipment and products. Western products cost more; moreover buying them for use in the Games would make it seem to outside observers that the Soviet economy lacked the capacity to produce the quality sports equipment needed for Olympic competitions. As head of the Orgcom Sports Department, Rodichenko had to purchase first from Soviet suppliers then from other socialist countries before turning to Western imports as a last resort.[60] One of the prime examples of the difficulty in balancing the need to "modernize" the staging of the Games with the limitations of the Soviet command economy was the Automated Control System, ACS-Olympiad. The main computers were housed at the ACS-Olympiad building at Luzhniki, and this complex was connected to five regional computer centers that gathered data from the various competition sites and relayed it to the main center for tabulation and reporting of results. Members of the Orgcom were keenly aware that Soviet computing technology was not up to Western standards and could be a source of embarrassment. When one member of the Orgcom commented at an August 1975 meeting that it would be impossible to develop the Automatic Control System based on Soviet computers and that therefore foreign computers should be purchased, Novikov questioned what foreign observers would think about the state of Soviet technology if they saw only imported computers.[61]

Similarly, in April 1976, the Sports Committee discussed the merits of developing domestic pole-vaulting poles using fiberglass. In February 1976, a chemist, E. N. Popov, denounced the head of Glavsportprom, V. V. Sumochkin, for "damaging Soviet prestige" by not developing quality, Soviet-made sports equipment out of fiberglass, and instead buying fiberglass products from capitalist countries. Popov appealed to the Central Committee to instruct the Sports Committee to bring domestic production of fiberglass sports equipment up to the "international standard."[62] Popov underscored the "great importance of producing various products for technical sports" due to the upcoming Olympic Games.[63] Since developing a domestic industry in fiberglass pole vaulting poles would be "inexpedient" because it would cost 200,000–230,000 rubles while current demand for such products was only a thousand per year, the Sports Committee found that it would be more cost effective to purchase the poles from an East German company.[64]

The chairman of the Moscow City Soviet, Promyslov, expressed similar concern for the USSR's international reputation when pushing to modernize service facilities. Calling the Olympics "a task for the prestige of our whole country," Promyslov insisted that it was not enough to build cafeterias and restaurants, but it was equally important to pay close attention to how they should be outfitted. Fearing that poor facilities would cause embarrassment, he shared a personal experience he had when taking representatives of a West German firm to a specialty grocery store, Eliseev's on Gorkii street. According to Promyslov, the foreign guests remarked that the cash registers in Eliseev's looked like they had been purchased in 1905. Promyslov noted the difference between Soviet registers, which could only calculate two purchases at a time, and Swedish machines that could process many items at once, wondering aloud what would happen if a shopper had forty or fifty items to purchase, "how many times must [you] return to the cash register to make that many purchases!"[65] Novikov also emphasized the significance of tourist facilities to Soviet prestige. Novikov argued that the existing Soviet currency exchange system was too slow and involved to serve the needs of thousands of foreign visitors coming for the Games, explaining, "here you have to fill out a form, then stand in line for two hours, and then three hours later receive the money."[66] Novikov recognized the need for an elevated level of services for foreigners. Insisting that "our [Soviet] people could not be housed in hotels," he noted that with students on vacation, student cafeterias could feed visitors from within the Soviet Union. "Foreigners," he insisted, "could not be sent to student dorms," suggesting that student dorms and cafeterias were of insufficient quality to make the desired impression on foreign guests.[67] Berating managers for construction delays, Novikov fumed, "We will have 7,500 journalists, and if even one of them doesn't have an international phone line, it will be a worldwide scandal" (see Figure 4.2).[68]

Novikov was not exaggerating. IOC President Killanin shared concerns over the quality of tourist accommodations and services. In a letter to Smirnov dated 26 November 1976, Killanin wrote, "I believe there will be a large problem in regard to training of staff. This is worldwide and is an area where visitors are most critical."[69] Western journalists doubted that adequate freedom and facilities would be afforded them in Moscow to report on the Games. In May 1976, K. D. Lawrence, sports editor for the *Daily Express* of London, complained to Killanin about his inability to get a visa for one of his reporters to cover the USSR versus Great Britain athletics meet in Kiev. Based on this one difficulty, Lawrence concluded "I can see no reason why the Olympics should be staged in Moscow when this is the way they behave."[70] To fault an entire country for one bureaucratic mishap seems rather small-minded, but it was a typical reaction by Western journalists in the run up to the 1980 Games.

Olympic construction revealed systematic problems and challenges posed by the Soviet bureaucratic apparatus and command economy. Novikov argued that the Orgcom must eliminate the many mistakes that typically take place in construction projects and make sure that Olympic preparations did not negatively impact the way of life of the Soviet people.[71] However, Olympic construction projects did sometimes impact peoples' lives. To accommo-

Figure 4.2. Because the media play such a key role in shaping the reputation of the host city, the press center, pictured here under construction in 1979, was one of the most important facilities built for the Moscow Olympic Games. Courtesy International Olympic Committee.

date a campground for tourists at Mikhalovo, the Orgcom relocated an entire village of eleven houses and thirty-six people. The relocation was scheduled for January 1978 but, at that time, furnaces were not yet installed in the new homes. Novikov called for bringing together everyone who was working on the resettlement to make sure they complete the "important project."[72]

When there was no significant progress in building hotels for the Games, Novikov grew frustrated with the lack of leadership displayed by those in charge of the construction projects. Railing that "we don't have a single hotel with 12,000 occupancy in the Soviet Union," Novikov criticized Kokhanenko who was responsible for building the Izmailovo hotel complex, whose four hotels when finished would accommodate 36,000, but on which construction was only in the beginning stages in January 1978.[73] Kokhanenko complained that he needed help with the ventilation systems, that he did not have enough natural stone, that he still lacked technical documentation, and that he needed electrical supplies. To these excuses, Novikov wondered "Can't you negotiate with Glavkom?" When Ravich from the Ministry of Communications gave similar explanations, Novikov queried "Can't you negotiate with Iashin yourself?" Then he turned on the group as a whole, ranting, "You are all important leaders, you should be able to resolve these issues yourself," and reminding them of the big picture.[74] Recognizing the impediments of working within the party-state apparatus, Novikov admonished Orgcom leaders to utilize informal networks and unofficial channels to ensure the timely construction of Olympic venues.

Novikov wanted individuals to recognize the full scale of the task before them and the implications of their actions for the project as a whole. Novikov also expected managers to take initiative to solve their own problems and to work with other departments and agencies to get the materials they needed. When Falaleev from the Ministry of Energy needed limestone, Novikov said "You know Demin, he makes limestone. Is it really the case that you can't order it?" He also advised Falaleev to deal directly with the glass factory for windows.[75] Novikov worked on the assumption that exploiting personal relationships to break through bureaucratic barriers was an essential feature of the system. When Falaeev bemoaned his lack of steel beams that needed to be taken up with Kovalev, Novikov remarked, "You are like brothers, solve the problem together, and don't bring it here."[76] At the same meeting, Novikov admonished managers,

> Stop taking it out on each other. Each one of you is a responsible person and obliged to make decisions on your own. And you are leaders, so don't say that so-and-so didn't send workers or so-and-so didn't send materials, etc. Truly you will answer for it before the party and the government, and I will answer along with you.[77]

Novikov seems to be asking for lateral, interdepartmental decision-making in a bureaucratic culture where administrators were accustomed to taking all their problems up the hierarchy. Novikov instead expected mid- and low-level managers take matters into their own hands to solve their problems.

Recognition of the shortcomings of the system did not equate to an overall lack of support for regime goals and ideals. Novikov was much more appreciative of officials who took initiative and demonstrated dedication to realize the Olympic project. Karaglanov too discussed shortages but noted that he was working with Promyslov and the Moscow City Soviet to solve them to ensure that venues were built "ahead of schedule and of high quality," because their work was "an honorable duty."[78] Novikov agreed stating, "It is an honorable task for all organizations—demanding, complicated, difficult, but also honorable, because it involves the prestige of the Soviet Union."[79] Novikov stressed that managers of Olympic construction projects should be motivated by their patriotism and devotion to the socialist motherland rather than by fear of disciplinary action if they failed to produce results, because "we don't have the right to disgrace the Soviet Union before the entire world."[80] Shoddy workmanship and endless delays might be okay under normal circumstances, but such problems were unacceptable for facilities that had to hold up to international scrutiny.

Ultimately, Olympic construction by itself could not cover up the less attractive elements in Soviet society, and the Orgcom reverted to "Stalinist practices" to ensure that visitors got the correct impression of the Soviet quality of life.[81] To create "normality" in Moscow during the Olympic Games, organizers took steps to limit the domestic traffic in and out of Moscow and to increase the availability of goods for that period.[82] Security forces worried about uncontrolled interactions between foreign visitors and Soviet residents, and suspected that foreign movements would try to infiltrate the Games as delegation members or tourists, in order to cause social disturbances. Therefore the KGB and MVD organized a series of raids called *Profilaktika*-80 to cleanse the Olympic city of potential criminal elements, and set up strict border searches to prevent the entry of dangerous elements.[83] They also ensured a heavy police presence as well as brigades of *druzhinniki* (civil police) to control the crowds and prevent disorder.[84] In the lead up to the Games, the Ministry of Internal Affairs (MVD) took action to "cleanse Moscow of chronic alcoholics and drug addicts" by sending them outside of the city. According to an MVD bulletin, 900 such persons were sent out of Moscow in August 1979.[85] Crime, dissidence, alcoholism and drug addiction should only exist in a capitalist society and not in "really existing socialism," so evidence of such problems in the Soviet capital had to be hidden in order to exhibit Moscow as an "exemplary communist city."

"ECONOMIC EXPEDIENCY AND RATIONAL USE": FINANCING THE GAMES

The cost of hosting the 1980 Games was a concern on all sides for a variety of reasons. As the Montreal Games of 1976 drew closer, it became clear that the Montreal Organizing Committee and the city of Montreal experienced serious financial strain and controversy in connection with the Games. Concerned about the Olympic image, IOC President Lord Killanin insisted that there be no similar "apparent waste of money" in Moscow.[86]

Along with the pressure to modernize, hosting the Olympics also provided opportunities to finance that modernization. Novikov secured permission from the Politburo to secure funding from wealthy Americans willing to send thousand-dollar checks to add to the Olympic fund and foreign firms offering their services for low costs in exchange for advertising and recognition as "official sponsors of the Olympic Games," as long as the Olympiad retained its "socio-political resonance."[87] Negotiations with foreign firms and companies occupied much of the Orgcom's energies. For example, Coca-Cola and Pepsi Cola both approached the Orgcom regarding the rights of "official sponsor."[88] The Orgcom also signed a contract with Adidas for providing free uniforms for 28,000 workers of the Orgcom and service personnel for the Games at an overall cost of 1.5 million dollars in exchange for the right to be named an "official sponsor." The agreement also called for the use of the Moscow emblem on football jerseys and bags, providing the Orgcom with 5 percent of the proceeds from the sales of those products. IBM, Siemens, and Philips likewise approached the Orgcom with proposals for providing various technologies in exchange for becoming official sponsors of the Games.[89] In August 1977, Novikov requested permission from the Council of Ministers to cooperate with socialist and capitalist firms in organizing services for the Olympic Village. Such services would include things such as shopping centers, repair shops, beauty salons, discotheques, and other services, and foreign firms competed for the right to become "official sponsors" of the Games by donating goods or setting up shops for selling goods to athletes and officials (see Figure 4.3).[90]

Figure 4.3.   Soviet athletes stayed in separate facilities in Helsinki in 1952. For the Moscow Olympic Village, pictured here under construction in 1980, the 1980 Organizing Committee tried to account for everything the athletes would need for a comfortable stay. Courtesy International Olympic Committee.

The Moscow organizers also experienced pressure to safeguard IOC interests when concluding foreign contracts. The IOC director, Monique Berlioux, insisted that all major contracts with foreign firms be sent to the IOC for review before signing in order "to avoid the 'fait accompli' situations which have arisen in the past."[91] Lord Killanin also worried about commercial contracts. In a telegram to Berlioux, who was visiting Moscow at the time, Killanin asked her to clarify with the Moscow Orgcom which contracts impacted IOC interests or protocol and needed to be countersigned by the IOC. He also requested that, in order to expedite the process, she agree *pro forma* any contracts for merchandising where final approval rested with the NOCs.[92]

For their part, the Moscow organizers also wanted to guard their own interests with regard to commercial negotiations, and Berlioux's tenacity in overseeing contracts seems to have annoyed the Moscow organizers. In a letter to Berlioux in November 1977, Smirnov asked "the IOC to take into account the interests of the organizing committee when signing contracts with commercial companies."[93] Novikov also expressed "anxiety over the desire of some officials to gain control over the financial side of the Olympic Games."[94] Killanin claimed ignorance of who Novikov meant, but Berlioux seems the likely source of Novikov's frustration. Again in January 1978, Novikov complained to Killanin about Berlioux's insistence that all contracts be approved by the IOC secretariat before signing. According to Novikov, this put an undue burden on the Orgcom and represented "moral and material damage" to it. He insisted that "we have fulfilled and will exactly fulfill all the rules of the IOC, but the rules did not specify that all contracts must receive approval by the IOC."[95] Reminding Killanin of the special problem the Orgcom had in securing foreign currency because of being a socialist country, Novikov argued that it was in both the Orgcom and the IOC's interests to "stop the activities that are preventing us from developing commercial dealings."[96]

Television coverage of the Games was a source of considerable income and another area of intense discussion and negotiation between the Orgcom and the IOC. Before the Montreal Games, the Moscow Orgcom had met with the IOC Television Technical Commission and foreign TV companies to discuss the practicalities of televising the 1980 Games. Novikov reported to the IOC session in Montreal that the Orgcom intended to provide color TV coverage through twenty channels, an "unprecedented" scope of coverage that would "entail considerable expenditures." He maintained that such coverage was necessary because of television's ability to "transform the world into a huge Olympic stadium" and to "turn scores of millions of sports enthusiasts throughout the world into eyewitnesses of this international sports festival and make them champions of the noble Olympic ideals of strengthening friendship, mutual understanding, and peace."[97] Novikov hoped the IOC would take this into account when deciding what share the Orgcom would receive from the sale of television rights. In January 1977, Novikov estimated that rights for the Games could bring in $80 million.[98] In February, the Orgcom signed an $85 million contract with NBC for broadcasting rights in the United States.[99] Berlioux urgently requested that the Orgcom provide the text of the speeches made by Novikov and Koval' when signing the contract.[100] In April 1978, Novikov informed Killanin that the European Broadcasting Union (EBU) offered to pay $5.75 million, and that the Orgcom had invited Canada's CBC to Moscow for final negotiations.[101] Killanin insisted that TV contracts should be concluded quickly because "it is in all our interests to obtain a maximum amount as quickly as possible."[102]

Commercial advertising proved an important source of funding for various aspects of the Games preparation, but the Orgcom also needed to clear advertising with the IOC, who wished to ensure that there was no unnecessary "commercialization" of the Games. Monique Berlioux wrote to Novikov in November 1975 clarifying that, according to the Olympic Charter, no airplane advertising banners should appear above Olympic venues, the last torch runner must wear no trademarks, and trademarks and logos on timing equipment and scoreboards must be no larger than at the Munich Games.[103] In August 1976, Andrianov asked the IOC director to confirm in writing that including advertisements in the Orgcom publications, *Olympiad-80* and *Olympic Panorama,* "would not infringe the IOC rules."[104] Later that month, Killanin wrote to Novikov addressing a number of issues from the Montreal Games that he hoped the Moscow organizers could avoid, pointing out that none of the official publications of the Games should include commercial advertisements.[105]

The Orgcom also had to work closely with the IOC when licensing Moscow Olympic emblems to generate revenue. In 1976, the Orgcom launched a worldwide licensing program whereby interested countries would pay for the right to produce and sell coins, medals, stamps, and other souvenirs with the Moscow Olympics emblem. By January 1977, forty-two countries had signed on, and the Orgcom had held around 700 negotiations with foreign firms as part of the commercial-licensing program that looked to bring in around 204 million rubles in foreign currency.[106] That October, Smirnov had requested a copy of the IOC's contract with Italcambio regarding commemorative medals to "avoid a possible clash of interests" as the Moscow Orgcom negotiated with other firms on distributing medals commemorating the Summer Games.[107]

In addition to licensing agreements and income from foreign companies, the Orgcom relied on other domestic sources to fund the Games. Novikov and Promyslov argued that each ministry and agency needed to help with financing construction of housing, telecommunications, and transport and listed the amounts they needed to pitch in.[108] The Soviet public also provided a significant source of funding. Two sports lotteries, Sprint and Sportlotto, brought in a considerable amount of money. Also, sales of Olympic stamps, tickets to training events and competitions, and Olympic publications in the Soviet Union provided revenue for the Orgcom.[109] That Soviet citizens bought these items demonstrates a degree of popular enthusiasm for the Olympic project. Novikov noted that although ticket sales for the Sprint lottery in Moscow "showed the enormous popularity" of the program, other ministries and departments had not done their part to guarantee the development of the Sportlotto.[110] Early problems with theft of Sportlotto tickets and revenue led the Orgcom to work out additional security measures with the Ministry of Internal Affairs (MVD) to protect Sportlotto distributers and to tighten control over rules for ticket sales.[111]

Novikov often talked of the need to reduce expenditures, but he never advocated cutting corners in any way. Financing the Games needed to be economical, but he insisted that the Olympics needed to be prepared in such a way as to fulfill the needs of both the Games and future development in Moscow and elsewhere in the Soviet Union. In 1976, Novikov articulated the need for economy in construction projects for the Games, advocating that housing projects for the Olympic Village and foreign and Soviet tourists to be constructed in a way that Muscovites could live in them later.[112] He also maintained that the infrastructure for color television transmission would make it possible for all Soviet citizens to have access to color TV after the Games.[113] In April 1976, the Presidium of the Orgcom decreed that "economic expediency and rational use of venues for the post-Olympic period should be the guiding principle in negotiations with IFs."[114] Similarly, the IOC was keen that the Games help each host city in its long-term development of services and infrastructure, insisting that Olympic construction plans be geared toward the future use of those facilities.

"CONSCIENTIOUS WORK" AND "NORMAL CONDITIONS": ORGCOM OFFICE CULTURE IN THE WORKERS' STATE

The Orgcom's departments oversaw the work of various commissions, and these were made up of representatives both from the Orgcom itself and from other Soviet agencies and departments.[115] This alone did not always ensure quality work, as these individuals did not report directly to the Orgcom leadership.[116] Novikov and his vice-presidents relied upon bureaucratic control measures, professional and material rewards, official sanctions and self-regulation to ensure the loyalty, dedication, and productiveness of Olympic workers.

To make sure that other Soviet agencies were on board, the Orgcom required regular reports from other departments and sections on their preparation work and requested that all plans and reports be approved in advance by an Orgcom vice-president. Each Orgcom committee was assigned a ministry, agency, or organization for which to be responsible.[117] The leaders of Orgcom subunits had to prepare their reports with other interested agencies, observing "strict adherence" to deadlines.[118] In addition, the Orgcom required all department and section heads to "expose existing deficiencies and report on what measures had been taken to eliminate them."[119] This form of self-criticism was a hallmark of bureaucratic leadership peculiar to the Soviet Union. Finally, delegations traveling abroad were to report directly to the Orgcom leaders who, in turn, would make all decisions regarding the proposals contained in those documents.[120] The Executive Bureau also instituted additional controls to ensure that reports for the Orgcom leadership followed the prescribed procedures and that all materials and reports to be presented were first approved by the appropriate vice-president.[121] By making the Orgcom committees responsible for guaranteeing that reports from outside agencies were completed and turned in on time, the Orgcom leadership hoped to keep closer tabs on how other bureaus contributed toward the Olympic project.

In keeping with established practice, Novikov continually reshuffled the workforce of the Orgcom, using personnel management as both a tool of control and as a means to increase the organization's efficiency in fulfilling its tasks. In August 1976, Novikov announced to the Orgcom Executive Bureau that the Council of Ministers had approved his recommendation to replace several members of the Orgcom.[122] That same month, the Executive Bureau of the Orgcom endorsed the decision to install the longtime head of the Soviet soccer federation and member of the USSR NOC, V. A. Granatkin, as a senior officer in the sports program department and S. I. Kalashnikov as the executive officer of the Orgcom in connection with his move from Gosstroi.[123] These moves suggest that Novikov wanted to build up the number of experienced administrators in the Orgcom.

Bureaucratic control of Orgcom representatives was especially significant with regards to the large number of delegations travelling abroad to observe Olympic Games, to meet with international sports representatives, and to secure foreign contracts and supplies. The Presidium criticized many Orgcom members for making extraneous trips, not giving enough attention to existing records on foreign experience, and wasting time abroad elucidating issues that were already known from written materials. They were also criticized for being slow in reporting on their trips, in carrying out recommendations based on negotiations with representatives of foreign firms and organizations, and in answering foreign correspondence.[124] The Presidium determined that Orgcom department heads needed to better train delegations going abroad and institute measures for controlling the distribution of information gathered from observing other organizing committees.[125]

The Executive Bureau of the Orgcom also tried to strengthen control over its international delegations, achieving "more well-defined coordination with planning and carrying out international relations of subunits of the Orgcom." Vice chairmen of the Orgcom were also to "systematically hear reports" from department heads on how their sections were utilizing previous experience in their work.[126] The international department under V.I. Prokopov was to give more practical help to subunits on how to incorporate the experience of previous Olympics, to clarify the division of functions with the protocol department for receiving foreign delegations, and to set up with the cadres department a team of qualified specialists to translate foreign information and materials. The translation needs of the Orgcom were significant given the volume of correspondence and informational materials being exchanged with the IOC, IFs, NOCs, and previous Olympic organizing committees, so the Orgcom poached qualified translators from other ministries and agencies. Leaders of Orgcom subunits were also supposed to exert more control over preparing workers traveling abroad to negotiate with foreign organizations and firms.[127]

The upcoming Moscow Games also provided an opportunity for athletes to criticize Orgcom and Sports Committee personnel, calling attention chronic shortages and corrupt practices characteristic of late Soviet socialism. In February 1978, a group of anonymous members of the Soviet cycling team complained that a lack of quality cycles, spare parts, and tires prevented them from achieving the highest sporting results, appealing to the Central Committee to "sort out certain shameful practices in cycling." In their letter, the cyclists bemoaned the fact that they could not buy quality cycles and parts in stores. Instead, they alleged that their money went into "the pockets of certain people, who use it to buy cars, dachas, and apartments and to maintain a dissolute lifestyle." The cyclists denounced their head trainer V. A. Kapitonov, who they said instructed them to buy cycles and equipment abroad with their per diems. They also alleged that Kapitonov took the prize money they earned and, telling them it would go to the Sports Committee to buy equipment, would spend it on other things.[128] In his report on the allegations contained in the letter, Pavlov insisted that the things described did not happen according to written statements by members of the cycling team, and were not borne out by financial documents. According to two of the accused, they obtained cars and apartments before beginning work in the Sports Committee and acquired them from their personal means and through the help of relatives.[129]

As one would expect when dealing with a high-profile undertaking such as the Olympic Games, disagreements arose between department heads, providing the opportunity for individuals to assert their authority and to defend the importance of their position. For example, when head of construction for the Games and vice-president of the Orgcom I. K. Koziulia felt that the head of the technical department, V. A. Polishchuk, overstepped his authority by meeting with West German television experts without Koziulia's permission, he complained to Novikov, requesting that Polishchuk be reprimanded for "willfulness and deceit." Koziulia further accused Polishchuk of neglecting his responsibilities by requesting unnecessary meetings with foreign firms while leaving work in designing, building, and equipping Olympic facilities unfinished.[130] Admitting that he made a mistake in not securing written permission before holding the meetings, Polishchuk insisted that Koziulia had approved the negotiations in question, that he had requested no unnecessary meetings with foreign firms, and that negotiations had not exceeded the budget for technical furnishings.[131] Rather than taking sides, Novikov instructed Koziulia to meet with Polishchuk and settle the matter.[132]

The responsibilities of organizing a sporting mega event would challenge any committee that signed on to host the Olympic Games, but the 1980 Orgcom had the added pressure of hosting the Games for the first time in a socialist country. Such a large influx of visitors presented special difficulties to a closed society more accustomed to hosting small, tightly controlled foreign delegations and tourist groups than accommodating many large delegations and individual tourists simultaneously. Welcoming the world to Moscow also meant that millions of foreign observers would see first-hand the level of development in Soviet society that in reality was far less modern than its Western rivals. Accordingly, Novikov called for cadres to be trained in the treatment and service of foreigners, including foreign language training. In a meeting with various Orgcom managers in January 1978, Novikov expressed anxiety over the need to train 97,000 students and workers from various ministries and departments as service personnel, and that they had not decided "where to train them, who to train, or when to train them."[133]

In order to complete construction of Olympic venues and tourist facilities, the Orgcom also had to attract thousands of skilled workers to Moscow. In a meeting with Novikov to discuss construction projects for the Games, Agitprop chief B. P. Goncharov groused that the country's "working potential" was not being used to its fullest, noting that around 19,000 soldiers, 10,000 Moscow city workers, and 7,000 workers from regional governments had been gathered for Olympic construction, but that many were abandoning their posts because of poor working conditions. Goncharov argued that the Orgcom had failed to provide the high wages, proper housing, and services it had promised. He insisted that they needed to treat Olympic construction workers better to keep them on the job.[134] Novikov agreed for different reasons. He informed the meeting that the Orgcom received many requests from foreign communist and workers' parties asking to show journalists and representatives Olympic facilities, but the Orgcom had dragged its feet for fear of how foreign visitors would describe the progress.[135] Novikov realized that using large-scale construction projects as propaganda for the successes of socialism could backfire if working conditions and daily lives of workers were not exemplary. Socialist observers visiting incomplete Olympic constructions and seeing thousands of workers without proper housing and food services could leave with a negative impression of Soviet socialism and, perhaps more importantly, might disparage the Olympic project and the Soviet Union in their domestic press.

In addition to all the construction necessary for the Games themselves, the Organizing Committee along with the Moscow City Soviet had to arrange office space for the committee's growing staff. The Sports Committee presented a proposal for the construction of a new building to house the Orgcom, press center, and all the television and radio equipment.[136] Then in early 1976, the Organizing Committee moved into new headquarters on Gorky Street.[137] In September of that year, the Executive Bureau instructed the housekeeping department to "establish normal conditions for work" and "improve catering" for the Orgcom staff. Similar measures were also needed at the Orgcom's second location, and Rogul'skii made sure this was done in a timely fashion.[138] Upon completion of the ACS Olympiad for the Games, a number of Orgcom departments relocated to that new building.[139] After the Games, the building would serve as the new headquarters of the Sports Committee and provide some offices for the Moscow City Soviet.[140]

To ensure loyalty and efficiency among their staff, the Orgcom leadership rewarded diligent and dedicated workers with cash incentives and other means of appreciation. For example, the Orgcom Presidium awarded twenty one-hundred ruble rewards to fifty-nine people for their "conscientious work" during the preparation for the Olympic Games.[141] In March 1977, the Executive Bureau charged I. I. Kholod propaganda head Shevchenko, and Rodichenko to create certificates of merit, diplomas, badges, and medals for recognizing Orgcom workers. The team also explored granting outstanding organizers tickets and tourist passes to Olympic events in honor of their hard work.[142] For dedicated service, Orgcom employees could also expect recognition on their birthdays.[143] By contrast, poor work performance could result in expulsion from the Organizing Committee: in January 1980, V. L. Mal'kevich was taken off the foreign relations commission after failing to show up to meetings for two years.[144]

Lower-level employees appealed to the Orgcom leadership to improve their working conditions, exposing tensions between increasing professionalization within the committee and remaining patrimonial styles of leadership. In February 1978, senior clerk of the propaganda department V. Shandrin complained to the Orgcom Executive Bureau about the head of the Propaganda Department, V.G. Shevchenko. Presenting himself as an experienced sports

photo-journalist and highlighting his many trips to international competitions and the awards he had earned for his work, Shandrin felt his skills were
underutilized. After his idea for setting up a photo-lab in the Orgcom was
shot down by Shevchenko, Shandrin asserted that "Initiative is punished!"
bemoaning, "I receive regular pay without any responsibility. I'm okay with
this, but I could be of more use." Shandrin contrasted his dedication to the
photographer's craft and professionalism to the other members of the propaganda department, who he believed "use[d] their positions for selfish goals,
bringing not only material but also moral damage" to the Orgcom. Calling for
a "corrective" to the "style of work" in the propaganda department, Shandrin
argued that the Orgcom had already expended more money on the purchase
of photographs and negatives than the cost of setting up a central photo-lab.
Though not explicitly stated, it seems safe to assume that Shandrin envisioned
himself as the manager of photo-services, being allowed to set up an Orgcom
photo-lab and perhaps taking advantage of the "more than 10,000 negatives"
in his personal collection.[145] Shandrin expressed frustration over lethargy in
the bureaucracy, but maintained commitment to the Olympic project, exhibiting personal initiative and a desire for meaningful work.

Some Orgcom workers leveraged the importance of the Olympic Games to
obtain a better apartment, demonstrating continued housing shortages and the
informal networks of authority used to overcome them. In 1975, Promyslov
had designated a building to resettle 350 workers' families and expressed
the need to find an additional 300–400 square meters to house people.[146] As
the head of the Administration of Affairs of the Orgcom, S. I. Kalashnikov
worked with members of the Orgcom Party Committee to oversee compensation and housing for Orgcom personnel. Owing to limited resources,
Kalashnikov often enlisted the help of Novikov to secure apartments from
municipal and regional party organs for Orgcom workers, underscoring the
needs of Orgcom personnel who often lived with large families in small
apartments or in communal flats. In February 1978, Kalashnikov and head of
the Orgcom Party Committee E. Korobov wrote to Novikov on behalf of A.
Kozlovskii, deputy chief of the Orgcom International Department. According
to their letter, Kozlovskii had been living in a small one-room apartment with
his wife and daughter. They requested that Kozlovskii be given a three-room
apartment, arguing that, in light of the "important and complicated task [of
the international department] to ensure broad representative participation in
the 1980 Olympic Games," Kozlovskii should be granted "better living conditions."[147] Novikov, in turn, asked the person in charge of that district "to
help."[148] Being a part of such an important project provided access to powerful patrons who could use their connections to improve the Orgcom workers'
living standards.

At times, Orgcom members appealed directly to Novikov to secure his help in obtaining better living conditions, emphasizing the personal hardships caused by their current circumstances. In May 1977, a member of the Orgcom Sports Department requested Novikov's help in securing an apartment in Moscow to be closer to his place of work, complaining of the distress caused by his almost four-hour commute.[149] In May 1978, Novikov intervened on behalf of V. A. Bykov, one of the vice-presidents of the Orgcom. In requesting housing on behalf of Bykov, Novikov cited Bykov's fifteen years working in the Central Committee apparat prior to joining the Orgcom to explain why he deserved a larger apartment.[150] When Orgcom propaganda chief Shevchenko asked for more living space to provide "normal" conditions for work and rest for him and his two daughters and to allow them to care for his ailing parents, Novikov described Shevchenko as a qualified leader, a "principled and exacting communist," and an able organizer who often worked at home on weekends and in the evenings to "fulfill [his] responsibilities."[151] Workers in other fields stressed any connection they had with the Moscow Games in appealing to Novikov to secure better apartments on their behalf. In June 1981, a doctor at a polyclinic asked Novikov's help in securing a better apartment. According to her letter, she and her family of four lived in a communal apartment in a nineteen-square-meter room with two other families, including a cancer patient who was fed through a tube and breathed through a tracheotomy tube which scared her young children. This doctor's claim to Novikov's assistance was based on her treating workers involved with building Olympic venues from 1972 to 1975.[152] Organizing the Olympic Games thus provided opportunities for rank and file bureaucrats to improve their working and living conditions as well as advance their professional careers.

CONCLUSION

Did being the first socialist nation to hold the Games serve as an advantage or disadvantage? Certainly the massive influx of foreign tourists would tax the underdeveloped tourist industry of a closed society, and lack of technological development in Soviet industry meant that most of the high-tech equipment needed for the Games had to be acquired abroad. Moreover, the system of many independently run government bureaus with no formal lateral contacts could cause delays and setbacks to a project that required coordination among nearly every state agency in Moscow. To overcome logistical problems, the leadership formed a separate committee, formally incorporating officials from various state bureaus and organizations into the effort of preparing for the Games. The Orgcom developed a system for overseeing the work of staff and commission members, including awards and cash incentives to ensure a job well done. The Orgcom leadership also expected individuals to take personal responsibility for their duties. At times, Novikov admonished Orgcom workers for failing to do so, demanding that they utilize informal channels to acquire the materials and cooperation they needed from other government bureaus. Throughout the process of organizing the Games, the Orgcom leadership demonstrated a keen awareness of the limits of the Soviet system and took steps to break through bureaucratic barriers and to work around obstacles.

The work of the Organizing Committee also reveals a significant degree of professionalization within the Soviet bureaucracy. Orgcom workers were chosen for their previous experience, and the Orgcom leadership instituted training and educational programs to ensure that their workers had the skills necessary to carry out their tasks. Technical expertise and pragmatism were valued alongside ideological commitment or personal connections. Though party members did make up a significant percentage of the Orgcom staff, this number grew over time, suggesting that work in the Orgcom provided an opportunity for enterprising junior administrators to achieve a degree of professional advancement in the developing gerontocracy. At the same time, limited resources meant that Orgcom employees still had to rely on informal networks to secure better working and living conditions.

Comparing the organization behind the Olympic Games with another ambitious project launched around the same time provides a useful means of evaluating the possibilities and limits of bureaucratic initiative in Brezhnev's Soviet Union. In his monograph on the construction of the Baikal-Amur Mainline Railway (BAM), Christopher Ward found the BAM project to be emblematic of the Brezhnev era as a whole, in that it revealed that Soviet officialdom was out of touch with growing social and cultural tensions in Soviet society and failed to recognize the real limitations and inadequacies of Soviet state-socialism.[153] For Ward, the BAM experience "completed the disenchantment by the mid-1980s of the generational cohort of twenty- and thirty-year olds" with the Soviet status quo.[154] Ward further notes that corruption, poor working conditions, and gross inefficiencies related to the construction of the railroad exposed foreign visitors to the problems of the socialist system it was meant to promote. Likewise workers on the BAM project embarrassed the Soviet leadership by their poor behavior abroad.[155]

The 1980 Olympic Organizing Committee escaped these problems and, on the whole, their efforts enhanced the Soviet image abroad, especially in the capitalist world. Foreign delegations coming to see preparations for the Moscow Games experienced not corruption and inefficiency but helpful guides who met them at the airport with gifts, escorted them to a ballet at the

Bolshoi Theater and a visit to the Kremlin, and accompanied them to building sites where construction on state-of-the-art stadiums and sports fields was progressing on-schedule. Seen in this light, the buildup to the 1980 Olympics (and Soviet sport in general) provided an important counter image to the Soviet construction of BAM. Olympic events were located in the largest Soviet cities, meaning that visitors from abroad could be offered the best services available in the Soviet Union. The central location also meant that resources were more readily available to Olympic construction projects than they were to BAM, located so far from Moscow. Plus, there were many powerful Soviet patron-advocates of the Olympics outside of the Kremlin who had a firm stake in making the Games a resounding success. Intense international scrutiny from the IOC and International Federations also helped make Olympic preparations a priority. Beyond the higher level of priority or funding for sports as compared to the BAM project, the success of Soviet Olympic endeavors speaks to the professionalism and managerial skill of all strata of sports administrators who, due to their experience staging large-scale sports events, were familiar with Western expectations and how to meet them.

If the BAM project symbolized the shortcomings of the Soviet system under Brezhnev's leadership, the Olympic project is an example of what could still be accomplished under Soviet-style "developed socialism." On one hand, staging the Olympic Games in Moscow could be seen as yet another example of Soviet leaders pouring energy and resources into maintaining the image of the USSR in competition with the West: focusing on outward-facing projects, modern Potemkin villages, and diverting limited resources to big-scale projects instead of reforming the economy and improving the quality of life for its citizens. Under Khrushchev and Brezhnev, rising standards of living meant that there were enough resources to do both. However, by the mid-1970s, when the standard of living began to decline while defense spending continued to grow, Soviet citizens became increasingly disillusioned. On the other hand, there was genuine enthusiasm for hosting the Olympics, both in the leadership and among the population. With support from the party leadership and the dedicated efforts of hundreds of administrators, Moscow could pull off a high-profile international festival such as the Olympic Games. Thousands of people bought Sport Lotto tickets, and most of the Olympic event tickets were purchased by Soviet citizens. Furthermore, while it is true that Soviet resources were poured into this large-scale project, the Games also brought in a significant amount of resources from the outside world, both in terms of funding and expertise, making long-term improvements to Moscow that would not have happened if the USSR had not hosted the Games.

Many Sports Committee bureaucrats acknowledged the realities facing a Soviet Olympics. They knew that the world was coming to see the Olympic

Games, and if they had no hotel room to stay in or could not find a decent restaurant to eat in, it would be humiliating for all concerned and could not be concealed from the public, abroad or at home. Despite the challenges, they formed a corps of pragmatic and professional "enlightened bureaucrats" who mustered all of their authority to make the Games happen.[156] They did so building upon decades of experience in international sports circles and first-hand knowledge of how Games were run in the past.

NOTES

1. Minutes of the First Meeting of the Organizing Committee for the 1980 Olympic Games, 7 March 1975, GARF f. 9610, op. 1, d. 3, ll. 18–19.
2. Ibid., l. 22.
3. Ibid., l. 21, 26.
4. Evans, *Between Truth and Time*, 5 and David-Fox, *Crossing Borders*, 17. In his sweeping analysis of Soviet historiography and cultural exchange, Michael David-Fox advocates for "a middle ground between the binary oppositions entrenched in this field, most notably the one between exceptionalism and shared modernity."
5. Yurchak, *Everything was Forever*; Raleigh, *Soviet Baby Boomers*, 220–28.
6. Kotkin, *Armageddon Averted*, 16–17.
7. Raleigh, *Soviet Baby Boomers*, 228–36.
8. Christopher J. Ward, *Brezhnev's Folly*, 152–53.
9. Ward, *Brezhnev's Folly*, 5; Evans, *Between Truth and Time*, 5.
10. Fainberg and Kalinovsky eds., *Reconsidering Stagnation*, vii.
11. Evans, *Between Truth and Time*, 7–8.
12. Ibid., 283.
13. Kristin Roth-Ey, *Moscow Prime Time*, 20, 23–24.
14. Ibid., 23.
15. Ryavec, *Russian Bureaucracy*, 5–6.
16. See for example, Steven l. Solnick, *Stealing the State: Control and Collapse in Soviet Institutions* (Cambridge: Harvard University Press, 1998); Stephen Kotkin, *Armageddon Averted*; Vera Dunham, *In Stalin's Time: Middle Class Values in Soviet Fiction* (Cambridge and New York: Cambridge University Press, 1976). Sergei Khrushchev, "The Military-Industrial Complex, 1953–1964," in *Nikita Khrushchev*, William Taubman, ed. (New Haven: Yale University Press, 2000): 242–74.
17. Nikolai Mitrohin, "'Back Office' Mikhaila Suslova."
18. Stephen F. Cohen, "Was the Soviet System Reformable?" *Slavic Review* 63.3 (2004): 473.
19. Ibid., l. 50.
20. Copy of Report to Council of Ministers on course of preparation for 1980 OG Moscow, 27 January 1977, GARF, f. 9610, op. 1, d. 119, ll. 3, 11.
21. Minutes of the First Meeting of the Organizing Committee for the 1980 Olympic Games, 7 March 1975, Ibid., ll. 27–28.

22. Decree of the Presidium of the Orgcom, 12 June 1975, GARF, f. 9610, op. 1, d. 4, l. 3.

23. Ibid., ll. 1–3.

24. Minutes of the First Meeting of the Organizing Committee for the 1980 Olympic Games, 7 March 1975, GARF, f. 9610, op. 1, d. 3, l. 24.

25. Ibid., 27–28.

26. Ibid., l. 24.

27. Work Plan of I. I. Kholod for Studying the Experience in Preparing and Staging the Olympic Games (questions of cadres), approved by Novikov, 9 July 1976, GARF, f. 9610, op. 1, d. 38, ll. 83–84.

28. Ibid., l. 42.

29. Report, On course of Fulfillment of Decree of Central Committee and Council of Ministers from 23 December 1975, Preparation and Training of Service Personnel during the OG 1980, GARF, f. 9610, op. 1, d. 255, l. 3.

30. Minutes of Meeting of the Orgcom, 4 August 1975, GARF, f. 9610, op. 1, d. 3, ll. 68–69.

31. Minutes of the First Meeting of the Organizing Committee for the 1980 Olympic Games, 7 March 1975, Ibid., ll. 25, 29–30.

32. V. Smirnov to M. Berlioux, 12 September 1977, COJO of the Summer Games in Moscow 1980 Correspondence 1975–78 (hereafter COJO 1980 Correspondence 1975–78), IOC Archives.

33. For a discussion of how the question of juridical entity related to another Soviet agency, TASS, see W. E. Butler, "Immunity of Soviet Juridical Persons," *The Modern Law Review* 35.2 (March, 1972): 189–93.

34. Minutes of the First Meeting of the Organizing Committee for the 1980 Olympic Games, 7 March 1975, GARF, f. 9610, op. 1, d. 3, ll. 33, 36.

35. Report of Orgcom Olympiada-80 for the 77th IOC Session, Innsbruck, 3 February 1976, GARF, f. 9610, op. 1, d. 34, l. 19.

36. Record of Meeting of the Executive Bureau of the Orgcom, 19 February 1976, GARF, f. 9610, op. 1, d. 39, l. 2.

37. Ibid., 9.

38. Record of Meeting of Orgcom 1980, 7 March 1975, GARF f. 9610, op. 1, d. 3, l. 9.

39. Ibid.

40. Minutes of the First Meeting of the Organizing Committee for the 1980 Olympic Games, 7 March 1975, ibid., l. 43.

41. Record of the Presidium of the Organizing Committee, 9 June 1975, GARF, f. 9610, op. 1, d. 5, ll. 36–37.

42. Minutes of the First Meeting of the Organizing Committee for the 1980 Olympic Games, 7 March 1975, GARF, f. 9610, op. 1, d. 3, l. 49.

43. Ibid., l. 49–50.

44. About Luzhniki, "Let There Be a City of Sports!," Olympic Complex "Luzhniki," available at http://www.luzhniki.ru/eng/luzh.aspx?id=1.

45. Record of Meeting of the Orgcom Presidium, 30 June 1977, GARF, f. 9610, op. 1, d. 122, ll. 54–55.

46. V. F. Promyslov to I. T. Novikov, 28 February 1977, GARF, f. 9610, op. 1, d. 141, l. 89 and V. S. Rodichenko and A. I. Romashko to I. T. Novikov, 22 March 1977, ibid., ll. 92–93.

47. *Official Report*, vol. 2, p. 72.

48. Decree of the Presidium of the Orgcom Moscow, 1 April 1976, On the Results of Establishment of International Relations for 1975, GARF, f. 9610, op. 1, d. 36, l. 40.

49. Meeting with K. Willing from the Munich Organizing Committee, December 1975, GARF, f. 9610, op. 1, d. 11, l. 7.

50. Ibid., ll. 8, 20.

51. Ibid., ll. 4–5.

52. Order No. 13 of the Sports Committee and Moscow Organizing Committee, 28 November 1975, GARF, f. 9610, op. 1, d. 10, l. 43.

53. Ibid., 9.

54. Ibid., 20.

55. Instruction of Orgcom, 29 December 1975, GARF, f. 9610, op. 1, d. 11, l. 3.

56. Record of Meeting of the Orgcom Presidium Olympiada-80, 1 April 1976, GARF f. 9610, op. 1, d. 36, l. 25.

57. Report on Delegation of Technical Observers to the 1976 Montreal Games, GARF f. 9610, op. 1, d. 34, l. 73.

58. Ibid., ll. 76–77.

59. Minutes of meeting with I. T. Novikov, 13 January 1978, GARF, f. 9610, op. 1, d. 242, l. 112.

60. Record of Meeting of the Orgcom Executive Bureau, 17 June 1976, GARF. f. 9610, op. 1, d. 39, ll. 26–27.

61. Minutes of Meeting of the Orgcom, 4 August 1975, GARF, f. 9610, op. 1, d. 3, ll. 68–69.

62. E. Popov to Politburo of the Central Committee, 23 February 1976, GARF, f. 7576, op. 31, d. 2626, l. 64.

63. E. I. Popov to I. T. Novikov, Ibid., l. 63. It is interesting to note that Popov addressed Novikov as vice chairman of the Council of Ministers and president of the Olympic Committee of the USSR, suggesting that the person was more important than the title and that Soviet citizens were not necessarily familiar with all the different positions and overlapping responsibilities between the Sports Committee, the Olympic Committee, and the 1980 Organizing Committee.

64. A. I. Kolesov, Vice Chairman of the Sports Committee to the Central Committee Department of Chemistry, 27 April 1976 and S. P. Pavlov to Novikov, President of Orgcom 1980, 9 March 1976, GARF, f. 7576, op. 31, d. 2626, ll. 58–60.

65. Minutes of Meeting of the Orgcom, 4 August 1975, GARF, f. 9610, op. 1, d. 3, ll. 80–81.

66. Ibid., l. 107.

67. Ibid., l. 92.

68. Minutes of meeting with I. T. Novikov, 13 January 1978, GARF, f. 9610, op. 1, d. 242, l. ll. 19–20.

69. Lord Killanin to V. Smirnov, 26 November 1976, COJO 1980 Correspondence 1975–78, IOC Archives.

70. K. D. Lawrence to Lord Killanin, 20 May 1976, Ibid.

71. Minutes of meeting with I. T. Novikov, 13 January 1978, GARF, f. 9610, op. 1, d. 242, l. 112.

72. Ibid., l. 33.

73. Minutes of meeting with I. T. Novikov, 13 January 1978, ibid., l. 16.

74. Ibid., l. 18.

75. Ibid., l. 22.

76. Ibid., l. 23.

77. Ibid., ll. 41–42.

78. Ibid., ll. 25–26.

79. Ibid.

80. Ibid., l. 28.

81. Carol Marmor-Drews, "To Guarantee Security and Protect Social Order," in *Surveilling and Securing the Olympics: From Tokyo 1964 to London 2012 and Beyond,* Vida Bajc, ed. Transnational Crime, Crime Control and Security Series (Palgrave Macmillan, 2016), 180–200.

82. Record of meeting with Vice-President of the Orgcom, G. M. Rogul'skii, 6 April 1978, GARF, f. 9610, op. 1, d. 244, ll. 20–22. See also Carol Marmor-Drews, "To Guarantee Security and Protect Social Order," 192–93.

83. Carol Marmor-Drews, "To Guarantee Security and Protect Social Order," 186–87, 191–92.

84. Ibid., 193–94.

85. MVD Bulletin for June-August 1979, 5 October 1979, RGANI, f. 5, op. 76, d. 205, l. 60.

86. Killanin to Smirnov, 8 December 1975, Vitaly Smirnov Correspondence 1971–1984, IOC Archives.

87. Minutes of the First Meeting of the Organizing Committee for the 1980 Olympic Games, 7 March 1975, GARF, f. 9610, op. 1, d. 3, l. 31.

88. Copy of Report to Council of Ministers on course of preparation for 1980 OG Moscow, 27 January 1977, GARF, f. 9610, op. 1, d. 119, l. 7. Coca-Cola proposed to provide ten million drinks free of charge, but Pepsi Cola had concluded an agreement with the Ministry of Foreign Trade to sell Pepsi in the Soviet Union. As a result the Orgcom could not take the Coke deal, but they were able to negotiate a deal on the same terms with Pepsi.

89. Report for Meeting of Orgcom, On participation of the Orgcom Delegation in the 78th Session of the IOC and Familiarization with the Experience of Montreal, 17 September 1976, GARF, f. 9610, op. 1, d. 34, ll. 65–66.

90. Novikov to Council of Ministers, 5 August 1977, GARF, f. 9610, op. 1, d. 118, ll. 1, 5–6.

91. M. Berlioux to I. Novikov, 15 December 1975, COJO 1980 Correspondence 1975–78, IOC Archives.

92. Telegram, Lord Killanin to M. Berlioux, 11 November 1977, ibid.

93. V. Smirnov to M. Berlioux, 9 November 1977, ibid. It is interesting to note that the Russian original of this letter was addressed "Dear Monique," but the English translation reads "Dear Mme. Berlioux."

94. I. Novikov to Killanin, 4 December 1975, ibid.

95. Notes on Meeting between Novikov and Killanin, 5 January 1978, GARF, f. 9610, op. 1, d. 267, l. 7.

96. Ibid., l. 8.

97. Minutes of the 78th IOC Session, Montreal, September 1976, IOC Archives.

98. Copy of Report to Council of Ministers on Preparations for the 1980 OG Moscow, 27 January 1977, GARF, f. 9610, op. 1, d. 119, l. 8.

99. "Warming Up for the 1980 Olympics," *Time*, 6 August 1979, http://www.time.com/time/magazine/article/0,9171,948761–1,00.html.

100. Telegram, M. Berlioux to M. Petrova, 11 February 1977, COJO 1980 Correspondence 1975–78, IOC Archives.

101. Telegram, I. Novikov to Lord Killanin, 10 April 1978, ibid.

102. Telegram, Lord Killanin to I. Novikov, 31 March 1978, ibid.

103. M. Berlioux to I. Novikov, 13 November 1975, ibid.

104. Telegram, K. Andrianov to M. Berlioux, 12 August 1976, ibid.

105. Lord Killanin to I. Novikov, 23 August 1976, ibid.

106. Notes on Meeting between Novikov and Killanin, 5 January 1978, GARF, f. 9610, op. 1, d. 267, ll. 7–8.

107. V. Smirnov to M. Berlioux, 14 October 1977, ibid.

108. Report of Meeting of Orgcom Moscow, 4 January 1976, GARF, f. 9610, op. 1, d. 33, l. 6.

109. Copy of Report to Council of Ministers on Preparations for the 1980 OG Moscow, 27 January 1977, GARF, f. 9610, op. 1, d. 119, l. 6.

110. Decree of the Presidium of the Orgcom, 12 June 1975, GARF, f. 9610, op. 1, d. 4, l. 6.

111. To Central Committee CPSU from the Department of Propaganda, 26 February 1976, GARF, f. 7576, op. 31, d. 2626, ll. 7–8

112. Report of Meeting of Orgcom Moscow, 4 January 1976, GARF, f. 9610, op. 1, d. 33, l. 6.

113. Ibid., l. 11.

114. Decree of the Presidium of the Orgcom Moscow, 1 April 1976, On International Relations of the Orgcom for 1975, GARF, f. 9610, op. 1, d. 36, l. 42.

115. Record of Meeting of the Orgcom Presidium Olympiada-80, 1 April 1976, GARF f. 9610, op. 1, d. 35, l. 14.

116. Ibid., l. 10.

117. Record of Meeting of the Orgcom, 17 September 1976, GARF, f. 9610, op. 1, d. 33, ll. 38–43.

118. Ibid., l. 23.

119. Ibid.

120. Ibid., l. 36.

121. Ibid., l. 48.

122. Record of Meeting of the Orgcom Executive Bureau, 11 August 1976, GARF, f. 9610, op. 1, d. 39, l. 33.

123. Ibid., ll. 41, 43.

124. Record of Meeting of the Orgcom Presidium Olympiada-80, 1 April 1976, GARF f. 9610, op. 1, d. 36, l. 41.

125. Ibid., l. 42.

126. Report of Meeting of the Orgcom Executive Bureau, 4 October 1976, f. 9610, op. 1, d. 39, ll. 50–51.

127. Ibid., ll. 64–65.

128. Anonymous Letter to the Central Committee from the Cycling Team USSR, GARF, f. 7576, op. 31, d. 3283, l. 202.

129. Pavlov to Central Committee, ibid., l. 196.

130. I. K. Koziulia to I. T. Novikov, 1 February 1977, GARF, f. 9610, op. 1, d. 141, l. 81.

131. V. A. Polishchuk to I. T. Novikov, 21 February 1977, ibid., ll. 82–83.

132. I. T. Novikov to I. K. Koziulia, handwritten note, 7 March 1977, ibid., l. 80.

133. Minutes of meeting with I. T. Novikov, 13 January 1978, GARF, f. 9610, op. 1, d. 242, l. 114.

134. Ibid., l. 38.

135. Ibid., l. 39.

136. Minutes of the First Meeting of the Organizing Committee for the 1980 Olympic Games, 7 March 1975, GARF, f. 9610, op. 1, d. 3, l. 29.

137. Telegram, V. Smirnov to M. Berlioux, 5 January 1976, COJO 1980 Correspondence 1975–78, IOC Archives.

138. Record of Meeting of the Orgcom Executive Bureau, 1 September 1976, GARF, f. 9610, op. 1, d. 39, l. 48.

139. Record of Meeting between the Orgcom President and Vice-Presidents, 20 November 1978, GARF, f. 9610, op. 1, d. 242, l. 108.

140. *Official Report*, vol. 2, p. 129.

141. Plan of Orgcom for Informational-Propaganda Measures Related to Olympiada-80, GARF, f. 9610, op. 1, d. 10, ll. 46–48.

142. Record of Meeting of the Orgcom Executive Bureau, 28 March 1977, GARF, f. 9610, op. 1, d. 127, ll. 40–41.

143. V. Bykov, Kh. Dzhatiev, and B. Shliapnikov to I. Novikov, 2 October 1978, GARF, f. 9610, op. 1, d. 256, l. 22.

144. Report of Commission for External Relations of Orgcom for 1979, 4 January 1980, GARF, f. 9610, op. 1, d. 439, l. 18.

145. V. Shandrin to the Orgcom Executive Bureau, 27 February 1978, GARF, f. 9610, op. 1, d. 251, ll. 4–9.

146. Minutes of the First Meeting of the Organizing Committee for the 1980 Olympic Games, 7 March 1975, GARF, f. 9610, op. 1, d. 3l, l. 47.

147. Kalashnikov and Korobov to I. Novikov, February 1978, GARF, f. 9610, op. 1, d. 250, l. 116.

148. I. Novikov to V. Novozhilov, 9 February 1978, ibid.

149. V. I. Lakhov to I. T. Novikov, 31 May 1977, ibid., l. 130.

150. I. T. Novikov to Administrator of Affairs of the Central Committee CPSU, G. S. Pavlov, 5 May 1978, GARF, f. 9610, op. 1, d. 216, l. 23.

151. V. G. Shevchenko to I. T. Novikov, 30 March 1978 and.I. T. Novikov to V. F. Promyslov, April 1978, GARF, f. 9610, op. 1, d. 252, ll. 19–20.

152. To Novikov from Minaeva, June 1981, GARF, f. 9610, op. 1, d. 679, l. 51.

153. Ward, *Brezhnev's* Folly, 155.

154. Ward, *Brezhnev's Folly*, 153.

155. Ward, *Brezhnev's Folly*, 149–50.

156. Bruce Lincoln, *In the Vanguard of Reform: Russia's Enlightened Bureaucrats, 1825–1851* (DeKalb, Northern Illinois University Press, 1982).

Chapter Five

A Job Well Done?

Welcoming the World to the 1980 Moscow Olympiad

On 3 August 1980, Moscow officially closed the Games of the XXII Olympiad. For a fortnight, Moscow had played host to over eight thousand athletes, officials, and trainers; over three thousand IOC, NOC, and IF representatives and their guests; nearly five thousand foreign and Soviet journalists; and over two million tourists. As Misha the bear mourned the end of the festival, the Moscow organizers symbolically passed the torch to Los Angeles, who had secured the bid for 1984. At the same time Lord Killanin, who had worked so closely with Soviet sports officials to secure the Games and ensure their success, retired as IOC President in favor of the newly elected Juan Antonio Samaranch. Despite the festive atmosphere of the closing ceremonies, the Games also struck a somber note as the 100,000 spectators in Lenin Stadium bid their final farewell to Misha as he floated out of the arena. In his official announcement closing the Games, Lord Killanin expressed hope that, despite the gloomy international context in which these Games had been held, the Olympics could continue to be a force for good. Praising "the sportsmen gathered here for the Games of the XXII Olympiad, [who] have shown their great friendship despite their varying colours, religious or political philosophies in fair competition," Killanin "implore[d] the sportsmen of the world to unite in peace before a holocaust descends."[1]

While the Orgcom's management of Olympic preparations serve as an example of what could be accomplished under "developed socialism," the inability of the Olympic Games in Moscow to overcome increasing international tensions and domestic social fissures shows the limits of "political modernization" in the Soviet bureaucracy. The same trend toward political stability that provided space for state bureaus to act without fear of repression also paved the way for political stagnation and ossification in the top party leadership. Brezhnev's success at building his own tight-knit group of trusted advisors meant that, especially from the mid-1970s on, decision-making again became the purview of a small group of leaders, isolated from the rest of the Soviet administrative system and society as a whole and unable or unwilling to address the more pressing problems facing the Soviet Union.[2] Furthermore, under Brezhnev's leadership, the emphasis on an expert-based, rational, and scientific form of "developed socialism," downplayed the human factor, adding to apathy among ordinary Soviet citizens.[3] Brezhnev's declining health and tendency to delegate responsibilities to his subordinates also hampered the Organizing Committee. The reliance on the expertise of a small group of party and state leaders, moreover, gave free reign to military, defense, and police organs to push Soviet power abroad and control dissent and instability at home. Increased defense spending not only drew resources away from other segments of the Soviet economy, including the Olympic Games preparations, but it raised doubts about the Soviet Union's peaceful intentions.[4] Furthermore, a stronger leader could have averted the decision to invade Afghanistan, which was pushed by Soviet Minister of Defense Dmitrii Ustinov and KGB chief Iurii Andropov.[5]

The developing gerontocracy lacked the energy and vision necessary to address the internal and external tensions that became much more apparent by the eve of the 1980 Games. While "stagnation" is a retrospective label for the period, it does capture the increasing malaise and alienation of the time. Christine Evans contends that "stagnation" also helps to integrate the Soviet Union into global developments of the 1970s "which were likewise marked by political repression and disaffection, economic crisis and malaise, and, correspondingly, the flourishing of (ostensibly) private identities and forms of expression."[6] These developments reflected in the international sports arena, and the Olympic Games became less able to avoid political entanglements. Moscow won the right to host the Olympic Games at a high point in East-West détente, but as the 1980 Games drew near, the international political atmosphere worsened, and Moscow risked becoming the third host city to fall victim to "the boycott era." Acts of protest, boycott, and even terrorism were seen by many as effective and appropriate ways to express anger at political conditions and to effect change, and individuals and groups found the Olympic Games and its worldwide television coverage a useful forum for spreading their message to a global audience.[7] The terrorist attack on eleven Israeli athletes by the Palestinian group Black September marred the Munich 1972 Olympics and alerted Olympic organizers that the Games had become a serious security risk.[8] Several African nations boycotted the Montreal 1976 Olympics to protest the system of Apartheid in South Africa, creating anxiety in the Moscow Organizing Committee (Orgcom) that such a boycott could happen to them too, and even before Moscow was officially elected, various groups had already begun discussing the possibility of boycotting a Moscow Olympiad.

The Organizing Committee showed that it could mobilize personnel and complete the construction and logistical aspects of the Games, but it also needed to ensure maximum participation in order to make the Games a propaganda success. In the lead-up to the Moscow Olympiad, the international and propaganda departments of the Organizing Committee sent legions of representatives abroad to promote the Games, and to secure guarantees from National Olympic Committees (NOCs) that they would send their athletes to Moscow. The Orgcom also worked closely with the IOC to manage the press surrounding the event, and assured International Federations that the sports venues and competitions would meet their standard. Sports diplomacy also played a crucial role in ensuring maximum participation in the 1980 Olympiad, and Soviet administrators increased their level of sports aid and exchange with the developing world to get more countries to compete. The possibility of a boycott united the USSR and IOC against what both saw as the inappropriate intrusion of politics, strengthening the Soviet representatives' position in the IOC for some time to come. However, despite their best efforts, the Moscow organizers could neither foresee nor prevent all eventualities. Ultimately they were overwhelmed by the spirit of the times, both at home and abroad.

Outside the control of the Orgcom, the invasion of Afghanistan undermined support in the West for détente and inspired fifty nations to boycott the 1980 Olympic Games. The invasion also undermined the image of Soviet socialist development as a society "that valued expression, cultivated excellence, and tolerated diversity," that sport bureaucrats had been promoting for decades. Since the picture could not obscure the reality of Soviet repression indefinitely, according to Nicholas Cull, Soviet cultural diplomacy failed in the long term to convince the world of Soviet peaceful intentions.[9] Domestically the war in Afghanistan strained the slowing economy and contributed to "disillusionment with the Soviet system."[10] The Olympic project reveals key paradoxes of Soviet society in the Brezhnev era. The party-state apparatus produced both the dynamism necessary to make the Games happen as well as the immobility that resisted real reform. The superbly organized Olympic festival, meant to demonstrate the achievements of "really existing socialism" could not mask completely the deep problems of everyday realities in the Soviet Union.[11] Likewise Olympism, meant to unite the world in peace and friendship, could no longer overcome Cold War tensions.

"ACTIVE, AGGRESSIVE, AND COORDINATED": BUSINESS AS USUAL IN THE SPORTS COMMITTEE

In some respects, it was business as usual for the Sports Committee after Moscow had secured the 1980 Games. At their June 1975 meeting, the Sports

Committee Collegium discussed the need to strengthen the position of Soviet and socialist sports organizations, as well as the need for Soviet representatives to be active proponents of Soviet policies in international sports organizations. Noting that all their recent efforts in international sport had brought results, from reviving the Olympic Congress to gaining the selection of Moscow to host the 1980 Games, Sports Committee chairman Pavlov remarked that these initiatives required "the most active, aggressive, and coordinated" efforts. Yet, he complained, "we have spread our representatives everywhere, they sit there for decades, and what do they do? On the whole they keep quiet." Pavlov argued that they needed to "clean up the act" not only of the Committee but of all Soviet sports organizations.[12] Furthermore, Soviet representatives had failed to secure IOC recognition for North Korea and the Mongolian People's Republic. UMSS head D.I. Prokhorov asserted the need to continue the struggle against "reactionary tendencies" in the IOC and gain more leadership positions in International Federations.[13] All of these recommendations were in keeping with the main trajectories of Soviet involvement in international sports organizations since the late 1940s.

Soviet IOC members continued to push for "democratization" of the Olympic Movement. At the 1977 IOC session in Prague, Andrianov and Smirnov called for IOC members to strengthen IOC connections with state sports organizations and establish close relations with UNESCO. Soviet representatives also recommended refusing entry into the Games to athletes participating in competitions in South Africa, and renewed their call for electing members of the IOC for each recognized NOC.[14] Predictably, the reaction to these proposals was split. Some members from Yugoslavia, Poland, and France supported the Soviet position, but members from England, India, Pakistan, Egypt, Norway, Sweden, and Kenya argued that the IOC needed to maintain its independence from governments and retain its practice of coopting members into the organization. Killanin attempted to bridge the two sides by highlighting the need for more cooperation with NOCs, but insisted that the IOC would proceed on an "evolutionary" rather than a "revolutionary" path.[15] Killanin cautioned that progressing "too rapidly" could "bring about the end of the Olympic Movement and the Olympic Games."[16] Smirnov and Andrianov concluded that many IOC members still regarded the organization as a "private club" and recommended that Soviet representatives continue efforts to democratize the organization.[17]

The selection of Moscow did galvanize the activities of the Sports Committee as its leaders reasserted control over athlete training. In order for the Moscow Games to be an unmitigated propaganda success, Soviet athletes had to dominate the competition. As the Orgcom began planning to host the Games in 1980, the Sports Committee stepped up its efforts to win the Olympic Games in 1976. As part of this, the Sports Committee requested additional funding for scientific research into training methods.[18] To inspire Olympic hopefuls to intensify their training, the Sports Committee organized a rally of all the potential members of the Olympic national team.[19] The Sports Committee also turned its attention to the construction of training bases for the national team for both the 1976 and 1980 Games.[20] Noting that U.S. President Carter recently authorized state funding of Olympic training, and that West Germany and the GDR had likewise strengthened their training systems, Pavlov asked Politburo member and secretary of the Moscow City Committee of the Communist Party V. Grishin to beef up "control" over Olympic preparations. Urging Grishin to make sure that the necessary repairs and renovations of Moscow sports bases were undertaken, Pavlov expressed his trust that the sports organizations of "the capital of our motherland, the hero-city of Moscow, would fulfill the tasks of preparing for the Olympic Games of 1980 . . . and win a minimum of fifteen gold medals and 182 points in the XXII Olympic Games in Moscow and three gold medals and fifty-two points at the XIII Winter Games in the United States.[21] These preparations proved successful, as Soviet athletes won ten gold medals in Lake Placid and eighty in Moscow.

"IN THE NAME OF PEACE, FOR THE GLORY OF SPORTS": PROMOTING THE GAMES

While the Sports Committee focused on preparing athletes and democratizing international sports, the Moscow Organizing Committee coordinated a worldwide campaign to promote the 1980 Summer Games. In August 1975, the Orgcom outlined a series of propaganda measures that were intended not only to publicize the ongoing preparations for the Games, but also sought to disseminate the principles and ideals of the Olympic Movement while promoting the success of the Soviet sports system as a whole, showcasing the large scale of public participation and the role of sport in a socialist society. Working with the Ministry of Culture, the State Committee for Television and Radio (Gosteleradio), the State Committee for Cinematography (Goskino), the Union of Artists, the Union of Composers, and the Union of Cinematographers, the Orgcom coordinated a number of exhibitions and contests designed to generate support among ordinary citizens at home and abroad. These events included international contests of children's drawings and posters, a radio festival of songs, a festival of amateur sports films, a competition for the official melody of the Games, and all-union exhibitions of Olympic-themed photographs and stamps, coins, medals, and souvenirs.[22] The Orgcom also sponsored a competition for designing the official emblem of the Moscow Olympiad, allocating over two thousand rubles as a prize for the contest winners (see Figure 5.1).[23] It called for tourist excursions to be promoted with the theme "Moscow Prepares for the Olympiad" and for the creation of an exhibition complex dedicated to the Olympic Games, instructing relevant departments to draw up the plans and itineraries.[24] The Orgcom also commissioned a series of documentary films to be made that emphasized the help and cooperation Soviet sports specialists were lending to Asian, African, and Latin American countries.[25] Throughout these various events and exhibitions, the Orgcom combined Marxist-Leninist ideals about the role of sport and physical culture, which "serves to encourage the health of the individual, his upbringing, and total development," with Olympic ideals of how sport and cultural contact "serves the cause of peace."[26]

The Games themselves would provide further opportunities to propagandize the Soviet project and its role in promoting the International Olympic Movement. The Propaganda Department, headed by V. G. Shevchenko and V. F. Kukharskii's Commission for Cultural Program and Cultural Services, would design and implement a number of "cultural measures" to take place during the Games, highlighting "the achievements of the Soviet multinational culture, the enormous artistic contributions of the [Soviet] peoples in the past and during the Soviet period" and to "depict the harmonious development of man in the conditions of triumphant socialism." To do this, the cultural commission would enlist the services of top-notch artists and tap the resources of "one of the largest centers of world culture": Moscow.[27] Similarly, the international and propaganda departments were charged, along with the Komsomol, to put together a "cultural-political" program for serving young Soviet and foreign tourists as well as participants in the international Olympic Youth Camp that would be held before the Games.[28] The 1979 Spartakiad, to which they would invite two thousand foreign athletes and many foreign journalists, would serve as a trial run of their cultural program and as a vital source of foreign currency.[29]

The opening and closing ceremonies represented the most significant propaganda opportunities offered by hosting the Olympics. I. M. Tumanov served as the lead director of these ceremonies, and V. N. Petrov was responsible for the sport exhibition segments. Their work had to meet the expectations of both the IOC and the Soviet leadership. To satisfy the IOC, the ceremonies must adhere to IOC rules, traditions, and protocol governing these events, and the final script would have to be approved in advance by the IOC director, its chief of protocol, and the IOC Executive Board.[30] To please Soviet leaders, the ceremonies also had to reflect the peace-loving politics of the party and government, the struggle of the Soviet people for peace and friendship, the multi-national character of the state, and the development of mass sports in the country. Numerous details had to be accounted for in

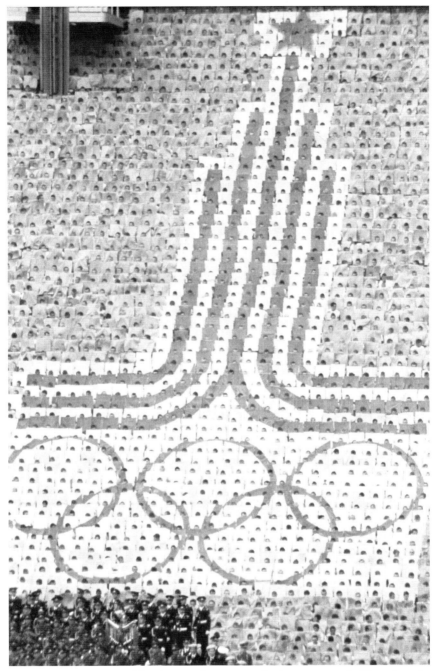

Figure 5.1.   Here created for the Opening Ceremonies by spectators holding placards, the Moscow 1980 logo blended Olympic and Soviet symbolism. Courtesy International Olympic Committee.

staging these ceremonies, from the number of athletes and dancers that could fit in the stadium, to whether the facility could accommodate a large net full of hot air balloons. Smirnov, I. F. Denisov, Rogul'skii, Koval', Shevchenko, Prokopov, Rodichenko, A. A. Gres'ko, and Andrianov were all authorized to oversee the planning of the events and address any problems as they arose.[31]

The opening and closing ceremonies' intricate planning and complicated logistics required coordination between many groups of people, and before drafting the proposal, the Orgcom leadership elicited input from other department and section heads. Their comments reveal a wide range of concerns and opinions among the stakeholders. While praising the overall concept of the script, Pavlov criticized the ceremony directors for not taking into account the "traditions of the Olympic Games." He suggested that the ceremonies would be too long and showy, with "unjustified elements of pomposity and adornment," asserting the directors needed to show more "rationality and economy" and produce a "more realistic, well-thought-out, and detailed script."[32] In contrast, the vice minister of culture and head of the cultural program commission of the Orgcom, V. Kukharskii, complained that the proposed opening ceremony did not incorporate enough original music by Soviet composers, including the established musical theme of the Olympiad-80, Shostakovich's "Festive Overture," and the pieces composed as part of a Soviet-wide contest organized by the Ministry of Culture and the Orgcom. He also insisted that all music for the ceremonies had to be approved by his ministry and the Composers Union. Kukharskii likewise questioned the feasibility of housing and transporting the number of regional dance and musical groups proposed by the directors on top of those already being brought to Moscow for other cultural events during the Games.[33] Here one can see the fine balance that had to be maintained between the interests of multiple groups: the need to please the IOC and other members of the international sports community, fulfill the propaganda goals of the regime, and appease the departments, ministries, and organizations whose work might be affected.

The Olympic Torch Relay constituted another key cultural component of the Games. The propaganda and international departments were responsible for the relay's overall organization, including proposing the route and procuring agreements from not only the IOC, but also the NOC of each country the torch would pass through.[34] Other departments, meanwhile, were charged with drawing up detailed plans, "guaranteeing the preparation and staging of the relay on a high ideological-political and organizational level." Propaganda head Shevchenko would prepare and submit the final plan for approval but, as with all activities of the Orgcom, he was instructed to first elicit input from the Sports Committee and various Orgcom commissions.[35]

While these internal preparations and discussions proceeded, other members of the Orgcom coordinated propaganda measures among socialist countries. In 1975 the vice-president of the Orgcom, Koval', and the head of the Orgcom International Department, Prokopov, set up a Joint Commission of Sports Organizations of Socialist Countries on Cooperation in Preparing and Staging the Games.[36] Meetings of the joint commission had both practical goals—coordinating the efforts of socialist representatives in international sports organizations—and the symbolic goal of creating a sense of socialist solidarity. The commission relied on ties that each country's representatives had with sports figures around the world—for example, Smirnov asked socialist sports leaders to mobilize their contacts among NOCs of Africa and Asia to help convince them to participate in the Games.[37] Similarly, Smirnov appealed to his socialist "colleagues and comrades" to use their influence on sports organizers in France to convince them to observe the isolation of apartheid sport and abandon plans to hold a rugby match with South African players.[38] East European countries worked together to propagandize the Games, publishing newspaper articles, informational pamphlets, radio broadcasts, and exhibitions on sport in the USSR and Olympic themes for distribution among their publics.[39]

Orgcom representatives also collaborated heavily with the IOC leadership to promote the upcoming Games abroad, and both Soviet and IOC international publications highlighted the Orgcom's progress in preparing for the Games. Sports Committee veterans Koval' and Smirnov supervised the creation of Soviet publications *Bulletin Olympiada-80* and *Olympic Panorama-80,* which incorporated the fundamental principles and ideals of the Olympic Movement, including "the development of international relations, improving mutual understanding, and furthering peace and friendship and cooperation between peoples."[40] The official Olympic publications produced by the IOC secretariat in Lausanne, *Olympic Review* and the monthly press analysis compiled by IOC director Monique Berlioux, provided another important means for disseminating information about the Orgcom and Games preparations to the Olympic community. Berlioux approached the Orgcom for material and information to be included in *Olympic Review* as well as articles for the monthly press roundup.[41] Orgcom secretary, A. A. Gresko and Orgcom translator Marina Petrova responded by providing a regular supply of content each month.[42] Expressing her appreciation for the "useful cooperation" of the Orgcom, Berlioux commissioned an article on the 1979 Spartakiad for the *Olympic Review* as well as a report on Killanin's trip to Moscow, providing the president's assessment of the preparations to date.[43]

Not all of the Orgcom's propaganda plans met with IOC approval. In May 1979, Berlioux chastised the Orgcom for not requesting IOC consent before translating the Olympic Charter into Russian, demanding that it limit distribution of the Russian version to the Orgcom staff and USSR NOC and not to the general public.[44] Prokopov dutifully requested permission to translate Pierre de Coubertin's "Ode to Sport" into Russian for domestic propaganda of the Olympics.[45] The Orgcom ran into further trouble when it proposed to adopt an official motto for the Games in Moscow, "From Friendship in Sport—To Peace on Earth," to highlight the "international social-political and cultural" contributions of the Soviet Union as well as its "peace-loving foreign policy."[46] The IOC rejected the proposed motto for the 1980 Games, deciding that only Coubertin's maxim that had been displayed in London or "*Citius, Altius, Fortius,*" the motto of the IOC, could be used.[47] The Orgcom proposed another motto: "In the Name of Peace, for the Glory of Sports." This motto had been approved by the Executive Board, but other members of the IOC objected to it, arguing that there was no precedent for it and that the IOC already had a motto.[48] These objections reflect the IOC's continuing sensitivity that host countries might attempt to coopt the Games for their own political purposes.

"FRUITFUL COLLABORATION" WITH THE IOC

Immediately upon Novikov's appointment as president of the Moscow Organizing Committee, the IOC sent a note of congratulations, expressing its "great joy" in working with his colleagues for the "success of this international festival of sport" and their "sincere wishes for fruitful collaboration."[49] Despite the differences of opinion and tense relationship at times, the collaboration between the IOC secretariat and the Moscow Orgcom did prove fruitful on many levels. The two organizations found much common ground not only in staging a well-ordered and spectacular festival, but also in safe-guarding the international reputation of the IOC and the Orgcom in the build-up to these highly controversial Games.

As preparations for the Games continued, the IOC and the Orgcom increasingly worked together to protect the licensing agreement and control the use of Olympic symbols. As director of the IOC, Berlioux handled all such licensing matters, including all the symbols and logos connected with the 1980 Games. As vice-president of the Orgcom responsible for propaganda, V. Koval' cooperated with Berlioux to ensure compliance with the Olympic Charter and licensing agreements on all materials produced in the USSR. Both worked with other National Olympic Committees who received permission from the IOC and the Orgcom for use of those symbols in their domestic markets.

The Orgcom assisted the IOC in protecting the use of Olympic symbols. In January 1976, Novikov insisted that all ministries and agencies of the USSR and union republics, councils of ministers of union and autonomous republics, regional and district executive committees, and the executive committees of Moscow and Leningrad had to comply with IOC rules regarding the use of Olympic symbols, stating that the appearance of unauthorized items with Olympic emblems could "seriously complicate the fulfillment of tasks entrusted to the Orgcom."[50] Both the Olympic Charter and a decision of the Central Committee and Council of Ministers gave the Orgcom the exclusive rights to use the Moscow Games emblem or other Olympic symbols for propaganda or advertising.[51] It was in the common interest of the IOC and the Soviet leadership that the Orgcom remain the sole entity with the right to use the Olympic symbols, in order to safeguard the reputation and financial interests of both. Selling licensing rights and official souvenirs was a significant source of revenue for the IOC and the host city. For this reason, Berlioux requested all designs, a list of articles they intended to put the designs on, information on whether those items would be sold in the USSR or worldwide, and to what use the Orgcom would put the proceeds of those sales.[52] There was considerable money to be made by exploiting the Olympic Games' brand, and Berlioux wanted to ensure that no one cashed in at the IOC's expense. In addition to the revenue to be gained, Soviet organizers wanted wide sales of souvenirs and other products with the official symbols of the Games "to contribute to the wide propaganda of the Games."[53]

As preparations continued for the Moscow Games, the Organizing Committee leaders developed a cordial personal relationship with the IOC director and president. This manifested itself in the many trips back and forth between Lausanne and Moscow, exchange of gifts, as well as the warmth of personal correspondence between IOC staff and Orgcom officials (see Figure 5.2). Berlioux and Killanin both travelled to Moscow several times between 1976 and 1980, and exchanges of gifts and souvenirs during and after these visits further strengthened the friendly relations between the Orgcom and the IOC secretariat. In January 1978, Berlioux wrote to Novikov that she was "very touched by the magnificent necklace and bracelet set" he gave her which she vowed to "treasure greatly."[54] Referring to the same trip, Killanin asked Smirnov what he owed for "the beautiful fur hat."[55] In his thank you note to Novikov, Killanin expressed his appreciation for the "amber necklace and bracelet for my wife" as well as "the vodka and caviar, which has already been sampled by us."[56] After a fall 1978 stay in Moscow, Berlioux expressed to Smirnov her "deep appreciation for their art of receiving guests."[57] Smirnov and Berlioux seemed to grow especially close. The two exchanged birthday greetings.[58] In expressing her sympathies to Smirnov upon hearing of him being ill, Berlioux joked "now you will have to start a diet!"[59]

Figure 5.2. Delegations of the Moscow Organizing Olympic Committee were a frequent feature at the IOC headquarters in Lausanne, Switzerland leading up to 1980, as the "colossal" task of hosting the games required close communication between the organizers and the IOC. Courtesy International Olympic Committee.

Despite the cordial relationship they cultivated with the IOC president and director, Orgcom leaders still found themselves defending their actions against criticism in the press and from the IOC itself at times. When Killanin requested help to "put an end to any propaganda against Moscow," Novikov confirmed that the Orgcom would invite all NOCs recognized by the IOC to the Games, and stage the Games in compliance with the rules and regulations of the IOC.[60] When the February 1976 edition of *Olympiad-80* stated that the working languages of the Games would be Russian and English, Berlioux cited Olympic Rules number 19 and 55, which state that the official languages of the Olympics were French and English, in that order.[61] In February 1977, the long-standing Soviet practice of tabulating medal counts by country, for internal publicizing of Soviet Olympic achievements, also came under scrutiny by the IOC when editions of *Olympiad-80* and *Olympic Panorama* included a medal tallies by country.[62] Killanin remarked that this was inappropriate in an official publication and asked Smirnov to "arrange for this to be discontinued, as it is a contravention of IOC rules and principles."[63] Smirnov responded in a brief telegram that "in the future we shall take steps so that all articles in the organizing committee's official publications correspond to the Olympic Rules."[64]

THE ORGCOM AND THE WESTERN PRESS

Soviet sports administrators often expressed frustration and dismay over a variety of activities of the Western press. Concerned over how Soviet press reports were used in the West, Pavlov remarked that the Soviet press too often let secrets slip out, insisting that it would be better to publish only articles about the achievements of Soviet athletes.[65] Whereas Soviet administrators used the sports press during the 1950s and 60s as a vehicle for publicizing the work of Soviet representatives in international sports bodies, Pavlov advocated for a more conservative approach to press releases about the Olympics.

The Orgcom delegation waged an ongoing battle against awarding Olympic press accreditation to Radio Free Europe and Radio Liberty, U.S.-funded radio stations that broadcast news into eastern bloc countries. Smirnov protested the "reactionary, subversive, and antagonistic activities" toward socialist countries by the radio stations at the Innsbruck Games in 1976, convincing the IOC to revoke the stations' accreditation.[66] This action by the IOC incited U.S. Secretary of State Henry Kissinger to send a memo to instruct the IOC representative from the United States, Roosevelt, to take action against the decision. Killanin instead informed the Soviet representative.[67] In this case, Smirnov convinced his colleagues in the IOC that Radio Free Europe and Radio Liberty represented purely political organizations and that the reaction from the United States constituted an attempt to bring politics into IOC business. In fact, the radio stations did form a part of U.S. cultural strategy in Cold War sports.[68] The Soviet delegation continued their "bitter struggle" to invalidate the accreditation of "that slanderous radio station."[69] Their efforts failed, but Soviet and East European representatives secured conditions for the accreditation, including a ban on broadcasting anything of a political nature or interviewing athletes from socialist countries. The Soviet delegation also convinced the IOC to change Rule 49 governing press accreditation to read that any international radio or television broadcast must be agreed upon by the two countries concerned.[70]

To avoid potential embarrassment, Killanin worked with the Orgcom to achieve a mutually agreeable solution to the accreditation issue. When Novikov, Andrianov, and Smirnov met with Killanin privately during the IOC session in Prague in July 1977, Novikov intimated that "there can be no discussion" of accrediting journalists from those stations in Moscow. Killanin, however, worried that President Carter might use their refusal as a pretext to keep American athletes from competing in Moscow.[71] After the session, Smirnov and Andrianov suggested that the Orgcom push for further changes to Rule 49 that would allow the Moscow organizers to deny accreditation to those radio stations.[72] Eventually, Killanin secured promises from the two radio stations that none of their journalists would pursue accreditation at the Moscow Games and relayed to Soviet authorities that "the problem virtually no longer exists."[73] Nevertheless, Killanin asked Willi Daume to be the point person on the issue, which he discussed with Novikov in Athens. Killanin asked both men to keep him informed of developments.[74]

INTERNATIONAL RELATIONS OF THE ORGCOM

The Moscow Organizing Committee's international relations advanced Soviet foreign policy interests. In their decree on international relations for 1975, the Orgcom linked hosting the 1980 Olympic Games with the "program of peace" announced at the 24th Congress of the Communist Party in 1971, as well as the "historic decision" taken at the Conference on Security and Cooperation in Europe held in Helsinki in the summer of 1975.[75] Connecting the 1980 Games with the Helsinki agreement was more than propaganda. The agreement reached at Helsinki did mention expansion of sports ties through encouraging "sports meetings and competitions of all sorts on the basis of the established rules, regulations, and practice."[76] The participating states agreed to expand ties and contacts in a number of other areas that would be facilitated by the Moscow Games as well as the activities of the Moscow Orgcom, including tourism, international conferences and meetings of international organizations, cultural exchange, information exchange, and education.[77] However, the Orgcom Presidium also used its activities to propagandize abroad "the Soviet way of life, the peace-loving foreign policy of the Soviet government, and the achievements of the Soviet people in building a communist society."[78] Détente was understood by the Orgcom as a means to promote the image of the Soviet Union abroad through peaceful, friendly interactions internationally.

The Orgcom's International Department and External Relations Commission worked together to manage world opinion of the Games and ensure maximum participation in Moscow. Headed by V. I. Prokopov, the Orgcom's International Department played a crucial role in managing key relationships within the international sports community. A former international relations specialist for the Soviet Committee for Youth Organizations, Prokopov brought expertise and experience to the Orgcom.[79] Staffed with a number of Sports Committee workers, including the head of UMSS, Prokhorov, the department drew up the international relations plan and signed sports exchange agreements and communiqués of partnership with sports administrators from other countries. The Commission for External Relations of the Orgcom dealt with coordinating their efforts with socialist countries, working with Olympic attachés, and negotiating with foreign companies. The external relations commission cooperated with Soviet embassies abroad to enlist the help of government representatives, IOC members, IF leaders, and NOC members to propagandize the 1980 Games.[80] Representatives of the external relations commission also organized teams to observe the Olympic preparations in Montreal, an international sailing regatta, the Pan American Games in Mexico, and various exhibitions and international symposia in the United States and West Germany to study the staging of such events.[81] Finally, the external relations commission worked with other commissions of the Orgcom to arrange visits by foreign IOC members, IF representatives, and agents of foreign firms.[82]

In the lead-up to 1980, the Organizing Committee worked to prevent possible boycotts of the Games on several different fronts. International tensions surrounding South Africa, Israel, and the People's Republic of China all threatened to mar the festival, and Soviet sports leaders spent three years attempting to defuse these sometimes overlapping issues.

The growing anti-Apartheid movement put Soviet organizers in an awkward position. Soviet and other socialist representatives to the IOC and IFs had long been vocal in persuading those organizations to expel South Africa and Southern Rhodesia from their ranks. The IOC banned South Africa from competing in the Olympic Games in 1970, formally revoking recognition of the South African NOC at their Amsterdam Session.[83] Many countries, however, maintained ties and competitions with South African teams in various sports. In protest over New Zealand's competitions with South African athletes, many African countries withdrew from the 1976 Montreal Olympics. Fearing that African countries might likewise boycott the Moscow Games, the Moscow Orgcom and Soviet representatives to international sports organizations fought to prevent individual countries from continuing sports ties with the racist regimes. The Sports Committee and Orgcom worked to strengthen sports ties with African countries as Soviet representatives continue to push for the full exclusion of South Africa and Rhodesia from IF-governed competitions.[84] At the same time, they used their contacts in the West to try to persuade their national sports federations not to pursue bilateral sports ties with the two countries. Soviet sports administrators hoped that this would bring as many third-world countries into the Olympic Movement as possible, to both further democratize the IOC and to ensure wide participation in the 1980 Games.

To appeal to sports leaders from developing nations, Orgcom representatives linked participation in the Moscow Games with anti-colonial and anti-Apartheid movements in the third world. For example, Smirnov told the head of the Yemen Ministry of Public, Work, and Youth Affairs that expanding participation of African, Asian, and Latin American countries in the Olympics was crucial to the struggle against Apartheid and racial discrimination, and promised that Soviet sports organizations would help the Yemen Arab Republic to become a part of the Olympic Movement and prepare athletes for the Moscow Games. The Yemeni representative promised to participate in the 1980 Games as a way to "decisively battle against the remnants of colonialism and racism in all its manifestations."[85] Similarly, the minister of culture of the Republic of Congo (Brazzaville), in his meeting with Orgcom representatives, intimated that Africans were "particularly sensitive to racial discrimination and would respond badly to the slightest manifestation of injustice." He expressed the hope that Moscow would be the most representative Olympic Games in history and promised that Congo (Brazzaville) would not participate in a boycott.[86]

Soviet representatives also courted developing nations to the Games with promises of material aid and assistance. Koval' promised Soviet help, in the form of expanded sports ties and assistance preparing athletes for the Games, to the representatives from Kuwait and Iraq, formalizing the terms of Soviet sports aid under the rubric of "sports cooperation."[87] Hundreds of coaches were working in over thirty developing countries by 1980.[88] All of these efforts required close cooperation between the Orgcom representatives and the Sports Committee. Orgcom representatives traveled to other countries and to large events such as the Asian or Central American Games, inviting representatives for negotiations in Moscow in order to fulfill their promises of Soviet aid and cooperation in developing their sports programs, while the Sports Committee had the necessary experts and budgetary resources for that purpose. As the head of UMSS in the Sports Committee, Prokhorov was in charge of arranging delegations of specialists to travel to developing countries.[89] The Orgcom also prevailed upon the Ministry of Defense and Profsoiuz sports sections to help expand sports ties with the developing world.[90] Along with Prokhorov, the head of the Dinamo sports society, the Ministry of Defense sports section, and the International Department of the Orgcom all used their resources to help supply third-world countries with sports equipment and inventory.[91]

Soviet sports administrators sometimes found it necessary to compromise between supporting the anti-Apartheid movement and the interests of the IOC and IFs, as African leaders pursued their own agendas by accepting Soviet support.[92] In 1978, the UN General Assembly considered an International Convention against Apartheid in Sport, making matters considerably more complicated for the Orgcom and the IOC, which viewed this action as an unwelcome intrusion of political interests, undermining their authority over governing international sports. At a meeting of socialist sports leaders, Smirnov expressed concern that such a resolution, and especially the proposed inclusion of sanctions, could cause a "schism in the Olympic Movement," because a number of capitalist countries maintained sports exchanges with South African and Rhodesian athletes.[93] To counter the proposed resolution, socialist representatives worked to prevent the resolution from passing while continuing other efforts to exclude South Africa from international competitive sport. Socialist representatives sought a meeting between the Tripartite Commission of the IOC and UN working group on Apartheid in sport.[94] Smirnov argued that such a meeting laid the basis for cooperation between the UN and the IOC in isolating South Africa from international sport and Olympic Movement "without allowing an international convention with sanctions to be taken."[95]

Soviet representatives also sought to convince African leaders to abandon the statute on sanctions and promise their participation in the Moscow Games. Leading the campaign to include the statute on sanctions, the president of the Supreme Council on Sport in Africa, Nigerian sports leader Abraham Ordia, warned that if Soviet representatives did not support the UN convention against apartheid in sport, including the proposal of sanctions, African nations "would be forced to hold their own private regional sports meets and would struggle against Apartheid in sport 'by their own methods.'"[96] Peter Onu, under general secretary of the Organization for African Unity (OAU), argued that Africans did not believe in the concept of "sport outside of politics," but saw sport as a place where they could achieve goals that they could not achieve in the political arena. He also believed that if they could get the support of Ordia, "no problems with the Olympic Games in Moscow would arise."[97] Soviet administrators exploited resentment felt by other African leaders over what they saw as Nigerian pretensions to power on the continent. For example, when the head of the Zimbabwe African People's Union (ZAPU), Samuel Munodawafa, remarked that Nigerian sports leaders "enjoy much less authority on the continent than they try to present," Prokopov sought to convince him not to support the resolution because it "could play into the hands of racists and reactionary circles."[98] Other African sports leaders sympathized with the Soviet side, but at the same time maintained that "African countries must use all opportunities to fight against Apartheid."[99]

By February 1979, Soviet leaders reported some success in their efforts to increase the participation of African countries in the Olympic Movement and of securing assurances that African countries would compete in Moscow. At the meeting of the Joint Commission of Socialist Sports Organizations, Smirnov noted that the forty-nine African countries represented in the Supreme Council of Sports in Africa had taken a unanimous resolution to support the Moscow Games.[100] He also informed the commission that the IOC had given temporary recognition to a number of NOCs, including Angola, Mauritius, Yemen, and Mozambique. Soviet administrators worked to make participation affordable for African and other developing nations and to help defray their expenses. R. S. Alexander, president of the Kenyan NOC, thanked Novikov in May 1979 for establishing "most generous" and "realistic [hotel] prices" that he hoped other cities would adopt in the future.[101] In June,

Alexander wrote to Smirnov to try to secure air transportation assistance for the team from Kenya.[102] Smirnov and Andrianov also worked to get IOC funds to help pay for transportation to bring athletes from poorer countries to the Olympics. At its meeting in San Juan in June 1979, the IOC's Solidarity Commission allocated one million pounds to subsidize travel expenses for athletes coming to the Games in Lake Placid and Moscow.[103]

While Soviet representatives worked to soothe tensions and address concerns in Africa, a separate set of difficulties related to Asia and the Middle East threatened the Moscow Games. The participation of Israeli athletes posed a challenge on a number of levels. Some members of the Jewish community in the United States remained convinced that the Moscow organizers would try to exclude Israel from the Games, based on the Soviet government's generally anti-Israel foreign policy and because of its restrictions on Soviet Jewish emigration.[104] Soviet officials also feared that various circles in the West that disagreed with Soviet government treatment of Jewish dissidents posed a significant boycott threat. One such organization, the Committee for the Boycott of the Olympic Games in Moscow, in fact wanted to organize a boycott of both Moscow and the 1980 Winter Games in Lake Placid because neither the United States nor the Soviet Union "respected human rights and democratic liberties" and because their rivalry "threatened peace throughout the world." Comparing both countries with Nazi Germany, the organization, formed in Paris, suggested that if the international community had boycotted the 1936 Berlin Olympics, "Hitler's barbarism and the triumph of national socialism perhaps could have been avoided."[105] Killanin believed that any call for boycott should be denounced because it was in the best interests of the Orgcom and the IOC "to have the maximum participation."[106] Despite the "ideological opponents" of the Soviet Union who were "using all means to crush the growing authority of the organizers of the Games," Smirnov believed that these calls elicited complaints from NOCs, the IOC, and IFs over the attempt to bring politics into the Olympic Games, resulting in stronger support for Moscow.[107]

The Moscow organizers also worried that oil-rich Arab countries, which tended to be either strongly anti-Israel or closely tied to the United States or Great Britain, might also initiate a boycott either as a protest against the participation of Israel, or to curry favor with the West, should the United States decide to boycott the Games in support of Israel.[108] Refusing to invite Israel would not only encourage boycotts from the West and its allies, but it would countermand the Olympic Charter and put the Soviet Union at risk of expulsion from the Olympic Movement. When the Indonesian government refused visas to athletes from Israel to compete in the IV Asian Games in Jakarta in the fall of 1962, the IOC withdrew its backing and threatened to revoke recognition of the Indonesian NOC.[109] To counter possible threats to the Games, the Orgcom increased their efforts to attract countries like Kuwait, Bahrain, Brunei, and the United Arab Emirates to the Olympic Movement.[110]

As with African sports leaders, Soviet representatives attempted to balance the expectations of Asian countries with IOC requirements for hosting the Olympic Games, publicizing their strict adherence to IOC rules, yet addressing Asian leaders' underlying concerns and offering sporting aid and assistance. The People's Republic of China, keen to "become the leading sports country in Asia," posed another boycott threat.[111] The status of Taiwan in the IOC continued to be an obstacle to PRC recognition. Killanin warned Moscow organizers that only full exclusion of Taiwan, and not merely renaming of its NOC, would compel the Chinese to apply for recognition and compete in the Games.[112] Soviet representatives feared that Communist China was coming out of its self-imposed international isolation and trying to build influence over other developing countries. Rogul'skii proposed working to expel Taiwan from the Olympic Movement and clarifying the Soviet position on China in order to head off possible actions by the PRC against the Moscow Olympics.[113] At the VIII Asian Games, the Orgcom delegation responded to a number of questions regarding the Peoples' Republic of China's participation in the Olympic Games. Assuring their Asian colleagues that the PRC would undoubtedly be invited to compete in 1980 if recognized by the IOC, Orgcom representatives also noted that, since Taiwan was recognized by the IOC, the committee was obligated to invite the Taiwanese athletes to participate. It defended its position by citing its intention to "strictly" fulfill the guarantee that it had given the IOC to follow the Olympic rules. Similarly, the Orgcom responded that as an NOC recognized by the IOC, Israel would be invited to the Games. The Orgcom insisted it was "taking all measures to assure broad representative participation of athletes of all countries with NOCs recognized by the IOC, including Asian countries." In the meantime, Soviet representatives continued to push for Taiwan's expulsion from the Olympic Movement.[114]

Rogul'skii recommended a number of other measures to promote the Moscow Games in Asia. Because an Indian representative was likely to be elected president of the Supreme Council of Sport in Asia, he believed the Orgcom should invite Indian sports leaders to the USSR. He also suggested that, since Japan was discomfited by the growing influence of Arab countries and China in the organization, the Japanese representatives could be a good channel through which to promote support of the Olympics in Moscow. Rogul'skii thought the Orgcom should invite representatives of Thailand to the USSR because of its role as a three-time organizer of the Asian Games and recommended that the MID and other Soviet bureaus help to organize

Orgcom exhibitions in foreign countries.[115] When the Asian Games Federation decided to exclude Israel from the event, Rogul'skii argued that Soviet representatives must prevent the International Amateur Athletic Federation from banning track and field teams from those countries that had participated in the Asian Games from entering the Olympic Games.[116] In addition to measures for promoting the Games in Asian countries, Rogul'skii judged it necessary to work within the IFs to ensure that there were no barriers to the participation of Asian countries in the Games.

As Soviet officials worked to defuse international tensions, a series of new sporting incidents threatened to renew difficulties in Africa and Asia. In October 1978, the daily London newspaper, *Morning Star*, reported that Israeli rugby teams planned to hold competitions with South African teams, potentially fueling boycott threats on multiple fronts with a single stroke. Smirnov asked Killanin to warn the Israeli NOC that any sports ties with South Africa "may cause serious complications." Smirnov asserted that should such competitions take place, "it will be clear to all that the Israeli sport bodies have done it with provocative purposes to bring harm to the Moscow Olympics."[117] Some Western countries also continued to anger African countries by holding sports competitions with South African teams. For example, the British rugby football union invited a South African rugby team, the Barbarians, on a tour of Britain in 1979.[118]

Despite the continuing tensions, Soviet organizers also received a steady flow of good news as the Games drew nearer. In March 1979, the Democratic Republic of Afghanistan NOC confirmed to the IOC that it would send ten freestyle wrestlers and officials to the Moscow Olympiad.[119] The Executive Board gave provisional recognition to Vietnam at its meeting in Nagoya in October 1979, along with the NOCs of Angola, Laos, Mauritania, and Mozambique. The EB accorded full recognition to Bahrain at that same meeting. In November, the IOC processed applications for recognition from Bangladesh, Botswana, British Virgin Islands, Djibouti, Grenada, Qatar, Sao Tome and Principe, Seychelles, and the Yemen Arab Republic and DPR of Yemen. The status of China was left to the full IOC membership through a postal vote.[120] By 31 December 1979, the National Olympic Committees of San Marino, Somalia, Monaco, Andorra, Uganda, and Honduras had confirmed their participation in the Moscow Games, although Albania and Saudi Arabia refused to participate, and the Orgcom still awaited final word from Malawi, Lesotho, Paraguay, Belize, Guatemala, and Haiti.[121] In February 1980, Berlioux informed Novikov that the NOCs of Angola, Bangladesh, Laos, Mauritania and Seychelles had received full recognition at the Executive Board Meeting at Lake Placid and could now be officially invited to participate in the Games.[122]

THE WHITE HOUSE'S "DARK DEED":
THE U.S.-LED BOYCOTT OF THE 1980 GAMES

As Moscow prepared to host the Games of the XXII Olympiad, the Brezhnev leadership took an increasingly aggressive line in its Cold War foreign policy which would help to undermine the Olympic project and contribute to the breakdown of East-West détente. Buoyed by American tentativeness following the disastrous Vietnam War and eager to maintain its status as leader of the socialist world, the USSR intervened along with its Cuban allies in several wars throughout the global south.[123] After costly proxy wars in Angola and Ethiopia, a 1978 communist coup in Afghanistan brought the superpower rivalry to the Soviet Union's southern border. As an Islamist insurgency and factionalism among Afghan communists continued to destabilize the regime, and fearing U.S. intervention, the Soviet politburo authorized Soviet military intervention to put down the insurgency and return control of the country to a reliable ally.[124] On 27 December 1979, Soviet troops invaded Afghanistan. Eager to send a message that such aggressive action would not be tolerated, on 14 January 1980, the Carter administration issued an ultimatum to the Soviet Union: exit Afghanistan by mid-February or the Games would be boycotted.[125]

On 22 January 1980, Soviet Orgcom leaders discussed the possible boycott with other socialist leaders at a meeting of the Joint Commission of Socialist Sports Leaders. At the meeting, Novikov commented on the "hysteria being raised by the U.S. administration around the 1980 Games," which he believed would influence American society. Yet he expressed confidence that most of the international community did not support the "crazy" idea of boycotting the Moscow Games.[126] In the Soviet domestic press, Afghanistan was never given as the reason behind the U.S. campaign, but Novikov acknowledged to his socialist compatriots that Carter's ultimatum was linked to what the U.S. administration referred to as "'Soviet aggression' in Afghanistan."[127] The White House's "dark deed" would never work, however, because "the whole world knows the truth" that the Soviet Union's "international duty" was to help developing countries in their fight against colonialism. He also provided an official explanation of the events in Afghanistan: the USSR was "helping the people of Afghanistan with a small number of soldiers" and not involved in "any kind of war."[128] Despite the efforts of the United States government, Novikov concluded, "the staging of the Games in a socialist country should give a new impulse to the development of the Olympic Movement, strengthen its unity, and encourage friendship and mutual understanding among the peoples of the world."[129] Smirnov decried the hypocrisy of Western leaders who insisted upon removing politics from sport, yet tried to push their political agenda on the IOC. He expressed bitterness at the actions of American politicians who espoused the boycott even though the Orgcom had not broken a single rule of the Olympic Charter and had not a single complaint from the IOC, IFs, or NOCs. Smirnov thanked the commission delegates for their support of Moscow and for publicizing in interviews and press reports that the Moscow Games would be held "in full accordance with the Olympic Charter."[130]

A few days later, the head of the Novosti press agency, Orgcom member Tolkunov, submitted a report to the Central Committee, outlining his strategy for dealing with the negative press surrounding the boycott campaign. Tolkunov described the many criticisms being laid at the feet of the Moscow organizers. According to him, Western forces reacted to the events in Afghanistan, but press reports renewed their criticisms of the Soviet human rights record and the lack of adequate tourist and hospitality services. To counter the boycott propaganda, Tolkunov recommended a counterpropaganda campaign, emphasizing the many hotels and restaurants available in Moscow, the high technical level of the Games, and the widespread support of the Olympic Games by the Soviet people.[131]

When Carter's threat failed to induce the Soviet leadership to abandon its mission in Afghanistan, Carter officially announced the boycott one month later, on 14 February 1980. After the House of Representatives and the Senate passed a resolution not to send athletes to the Games, the United States Olympic Committee (USOC) agreed. In mid-April the USOC announced its decision to support the Carter Administration's boycott, and the government warned its athletes that they could lose their passports if they traveled to the Games. Carter then began work to convince U.S. allies to support the boycott. While Carter and other Western leaders, such as British Prime Minister Margaret Thatcher, saw the boycott as an opportunity to take a hard line against Soviet belligerence, Olympic supporters, athletes, coaches, and officials around the world decried the boycott as an unacceptable political interference into the Olympic Games.[132]

The USOC decision to boycott the Games set off a flurry of telegram and phone activity between Smirnov and the IOC secretariat. On 14 April 1980, Smirnov telegrammed Killanin, asking him to put the USOC's decision on the agenda for the Executive Board meeting scheduled for the following week in Lausanne and to invite representatives from the USOC to take part in the discussion "in order to avoid any misunderstandings or use of other sources."[133] Upon rumors that Smirnov had hinted at possible implications for the 1984 Games in Los Angeles, Killanin begged him to "please, please remain silent until we meet next week."[134] The previous month, Smirnov had written to Berlioux that there were rumors that the Los Angeles Orgcom was attempting to organize rival "alternative" games to the Olympics in Moscow.

He noted that such action would jeopardize its right to host the 1984 Olympics.[135] Berlioux assured him that the LA Organizing Committee confirmed that it had no intention of staging alternate games.[136]

On 23 April, Killanin sent identical telegrams to Brezhnev and Carter, offering to visit each leader personally to discuss the proposed boycott.[137] Killanin had also appealed to Brezhnev in a February letter, conveyed by Novikov to the Soviet leader. The letter referenced Killanin's statement to the press in which he asked the Organizing Committee and the USSR NOC "to inform the highest authorities of their government of the reactions which have created these difficulties for so many NOCs."[138] Novikov assured Killanin that he delivered the letter to the Soviet premier, who answered in a speech delivered on 22 February, in which he declared, "We will be ready to commence withdrawing our troops as soon as all forms of outside interference directed against the government and people of Afghanistan fully cease. If the United States together with the neighbors of Afghanistan guarantee this, then there will no longer be any need for Soviet military assistance."[139] Novikov added his own belief that the issue went "beyond the sphere of cooperation" between the Orgcom and the IOC, because it concerned "purely political problems." Insisting that the United States government created the current problem for the IOC in its attempt to undermine the Games in Moscow "for far-fetched, purely political reasons," he expressed the wish that "our good relations of mutual understanding and trust will permit us to avoid any misunderstandings that can arise at times from incorrect information."[140] Novikov alluded to his close working relationship with Killanin, developed working together during the preparations for the Games, in hopes of maintaining the IOC president's support despite his inability to change the Soviet leadership's foreign policy. Despite its propaganda efforts, the Moscow Orgcom could not prevent the interference in Afghanistan nor avert the U.S.-led boycott the invasion had precipitated. Although outside the control of the Orgcom, the Soviet invasion of Afghanistan undermined support in the West for détente and inspired sixty nations to boycott the 1980 Olympic Games, demonstrating the limits of sports diplomacy.

CONCLUSION

When the Olympic Torch was extinguished, signaling the end of the Moscow Olympiad, the Orgcom and Soviet leadership had reason to be proud. Soviet athletes accumulated an impressive 195 medals during the fortnight of competition, 80 of them gold. Moreover, 74 Olympic records as well as 36 world records were set during the Games. Despite the absence of 60 countries, Moscow still welcomed 80 nations to the Games, where 5,179 athletes competed in 203 events. Furthermore, the Orgcom could boast good results for its efforts in international sports relations over the last decades, with several developing nations competing in the Olympic Games for the first time, including Angola, Vietnam, Botswana, Laos, Nicaragua, Seychelles, Mozambique, and Cyprus. In addition, women accounted for 1,115 of the athletes, marking the largest percentage of female athletes ever in the Olympic Games. Not only that, but many Western nations and U.S. allies attended the Games despite the boycott, among them NATO countries—Great Britain, France, Belgium, Greece, Iceland, Italy, Luxembourg, the Netherlands, Denmark, and Portugal—and countries of the British Commonwealth, Australia, and New Zealand. Some of these countries sent smaller delegations and marched under the Olympic instead of their national flags, but the presence of their athletes significantly reduced the impact of Carter's boycott.

Perhaps one of the biggest lessons to be learned from the Moscow Olympiad is that, over the course of Soviet involvement in the Olympic Games, Soviet and Western sports leaders shared an affinity for tightly controlled spectacle and perfectly organized competitions that relied on a combination of technical innovation and clearly recognizable rules and regulations.[141] They shared a common vision of modern sport, and both the Orgcom and the IOC believed this had been achieved at the 1980 Summer Games in Moscow. The following excerpt from the Official Report of the Games of the XXII Olympiad is not far off the mark in explaining how the 1980 Summer Games in Moscow were made possible:

The Organizing Committee consisting of representatives from government bodies and of experienced leaders in the national economy, who possessed both professional knowledge and the required authority in their particular fields, made it possible for the OCOG to resolve efficiently the complex problems involved in the preparation of the Games of the XXII Olympiad and to ensure their eventual success.[142]

This excerpt also demonstrates the main focus of the Organizing Committee: efficiency. The IOC representatives appreciated the "high organizational level" the Orgcom achieved. The newly elected IOC president, Juan Antonio Samaranch, applauded the "magnificent organization" of the Moscow Olympiad (see Figure 5.3).[143] Berlioux praised the "diligence and hard work which made the Games of the XXII Olympiad the success they were."[144] Even Western critics noted the well-organized and "mechanical" nature of the opening and closing ceremonies, although they attributed them to the ills of communism.[145]

The Politburo also gave its official approval of the Games and the hard work that went behind them. From the Orgcom down to ordinary "work-

Figure 5.3. Exchanges of gifts were a common feature of international sports diplomacy. Here the newly elected IOC President Juan Antonio Samaranch exchanges presents with Ignatii Novikov and other members of the Moscow Organizing Committee. Courtesy International Olympic Committee.

ers of Moscow," the Communist Party leadership praised the efforts of all those involved making the 1980 Olympics a sporting as well as a "huge moral-political" success. According to the Politburo decree, the Games not only succeeded in "consolidating peace, friendship, cooperation and mutual understanding between peoples," but it also "demonstrated the advantages of the Soviet way of life, our socialist democracy, political solidarity and ideological unity of the Soviet society, discipline, high moral quality of Soviet people, their hospitality, internationalism and friendliness." More importantly the "humanitarian principles and ideals of the Olympic Movement" were "clearly manifest."[146]

NOTES

1. *Official Report of the Games of the XXII Olympiad*, Vol. 2 "Organization," part 1, p. 301, available from http://www.la84foundation.org/5va/reports_frmst.htm.
2. Thatcher, "Brezhnev as Leader," 32.

3. Sandle, "Brezhnev and Developed Socialism," 185. See also Yurchak, *Everything Was Forever*.

4. Mike Bower, "Brezhnev and Superpower Relations," in *Brezhnev Reconsidered*, Edwin Bacon and Mark Sandle, eds. (Houndmills, Basingstoke, Hampshire: Palgrave, 2002), 90. See also Kotkin, *Armageddon Averted*. Defense spending accounted for about 15 percent of the Soviet GDP by 1982.

5. Bacon, "Reconsidering Brezhnev," 15. See also Zubok, *Failed Empire*, 259–64.

6. Christine Evans, *Between Truth and Time*, 6.

7. Douglas Booth, *The Race Game*; Aviston D. Downes, "Forging Africa-Caribbean Solidarity within the Commonwealth?: Sport and Diplomacy during the Anti-Apartheid Campaign," in *Diplomatic Games*, Dichter and Johns, eds., 145–86; Damion Thomas, "Playing the 'Race Card': US Foreign Policy and the Integration of Sports," in *East Plays West*, Stephen Wagg and Andrews, eds., 216.

8. Jorn Hansen, "The Most Beautiful Olympic Games that were ever Destroyed (Munich 1972)," in *Surveilling and Securing the Olympics*, Vida Bajc, ed., 2016, 144–61.

9. Cull, "Public Diplomacy," 45.

10. Theodore C. Mataxis, "Foreword," *The Soviet-Afghan War: How a Superpower Fought and Lost*, trans. and ed. by Lesster W. Grau and Michael A. Gress, (Lawrence: University of Kansas Press, 2002), xxv.

11. Yurchak, *Everything Was Forever*, 9–11. Yurchak argues that the key Soviet paradox was the intent to liberate society through party control.

12. Record of Meeting of the Sports Committee Collegium, 4 June 1975, GARF f. 7576, op. 31, d. 2274, l. 169.

13. Ibid., l. 168.

14. Report of participation of Soviet Representatives in work of 79th IOC session Prague, 10–18 June 1977, by Smirnov and Andrianov, 6 July 1977, GARF, f. 9610, op. 1, d. 144, l. 5. For more on the previous Soviet proposal to "democratize" the IOC, see chapter 2.

15. Ibid.

16. Minutes of the 79th IOC Session, Prague, 15–18 July 1977, IOC Archives.

17. Report of participation of Soviet representatives in the 79th IOC session Prague, 10–18 June 1977, by Smirnov and Andrianov, 6 July 1977, GARF, f. 9610, op. 1, d. 144, ll. 13–14.

18. Minutes of Meeting of the Sports Committee Collegium, 29 January 1975, GARF, f. 7576, op. 31, d. 2274, l. 10.

19. Minutes of Meeting of the Sports Committee Collegium, 27 August 1975, Ibid., l. 40 and Record of Meeting of the Sports Committee Collegium, 27 August 1975, GARF, f. 7576, op. 31, d. 2273, l. 48.

20. Ibid.

21. S. P. Pavlov to V. V. Grishin, n.d. (1979), GARF, f. 7576, op. 31, d. 4754, ll. 15–20.

22. Orgcom Plan for Informational-propaganda Measures Related to Olympiada-80, GARF, f. 9610, op. 1, d. 10, l. 14.

23. Report of Meeting of the Orgcom Presidium, 4 May 1975, GARF, f. 9610, op. 1, d. 5, l. 20.

24. Ibid., l. 13.

25. Orgcom Plan for Informational-propaganda Measures Related to Olympiada-80, GARF, f. 9610, op. 1, d. 10, l. 16.

26. To Central Committee CPSU, on Results of Exhibition Activities of the Orgcom for 1977, 28 February 1978, GARF, f. 9610, op. 1, d. 216, l. 7.

27. Material for Meeting of the Orgcom Presidium, 13 December 1976, GARF, f. 9610, op. 1, d. 37, ll. 70–71, 76, 81–82.

28. Orgcom Plan for Informational-propaganda Measures Related to Olympiada-80, GARF, f. 9610, op. 1, d. 10, l. 14.

29. Material for Meeting of the Orgcom Presidium, 13 December 1976, GARF, f. 9610, op. 1, d. 37, ll. 70–71, 76, 81–82.

30. See Berlioux to Smirnov, 12 December 1979, IOC Archives/COJO of the Summer Games in Moscow 1980 Correspondence 1979 and Berlioux to Novikov, telegram, 3 March 1980, IOC Archives/COJO of the Summer Games in Moscow 1980 Correspondence 1980–1993, Olympic Studies Center, Lausanne, Switzerland.

31. Record of Meeting with the Orgcom President, 19 June 1978, GARF, f. 9610, op. 1, d. 242, ll. 71–72.

32. S. Pavlov to I. Novikov, 12 December 1978, GARF, f. 9610, op. 1, d. 242, l. 92.

33. V. Kukharskii to I. Novikov, 16 February 1979, Ibid., ll. 96–98.

34. Order No. 43 Orgcom, 31 December 1976, GARF, f. 9610, op. 1, d. 48, ll. 211–12.

35. Ibid., l. 210.

36. Decree of the Presidium of the Orgcom Moscow, 1 April 1976, On the Results of International Relations for 1975, GARF, f. 9610, op. 1, d. 36, l. 41–42.

37. Minutes of the Meeting of the Joint Commission of Sports Organizations of Socialist Countries for Cooperation in Preparation and Staging of the Olympic Games, 26 February 1979, GARF, f. 9610, op. 1, d. 440, l. 22.

38. Ibid., 30.

39. Report of Joint Commission of Representatives of Socialist Countries for holding the 1980 Games and Measures for Fulfilling Recommendations of the Meeting, 31 March 1978, GARF, f. 9610, op. 1, d. 216, l. 17.

40. Order of the Orgcom, 25 September 1975, GARF, f. 9610, op. 1, d. 10, l. 9.

41. M. Berlioux to A. Gresko, 14 July 1975, COJO 1980 Correspondence 1975–78, IOC Archives.

42. A. Gresko to M. Berlioux, 11 June 1975, ibid.

43. M. Berlioux to A. Gresko, 31 July 1975 and Telegram, M. Berlioux to V. Shevchenko, 13 December 1976, Ibid. See also M. Berlioux to V. Smirnov, telegram, Vitaly Smirnov Biography and Press Articles, IOC Archives.

44. M. Berlioux to V. Smirnov, 8 May 1979, COJO 1980 Correspondence 1975–78, IOC Archives.

45. M. Berlioux to Prokopov, 13 June 1979, COJO 1980 Correspondence 1979, IOC Archives.

46. To Smirnov from V. Shevchenko, Orgcom Department of Propaganda, 10 June 1976, GARF, f. 9610, op. 1, d. 37, ll. 42–43.

47. M. Berlioux to V. Smirnov, 17 May 1979, COJO 1980 Correspondence 1979, IOC Archives.

48. Minutes of the 81st Session of the IOC, Montevideo, 5–7 April 1979, IOC Archives.

49. M. Berlioux to I. Novikov, 3 April 1975, COJO 1980 Correspondence 1975–78, IOC Archives.

50. I. T. Novikov to Ministries and Agencies of the USSR and Union Republics, Councils of Ministers of Union and Autonomous Republics, Regional, Provincial, Moscow, and Leningrad Executive Committees, 23 January 1976, GARF, f. 9610, op. 1, d. 49, ll. 1–2.

51. Koval' to Iu. S. Rudakov, Vice Chairman of the All-Union Copyright Agency, January 1976, Ibid., ll. 6–7.

52. M. Berlioux to V. Kondratiev, Chief Economic Program Department, Organizing Committee of the Games of the XXIInd Olympiad, 11 August 1978, USSR Correspondence 1977–79, IOC Archives.

53. V. Koval to M. Berlioux, n.d., ibid.

54. M. Berlioux to I. Novikov, 18 January 1978, ibid.

55. Lord Killanin to V. Smirnov, 12 January 1978, ibid.

56. Lord Killanin to I. Novikov, 11 January 1978, ibid.

57. M. Berlioux to V. Smirnov, telegram, 10 October 1978, ibid.

58. V. Smirnov to M. Berlioux, telegram, 9 January 1979 and Telegram, M. Berlioux to V. Smirnov, 12 February 1979, Vitaly Smirnov Biography and Press Articles, IOC Archives.

59. M. Berlioux to V. Smirnov, telegram, 4 December 1979, COJO 1980 Correspondence 1979, IOC Archives.

60. I. Novikov to Lord Killanin, October 1976, COJO 1980 Correspondence 1975–78, IOC Archives.

61. M. Berlioux to A. Gresko, telegram, 25 January 1977, ibid.

62. M. Berlioux to V. Smirnov, 18 February 1977, ibid.

63. Lord Killanin to V. Smirnov, 4 May 1977, ibid.

64. V. Smirnov to Lord Killanin, telegram, 30 May 1977, ibid.

65. Record of Meeting of Sports Committee Collegium, 4 June 1975, GARF f. 7576, op. 31, d. 2274, ll. 170–71.

66. Record of Meeting of the Orgcom Presidium, 1 April 1976, GARF f. 9610, op. 1, d. 36, l. 23. Minutes of the 77th Session of the IOC, Innsbruck, 2–3 February 1976, IOC Archives.

67. Record of Meeting of the Orgcom Presidium, 1 April 1976, GARF f. 9610, op. 1, d. 36, ll. 23–24.

68. See Rider, *Cold War Games*, 163–64.

69. Report on Participation of the Orgcom Delegation to the 78th Session of the IOC and Familiarization with the Experience of Montreal, 17 September 1976, GARF, f. 9610, op. 1, d. 34, l. 53.

70. Ibid., see also Minutes of the 78th IOC Session, Montreal, September 1976, IOC Archives.

71. Report on Participation of Soviet Representatives to the 79th IOC session Prague, 10–18 June 1977, GARF, f. 9610, op. 1, d. 144, ll. 19–20.

72. Ibid., ll. 22–23.

73. V. P. Zakhavin to Central Committee, 7 April 1978, RGANI, f. 5, op. 75, d. 310, l. 12. See also Prozumenshchikov, *Bol'shoi sport*, 189.

74. Lord Killanin to I. Novikov, 30 May 1978, COJO 1980 Correspondence 1975–78, IOC Archives.

75. Decree of the Presidium of the Orgcom Moscow, 1 April 1976, On the Results of establishment of international relations for 1975, GARF, f. 9610, op. 1, d. 36, l. 39.

76. Final Act, Conference on Security and Cooperation in Europe, The Organization for Security and Cooperation in Europe, Helsinki, 1975, p. 41, available at http://www.osce.org/documents/mcs/1975/08/4044_en.pdf.

77. Ibid., pp. 41–56.

78. Decree of the Presidium of the Orgcom Moscow, 1 April 1976, On the Results of International Relations for 1975, GARF, f. 9610, op. 1, d. 36, l. 39.

79. The Committee for Youth Organizations was founded in 1956 from the Anti-fascist Committee of Soviet Youth that existed from 1943 to 1956.

80. Record of Meeting of the Orgcom Commission for External Relations, Moscow, 27 November 1975, GARF, f. 9610, op. 1, d. 16, ll. 4–6.

81. Ibid.

82. Ibid.

83. Minutes of the Meeting of the 69th IOC Session, Amsterdam, 12–16 May 1970, IOC Archives. The vote to expel South Africa from the Olympics was close, thirty-five in favor, twenty-eight against, and three blank ballots.

84. Report on Participation of Soviet Representatives to the 79th IOC session Prague, 10–18 June 1977, GARF, f. 9610, op. 1, d. 144, l. 22.

85. Notes of Meeting of V. Smirnov with the Manager of the Office of the Minister of Public, Work, and Youth Affairs, 12 July 1977, GARF, f. 9610, op. 1, d. 194, ll. 6–7.

86. Notes from Meeting with Minister of Culture, Art, and Sport of the Republic of Congo, 8 December 1977, GARF f. 9610, op. 1, d. 195, ll. 1–2.

87. Notes of Meeting of Koval' and Minister of Work and Public Affairs of Kuwait, n.d. 1977 and Notes of Meeting of Koval with Minister of Youth of the Iraqi Republic, 29 November 1977, GARF f. 9610, op. 1, d. 195, ll. 7, 22–23.

88. Riordan and Peppard, 109.

89. Decree of the Orgcom Executive Bureau and the Sports Committee Collegium, 24 April 1978, GARF, f. 9610, op. 1, d. 226, l. 6.

90. Ibid.

91. Ibid.

92. Alegi, *African Soccerscapes* and Talton, "1960s Africa in Historical Perspective." See also Booth, *The Race Game*.

93. Minutes of the Meeting of the Joint Commission of Sports Organizations of Socialist Countries for Cooperation in Preparing and Staging the Olympic Games, 26 February 1979, GARF, f. 9610, op. 1, d. 440, l. 27.

94. Ibid., l. 28.

95. Report of the Orgcom Delegation to Belgium, 21–25 April 1979, GARF, f. 9610, op. 1, d. 416, l. 94.

96. Report of trip to the United States of the Orgcom Delegation, June 1978, GARF, f. 9610, op. 1, d. 279, l. 32.

97. Notes of Meeting of V. Kudriavtsev with Peter Onu, under general secretary of Organization of African Unity (OAU), GARF, f. 9610, op. 1, d. 300, ll. 17–18.

98. Notes of Meeting of Prokopov with Samuel Munodavafa, National Chairman of ZAPU (Zimbabwe), 6 October 1978, ibid., ll. 12–13.

99. Note of Meeting of V.I. Prokopov with Jo Jeli, member of Executive Bureau ANK South Africa, 3 August 1978, ibid., l. 11.

100. Minutes of the Meeting of the Joint Commission of Sports Organizations of Socialist Countries for Cooperation in Preparation and Staging of the Olympic Games, 26 February 1979, GARF, f. 9610, op. 1, d. 440, l. 19. See also Resolution from Supreme Council of Sport in Africa, 11 July 1978, COJO1980 Correspondence 1975–78, IOC Archives.

101. R. S. Alexander to I. Novikov, 10 May 1979, COJO 1980 Correspondence 1979, IOC Archives.

102. R. S. Alexander to V. Smirnov, 19 June 1979, ibid.

103. Lord Killanin to I. Novikov, 21 August 1979, ibid.

104. Len Alpert to Congressman Jack Kemp, 26 September 1977, USSR Correspondence 1977–79, IOC Archives.

105. Committee for the Boycott of the Olympic Games in Moscow to M. Berlioux, 7 September 1979, COJO 1980 Correspondence 1979, IOC Archives.

106. Lord Killanin to V. Smirnov, 24 May 1978, COJO Moscow 1980 Correspondence 1975–78, IOC Archives.

107. Minutes of the Meeting of the Joint Commission of Sports Organizations of Socialist Countries for Cooperation in Preparing and Staging the Olympic Games, 26 February 1979, GARF, f. 9610, op. 1, d. 440, l. 19, 22.

108. Report on the Work of the Delegation of Orgcom in Bangkok as Observers at VIII Asian Games, December 1978, GARF, f. 9610, op. 1, d. 301, ll. 32–33.

109. Report of the EB IOC meeting and meeting of the EB with IFs, 7–8 February 1963, RGANI, f. 5, op. 55, d. 11, l. 57.

110. Report on the Work of the Delegation of Orgcom in Bangcok as Observers at VIII Asian Games, December 1978, GARF, f. 9610, op. 1, d. 301, l. 33.

111. Ibid. See also Fan Hong and Lu Zhouxiang, "Politics First, Competition Second."

112. Report of Soviet Representatives in Meetings of the EB IOC, Commission for Olympic Solidarity and EB IOC with IFs in Lausanne, 16–22 October 1977, GARF, f. 9610, op. 1, d. 152, l. 33.

113. Report on the Work of the Delegation of Orgcom in Bangcok as Observers at VIII Asian Games, December 1978, GARF, f. 9610, op. 1, d. 301, l. 33.

114. Ibid., l. 31.

115. Ibid., l. 34.

116. Ibid., l. 35.

117. V. Smirnov to Lord Killanin, 26 October 1978, IOC Archives/ Vitaly Smirnov Biography and Press Articles, Olympic Studies Center, Lausanne, Switzerland.

118. Lord Killanin to V. Smirnov, 3 October 1979, Vitaly Smirnov Biography and Press Articles, IOC Archives.

119. Democratic Republic of Afghanistan NOC to IOC, 6 March 1979, COJO 1980 Correspondence 1979, IOC Archives.

120. M. Berlioux to I. Novikov, 8 November 1979, ibid.

121. V. Popov to M. Berlioux, telegram, 31 December 1979, ibid.

122. M. Berlioux to I. Novikov, 16 February 1980, COJO 1980 Correspondence 1980–1993, IOC Archives.

123. Roger E. Kanet, "The Superpower Quest for Empire: The Cold War and Soviet Support for 'Wars of National Liberation,'" *Cold War History* 6.3 (2006): 337. See also *The Global Cold War*, 214–15.

124. Westad, *The Global Cold War*, 325.

125. For more on Carter and the boycot,t see Nicholas Evan Sarantakes, *Dropping the Torch: Jimmy Carter, the Olympic Boycott, and the Cold War* (New York: Cambridge University Press, 2010).

126. Minutes of Meeting of Joint Commission of Socialist Sports Organizations on Cooperation in Preparing and Staging the Olympic Games, 22 January 1980, GARF, f. 9610, op. 1, d. 603, l. 12.

127. Ibid. For more on the domestic press explanation of the boycott, see Evelyn Mertin, "The Soviet Union and the Olympic Games of 1980 and 1984: Explaining the Boycotts to their Own People," in *East Plays West*, Wagg and Andrews, eds., 241–42.

128. Ibid., 13

129. Ibid.

130. Ibid., 34.

131. Mertin, "Explaining the Boycott," 240.

132. For more on the 1980 boycott movement and its effects see Nicholas E. Sarantakes, *Dropping the Torch*; Paul Corthorn, "The Cold War and British Debates over the boycott of the Olympics," *Cold War History* 13.1 (2013): 43–66; Daniel James Lahey, "The Thatcher Government's response to the Soviet Invasion of Afghanistan 1979–80," *Cold War History* 13.1 (2013): 21–42; and Derick L. Hulme, *The Political Olympics*.

133. V. Smirnov to Lord Killanin, telegram, 14 April 1980, COJO 1980 Correspondence 1980–1993, IOC Archives.

134. Ibid.

135. Ibid.

136. Ibid.

137. Killanin to L. Brezhnev, President of The Presidium of The USSR Supreme Soviet, telegram, 23 April 1980, Konstantin Andrianov Biography and Correspondence 1951–84, IOC Archives.

138. Lord Killanin to L. Brezhnev, 13 February 1980, ibid.

139. I. Novikov to Lord Killanin, 2 April 1980, ibid.

140. Ibid.

141. Chatziefstathiou, "Ideology of Olympism," 26–27.

142. *Official Report of the Games of the XXII Olympiad*, Vol. 2 "Organization," part 1, p. 10, available from http://www.la84foundation.org/5va/reports_frmst.htm.

143. Samaranch to Novikov, telegram, 14 January 1981, COJO 1980 Correspondence 1980–1993, IOC Archives.

144. Berlioux to Novikov, 12 January 1982, ibid.

145. John Hoberman describes the Moscow Olympiad as a "Totalitarian Spectacle," and cites Western journalists who criticized the 1980 Games as being too well-ordered and lacking spontaneity. John Hoberman, *Olympic Crisis*, 71–73.

146. Decree of the Politburo of the CC CPSS "On Results of the Games of the XXII Olympiad 1980," 14 August 1980, RGANI f. 3, op. 72, d. 984, ll. 7–11. quoted in T. Iu. Konova and M. Iu. Prozumenshchikov, eds., *Piat Kolets pod Kremlevskimi Zvezdami: Dokumental'naia Khronika Olimpiady-80 v Moskve* (Moscow, Russia: MFD, 2011), 794–95.

Epilogue

After the Soviet Union's entrance into the Olympic Games in 1952, Soviet athletes' impressive performance served as a highly visible symbol of Soviet power, as well as providing an important counterbalance to the image of a communist empire bent on subjugating the peoples of the world. Where the Soviet Union of the arms race was belligerent, combative, and uncooperative, the Soviet Union of the Olympics was friendly and engaging as well as competitive. Hosting the Olympic Games in Moscow was an idea born of the optimism that accompanied the allied victory in World War II, the expansion of international cultural ties under the rubric of peaceful coexistence, and the conviction that the Soviet Union should be a world leader in the spread of peace and mutual understanding between nations, underscoring the movement toward détente. Sports bureaucrats were crucial to cultivating this peaceful side of Soviet power during the Cold War.

If the Soviet Union's participation in the Olympic Games provided an important outlet for friendly contact and exchange to balance the highly charged climate of international politics, the boycotts of 1980 and 1984 reveal sport's limitations in reducing international tensions. The U.S.-led boycott of the Moscow Olympics, like the subsequent eastern bloc boycott of the 1984 Games in Los Angeles, caused many observers to conclude that the modern Olympic Movement had outlived its usefulness as a forum for promoting peace and understanding between nations.[1] In their eyes, the Olympic Games had proved unable to rise above international politics to diffuse tensions between East and West, between capitalism and socialism.

The mixed success of the 1980 Olympic Games also demonstrates the limits of sport to overcome the underlying tensions and problems of late socialism. The evolution of the Sports Committee shows that given sufficient time, space, and resources, Soviet governance could evolve into a more rational, effective, and professional endeavor. However, the invasion of Afghanistan serves as a reminder of how years of careful planning and coordination could be threatened by poor decisions made by the General Secretary and his small group of top advisors. Even the most exquisitely organized Olympic festival could not permanently obscure the growing economic, political, and moral crisis that was increasingly apparent by the time that Mikhail Gorbachev assumed leadership.

Emblematic of this disconnect, tragedy befell the former Olympic Stadium at Luzhniki on October 20, 1982. The same arena that once had treated one hundred thousand spectators to a highly ritualized festival and record-breaking performances of elite athletes, Luzhniki now played host to a mere ten thousand Spartak fans, arriving to an early round UEFA cup match on a cold and snowy evening. At Soviet soccer matches, tensions had been building for decades between increasingly exuberant and sometimes violent soccer hooligans and disaffected youths and the "overzealous guardians of order" trying to control them.[2] Seeking to organize the flow of spectators into the Moscow subway system, the stadium administration blocked all but one of Luzhniki's exits. As fans were leaving through the narrow tunnel toward an icy stairway, a last-minute goal by the Spartak striker brought many of them rushing back. As the two groups collided, dozens, if not hundreds, of fans slipped, were trampled or became crushed in the chaos. Blaming the tragedy on the hooliganism of the crowd, Soviet officials tried to cover up the scope of the disaster and failed to initiate reforms to prevent a similar catastrophe in the future, exhibiting a callous disregard for the safety of the spectators and the lives of the victims.[3] The incident serves as one of many examples of bureaucratic indifference and corruption exposed as dissatisfaction with the party-state grew into pessimism and apathy.

As the full scale of the crisis facing Soviet society became increasingly apparent and as reforms hurdled the Soviet economy faster toward the brink, the fatigued Soviet populace could not bear yet another call to mobilize, and the regime's inability to rally the administrative apparatus in particular may have been a key cause of the Soviet system's failure. *Glasnost'* gave a voice to hard-working, goal-oriented Soviet citizens of all walks of life; not only dissidents but also state bureaucrats took the opportunity to critique the failings of the system and offer suggestions for reform. Rather than an entrenched force opposing reform, many members of the *nomenklatura* and administrative elite supported the Gorbachev initiatives and participated actively in their articulation and implementation.[4] *Perestroika*, however, inspired resistance from those established bureaucrats who saw it as a threat to their job security and their privileges.[5] The regime seemingly had relied too long on coercive and motivational measures that spurred bureaucratic sectors to lobby for their own interests at the expense of larger needs and goals.

As in other realms of Soviet society, *glasnost'* and *perestroika* also ushered in a mood of "revelatory cynicism" regarding the Soviet elite sports system.[6] During this time, a general image emerged of the state-run sports system as one in which athletes and trainers had been treated as mere tools of the state, abused by the Sports Committee and Communist Party bureaucrats, who lauded and rewarded athletes' international successes but then hung them out to dry once their medal-winning days were over.[7] Former athletes and trainers criticized Sports Committee bureaucrats as being incompetent functionaries "trained in administration and not sport."[8] *Perestroika*-era revelations from sports insiders, primarily trainers and athletes, revealed the growing chasm between the stated purposes of Soviet sport—to inspire ordinary Soviet citizens to participate in sports in order to build healthy, more productive workers and a happier society—and the realities of an exploitative, elite training program.[9] This imputed a cynicism to the Soviet state-run sports system that did not fully capture the intentions and aspirations of many Sports Committee functionaries. As the Sports Committee sought to retain control, it also received considerable public criticism from trainers, athletes, referees, and journalists who wanted to develop professional, commercial sport outside the confines of the bureaucratic apparatus.[10] Furthermore, sport could no longer uphold socialist internationalism through the friendship of nations, even within the USSR itself—whereas at one time sport had brought together the diverse republics of the Soviet Union in "a multiethnic, transnational cultural practice that connected people of different national backgrounds," by the 1980s sports bolstered national identities and heightened divisions between the Soviet republican peripheries and the Russian core.[11]

Official ideology could no longer inspire a sense of socialist identity and faith in the Soviet project, especially as disconnects between official discourse and the realities of Soviet life were laid bare.[12] While many embraced the newly liberating political environment, they also feared falling living standards. As one man who lived through these turbulent years noted, "On the one hand, people wanted freedom; on the other hand, they didn't want to lose what they had."[13] Facing seemingly insurmountable obstacles and with a leader unwilling to hold the country together by force, the Soviet Union pulled itself in too many different directions, and the first nominally socialist country ceased to be.

The breakup of the Soviet Union severely tested the sports system that had developed throughout the Cold War. Ex-Olympians found it hard to make a living under these new circumstances.[14] At the same time, sports facilities, including those built for the 1980 Games, fell into disuse. Despite the challenges and the economic crises of the 1990s, former Soviet athletes again topped the medal charts, competing in 1992 as the Unified Team and winning

112 medals, including 45 gold, to the U.S.' 108 medals, only 37 of which were gold. The new Russian Federation continued to be an important player in Olympic Sport, winning the most gold medals in the 1994 Winter Games in Lillehammer despite the loss of team members from the former Soviet republics. After that, however, Russia would not top the medal count again until the 2014 Winter Games, hosted once again on Russian soil: the Black Sea resort town of Sochi.

The Sochi Winter Games serve as a useful comparison to the Moscow Olympiad in a variety of ways, from the bidding process to the difficulties encountered during the preparations and the political controversies attending the Games themselves. After a failed bid to host the Summer Games again in Moscow, Russian president Vladimir Putin pursued the Winter Games in Sochi as an opportunity to reassert Russia's importance and authority, just as the Soviet leadership had sought to host the 1980 Games in order to demonstrate the world power status of the Soviet Union. In order to ensure a successful bid, President Putin borrowed from the same playbook that had enabled Soviet sports bureaucrats to secure the 1980 Games for Moscow: emphasize Russia's proven ability to host large sporting events, tout Russia's importance to the sporting world and to the Olympic Movement in particular, but above all, use the personal authority that had been cultivated both domestically and within the international sporting community. These negotiating tactics again emphasized face-to-face meetings, personal guarantees, and positioning one's self as a like-minded leader whom IOC members could respect and trust.

Like the 1980 Games, the success of the Sochi Olympics depended on a powerful patron of sport in the Kremlin. However, unlike his Soviet General Secretary predecessors, Putin himself attended the IOC Session in Guatemala City, demonstrating his personal commitment to the Games. Addressing the members of the IOC in English and French, Putin spoke with the confidence of knowing what would appeal to his Olympic audience. He highlighted Russian athletes' "major contributions to the Olympic Movement" and drew a historical connection between the site of Sochi and ancient Greece.[15] Putin promised full support for the bid from the people of Russia and the Russian government, assuring the IOC that Sochi would be transformed into a world-class winter sports center, and noting that the Russian state had pledged $12 billion to make the Games a success. Most importantly, Putin's speech of support reassured the IOC members that he was like them: a sportsman and sports enthusiast committed to upholding the ideals of Olympism (see Figure E.1). Putin and the IOC also could rely on the experience and expertise of administrative continuity in the person of Vitalii Smirnov—though he had retired as chairman of the Russian NOC in 2001, Smirnov helped to secure the 2014 Winter Games for Sochi (see Figure E.2).

Figure E.1. The personal address in English by Russian President Vladimir Putin to the 119th IOC Session in Guatemala City in 2007, helped to convince the organization to award the 2014 Winter Games to Sochi, Russia. Courtesy International Olympic Committee.

The task facing the Sochi organizing committee was even more "colossal" than the one Ignatii Novikov had spoken of as the 1980 Games approached.[16] Whereas Moscow had begun Olympic preparations as a world capital with modern sports facilities and transportation networks, the sleepy Black Sea resort of Sochi required a complete urban infrastructure to be built practically from scratch. In the lead-up to Sochi, Western observers called for a boycott of the Games on human rights grounds over Russian law banning "propaganda of non-traditional relationships to minors."[17] Western journalists reported construction delays, environmental damage, lack of tourist facilities, and human rights abuses, among other complaints. Sochi organizers struggled right up to the Opening Ceremonies, as journalists tweeted photos from their unfinished hotel rooms with the Twitter hashtag #sochiproblems, wondering if, when push came to shove, Russia was ready to welcome the world again.[18] Smirnov responded affirmatively, arguing that Russia was deploying its "administrative resources" to ensure success in Sochi, just as Soviet leaders had done for the Moscow Games. "Russians' character makes them believe they need to host, even if it kills them," Smirnov said. "They take everything they have and put it on the table. This is what we will do in Sochi. Everything will be ready."[19]

Figure E.2. IOC President Jacques Rogge meets with Russian president Vladimir Putin and Vitalii Smirnov at the 119th IOC Session in Guatemala City in 2007. Putin drew upon Smirnov's experience in presenting Sochi Russia's bid to host the Winter Games. Courtesy International Olympic Committee.

Other elements of the Sochi Games reflect the new realities of post-Soviet Russia in an uncertain global context. Endemic corruption in Russia's crony capitalist economy threatened to mar the festivities as sporting venues remained incomplete despite the soaring $50 billion price tag. Whereas Soviet organizers were able to compel other departments and bureaus to deliver with limited resources, officials of the New Russia distributed wealth among themselves while Olympic venues went unfinished.[20] While the 1980 organizers feared boycott most of all, security was one of the prime concerns surrounding Sochi. Located in the volatile Caucasus, the Games served as a litmus test for Russian power in the region. With terrorist attacks in nearby Volgograd a month before the Games, a peaceful fortnight of competition seemed uncertain.[21] Whereas Moscow organizers had boasted of their state-of-the-art computer network, Sochi officials worried about cyber-attacks and vulnerable firewalls.[22]

Finally, both Games were marred by cross-border military actions that reinforced the image of an aggressive Russia bent on domination. The Soviet action in Afghanistan came before the Games opened in 1980, but the torch had barely been extinguished in Sochi before Russian troops seized Crimea, leading to Russian annexation of the region less than a month later. Like the conflict in Afghanistan, Russian action in neighboring Ukraine marked the beginning of renewed tensions between East and West.

In other ways, Putin's Olympic project has more in common with his pre-Soviet Russian antecedents. Through the sparkling high-tech display of Russia's national story in the opening ceremonies, Sochi organizers deliberately sought to connect to Russia's imperial greatness and a uniquely Russian national history and culture. Even the choice of Sochi reflects a self-conscious association with Russia's imperial legacy: located on the Black Sea, Sochi represented the successful, centuries-long tsarist quest for a warm-water port. Just as Peter the Great fashioned a new Russian capital out of the swamps of the Neva, Vladimir Putin carved a winter sports complex out of a subtropical summer resort town. Like Peter who "found only a blank page when he came to power" and "wrote on it the words Europe and the West," Putin found a blank slate on the Black Sea coast and wrote on it "a new world class resort for the new Russia—and the whole world."[23]

In August 2016, as the XXXII Olympiad progressed in Rio de Janeiro, Russian sport was once again in the spotlight for controversial reasons. Dozens of Russian athletes had been banned from competing after the World Anti-Doping Agency (WADA) alleged widespread, state-directed use of performance enhancing drugs and falsification of doping-control results. Fielding a dramatically reduced contingent, the Russian delegation in Rio put up a rather disappointing performance, winning only 56 medals to the American team's 121. The scandal also earned the team suspicion and ire from other competitors, especially from their old Cold War rivals.[24]

President Putin's reaction to the damning WADA report also harkens to the Soviet past. Responding to calls for the entire Russian Olympic team be banned from Rio, Putin blamed the United States for bringing politics into the Games and threatening a "schism" in the Olympic Movement by singling out the Russian Federation athletes.[25] He proposed that the IOC organize an objective committee to investigate the report, and recommended none other than Vitalii Smirnov to be its head. Citing Smirnov's long commitment to Olympic sport, his widespread respect from international sports leaders, and his "unimpeachable reputation," Putin argued that Smirnov would be the perfect man to guide the committee and discern the allegations' truth or lack thereof.[26] IOC members indeed held Smirnov in high esteem, having recently elected him as an honorary member at the 129th IOC Session in August 2015 in Kuala Lumpur, where IOC President Thomas Bach said of him, "All of us in the Olympic Movement have been privileged to witness his strong dedication and commitment to our values. For over 40 years within the IOC, he has never failed in his tasks as an IOC Member and Doyen. He is a great Olympic leader. His contribution to our Movement cannot be overestimated."[27]

Speaking to journalists after the second day of the IOC meeting in Rio, Smirnov sought to deflect the recent allegations by setting them in a context of longstanding prejudice and discrimination against Russia and its Soviet predecessors. He remarked that over the twenty-seven Olympic Games with which he had been involved, he did not remember a single one where Russian and Soviet athletes had not faced some sort of problem. Suggesting that judges historically had ruled against Soviet and Russian athletes because of those athletes' dominant position, Smirnov insisted that "the attitude toward our country is obviously purely political" and that Russia was again being singled out.[28] He affirmed that Russia would cooperate with any effort to eliminate doping—as long as it was uniformly applied to all NOCs and Russia was not treated like a "black sheep." Bemoaning that Russia had "lost our positions" in international sport bodies, Smirnov argued that Russian officials again needed to be afforded greater involvement and influence in the sporting world, stating, "we need our people everywhere, not just in WADA, but in the [sports] federations."[29] By asserting discrimination and mistreatment of Russian athletes and officials by the media, by rival athletes, by judges, and by other leaders of the sporting world, the Russian reaction to the WADA report calls into question the degree to which the Soviet Union and its Russian successor state has been integrated into global sports. Only time will tell if Russian athletes, trainers, and sports officials will ever truly be counted as the "same general type" as their Western peers.

NOTES

1. See for example John Hoberman, 1986.
2. Edelman, *Spartak Moscow*, 294.
3. Ibid., 294–95. The official report at the time numbered the victims at sixty-six, but according to the families of the dead, the number lost was 340.
4. Stephen F. Cohen, "Was the Soviet System Reformable?" *Slavic Review* 63, no. 3 (2004): 474.
5. Kotkin, *Armageddon Averted*, 48, 65.
6. Riordan, "Rewriting Sports History," 247.
7. Ibid., 253.
8. Robert Edelman, "The Professionalization of Soviet Sport: The Case of the Soccer Union," *Journal of Sport History* 17, no. 1 (1990): 49.
9. Edelman, "The Professionalization of Soviet Sport," 54; Riordan, "Rewriting Sports History," 247.
10. Edelman, "The Professionalization of Soviet Sport," 47.
11. Manfred Zeller, "Our Own Internationale, 72, 67; see also Cingiene and Laskiene, "A Revitalized Dream," 762–79.

12. Yurchak, *Everything was Forever*, 293.

13. Raleigh, *Soviet Baby Boomers*, 291.

14. Riordan, "Rewriting Sports History," 254.

15. Vladimir Putin, Speech delivered to the 119th Session of the International Olympic Committee in Guatemala City, 4 July 2007, transcription available at American Rhetoric Online Speech Bank, http://www.americanrhetoric.com/speeches/vladimirputiniocsochipitch.htm.

16. Minutes of the First Meeting of the Organizing Committee for the 1980 Olympic Games, 7 March 1975, GARF f. 9610, op. 1, d. 3, l. 50.

17. Jules Boykoff and Matthew Yasuoka, "Media Coverage of the 2014 Winter Olympics in Sochi, Russia: Putin, Politics, and Pussy Riot," *Olympika* 23 (2014): 35.

18. Gabrielle Farber, "A Tale of Two Olympic Cities: Moscow 1980 and Sochi 2014," *The Moscow Times*, 29 November 2013, https://themoscowtimes.com/articles/a-tale-of-two-olympic-cities-moscow-1980-and-sochi-2014-30036.

19. Ibid.

20. James Surowiecki, "The Sochi Effect," *The New Yorker*, 10 February 2014, http://www.newyorkcr.com/magazine/2014/02/10/the-sochi-effect. Surowiecki points out that the Sochi Games are not an isolated example of corruption surrounding large construction projects. See also "Sochi 2014: Encyclopedia of Spending—The Cost of Olympics Report," The Anti-Corruption Foundation, http://sochi.fbk.info/en/report/.

21. Bo Petersson and Karina Vamling, eds., *The Sochi Predicament: Contexts, Characteristics and Challenges of the Olympic Winter Games in 2014* (Newcastle upon Tyne: Cambridge Scholars Publishing, 2013).

22. Mark Clayton, "The Other Security Concern at Sochi Olympics: Cyberthreats," *Christian Science Monitor*, 6 February 2014, http://www.csmonitor.com/World/Security-Watch/2014/0206/The-other-security-concern-at-Sochi-Olympics-cyberthreats.

23. The quote about Peter the Great comes from Peter Chaadaev, "Apology of a Madman," quoted in Thomas Riha, *Readings in Russian Civilization*, vol. 2 (Chicago: University of Chicago Press, 1969), 311. Putin, Speech delivered to the 119th Session of the International Olympic Committee.

24. Nathan Fenno, "U.S. Swimmer Lilly King Spars with Russia's Yulia Efimova Over Doping," *LA Times*, 27 August 2016, http://www.latimes.com/sports/la-sp-oly-rio-2016-u-s-swimmer-trash-talks-russian-who-1470622298-htmlstory.html.

25. Neil Macfarquhar, "Putin's Swift Reaction to Doping Report Blames Anti-Russian Politics," *New York Times*, 19 July 2016, http://www.nytimes.com/2016/07/19/sports/olympics/vladimir-putins-swift-reaction-to-doping-rcport-blames-anti-russian-politics.html.

26. "Rio 2016 Olympics: Vladimir Putin Says 'No Place for Doping in Sport,'" BBC.com, http://www.bbc.com/sport/athletics/36869273.

27. "IOC Elects Two New Members on Final Day of 128th Session," Olympic.org, https://www.olympic.org/news/ioc-elects-two-new-members-on-final-day-of-128th-session.

28. "Vitalii Smirnov: Rossiia poteriala pozitsii ne tol'ko v VADA no l v riade drugikh organizatsii," *Sport-Ekspress*, 4 August 2016, http://www.sport-express .ru/olympics/rio2016/doping/reviews/vitaliy-smirnov-rossiya-poteryala-pozicii-ne -tolko-v-vada-no-i-v-ryade-drugih-organizaciy-1028920/.

29. Ibid.

Bibliography

ARCHIVES AND PUBLISHED ARCIIIVAL COLLECTIONS

Gosudarstvennyi arkhiv Rossiiskoi Federatsii (State Archive of the Russian Federation)

F. 7576   Committee of Physical Culture and Sport, 1920–1959, 1968–1991

F. 9610   Organizing Committee for Preparation and Staging of the Twenty-fourth Summer Olympic Games 1980 in Moscow, 1975–1980

F. 9570   Central Soviet of the Union of Sports Societies and Organizations USSR, 1959–1968

Rossiiskii gosudarstvennyi arkhiv sotsial'no-politicheskoi istorii (Russian State Archive of Socio-Political History)

F. 17   Central Committee of the Communist Party of the Soviet Union
   Op. 132   Department of Propaganda and Agitation (1948–1953)
   Op. 137   Foreign Political Commission for Relations with Foreign Communist Parties

Rossiiskii gosudarstvennyi arkhiv noveishei istorii (Russian State Archive of Contemporary History)

F. 5   Apparat of the Central Committee of the Communist Party of the Soviet Union
   Op. 16   Department for Propaganda and Agitation, 1948–1956
   Op. 33   Department for Propaganda and Agitation in the Soviet Republics and Department for Propaganda and Agitation, 1956–1962, 1965–1966
   Op. 55   Ideological Department of the Central Committee, 1962–1965
   Op. 58   Department for Propaganda and Agitation, 1966
   Op. 59   Department for Propaganda and Agitation, 1967

Op. 60   Department for Propaganda and Agitation, 1968
Op. 61   Department for Propaganda and Agitation, 1969
Op. 62   Department for Propaganda and Agitation, 1970
Op. 63   Department for Propaganda and Agitation, 1971
Op. 64   Department for Propaganda and Agitation, 1972
Op. 66   Department for Propaganda and Agitation, 1973
Op. 67   Department for Propaganda and Agitation, 1974
Op. 68   Department for Propaganda and Agitation, 1975
Op. 69   Department for Propaganda and Agitation, 1976
Op. 73   Department for Propaganda and Agitation, 1977
Op. 75   Department for Propaganda and Agitation, 1978
Op. 76   Department for Propaganda and Agitation, 1979
Op. 77   Department for Propaganda and Agitation, 1980

Avery Brundage Collection. University of Illinois Archives Record Series 26/20/37

Box 50   IOC Members, Andrianov; Konstantin, USSR. , 1954–69, 1970–72
Box 62   IOC Members, Romanov, Aleksei; Russia, 1954–55, 1962
Box 70–74   Circular Letters
Box 76–95   IOC Meetings
Box 112   USSR Olympic Committee Proposal for Reorganization of IOC, 1959–61
Box 113   Russia, 1946, 1950–56
Box 149   Union of Soviet Socialist Republics Comite Olympique d'U.S.S.R., 1947, 1950–69, 1970–72
          General, 1956, 1960–69, 1970–73
          Newspaper Clippings, 1956–68
Box 194 Olympic Games Bids, XXI Olympiad 1976 Moscow, Russia, 1969–70
Box 195 Olympic Games Bids, XXII Olympiad, 1980 Moscow, 1971
Box 277 Clippings, U.S.S.R., 1968–70

Russian State University of Physical Culture Museum, Moscow, Russia

Olympic Winter Games 1964, Innsbruck, 1964
Olympic Games 1964, 2 volumes, Tokyo, 1964
Olympic Winter Games 1968, Grenoble, 1968
Olympic Games 1972, 2 volumes, Munich, 1972
Olympic Winter Games 1972, Sapporo, 1972

International Olympic Committee Archives, Olympic Studies Center, Lausanne, Switzerland

IOC Members, Vitaly Smirnov, Biography and Press Articles, 1971–1984
IOC Members, Vitaly Smirnov, Correspondence, 1971–1984

IOC Members, Konstantin Andrianov, Biography and Correspondence, 1951–1984
IOC Members, Aleksei Romanov, Biography and Correspondence, 1947–1979
National Olympic Committees (NOCs), USSR, Correspondence, 1951–1981
NOCs, USSR Statutes, 1963–1983
NOCs, USSR Executive Board, 1963–1983
Olympic Games of Moscow 1980, Correspondence 1976–80
Olympic Games of Moscow 1980, Political Affairs, Correspondence 1976–1980
Olympic Games of Moscow 1980, Boycott, Correspondence with Jews and Israel
    NOC 1975–1980
Olympic Games of Moscow 1980, Congresses, 1980
Organizing Committee of the Summer Games in Moscow 1980, 1975–1980
President Killanin, Memoranda, 1976–1980
President Killanin, Correspondence, 1972–1980

Published Archival Collections

Konova, T. Iu,. and M. Iu. Prozumenshchikov. *Piat Kolets:Pod Kremlevskimi Zvezdami, Dokumental'naia khronika Olimpiady-80 v Moskve*. N.G. Tomilina ed. Mezhdunarodnyi fond "Demokratiia" (Fond Aleksandra N. Iakovleva). 2011.
Sorokin, Andrei. "Olimpiada-52 v Zerkale Partiinykh Dokumentov." *Rodina* 1 (2014): 66–75. http://rgaspi.org/nauka/rodina.
The Soviet Union and the Olympics. History and Public Policy Program Digital Archive. Cold War International History Project (CWIHP). http://digitalarchive .wilsoncenter.org/collection/266/soviet-union-and-the-olympics.
Vartanian, Aksel'. "Sekretnyi arkhiv Akselia Vartaniana." Parts 1–7. *Sport-ekspress*, 2002, http://www.sport-express.ru.

PUBLISHED MEMOIRS AND AUTOBIOGRAPHIES

Baklanov, Gleb. *Tochka opory*. Moscow: Molodaia gvardiia, 1971.
Romanov, Nikolai. *Trudnye dorogi k olimpu*. Moscow: Fizkul'tura i sport, 1987.

NEWSPAPERS AND JOURNALS

Bulletin du Comité International Olympique
Fizkul'tura i sport (Moscow)
New York Times
Olympic Review
Online *Pravda*, available at http://english.pravda.ru
Pravda (Moscow)
Sovetskii sport (Moscow)

WEBSITES

American Rhetoric Online Speech Bank, http://www.americanrhetoric.com/
Anti-Corruption Foundation, https://fbk.info/
Emetsk online: Site of Emetsk Arkhangel'skoi oblasti, http://www.emezk.ru/forum/ topic.aspx?topic_id=23&page=6.
Olympic Complex "Luzhniki," http://www.luzhniki.ru/eng/luzh.aspx?id=1
Olympic.org: Official Website of the Olympic Movement, http: //www.olympic.org
Organization for Security and Cooperation in Europe, Helsinki, 1975, http://www. osce.org/

BOOKS, ARTICLES, AND DISSERTATIONS

Adler, Nanci. *Keeping Faith with the Party: Communist Believers Return from the Gulag*. Bloomington: Indiana University Press, 2012.
Alegi, Peter. *African Soccerscapes: How a Continent Changed the World's Game*. Athens: Ohio University Press, 2010.
Alexopoulos, Golfo. *Stalin's Outcasts: Aliens, Citizens, and the Soviet State, 1926–36*. Ithaca, NY: Cornell University Press, 2003.
Arnaud, Pierre and James Riordan, eds. *Sport and International Politics: The Impact of Facism and Communism in Sport*. New York: Routledge, 1998.
Bacon, Edwin and Mark Sandle, eds. *Brezhnev Reconsidered*. New York: Palgrave, 2002.
Bajc, Vida, ed. *Surveilling and Securing the Olympics: From Tokyo 1964 to London 2012 and Beyond*. Transnational Crime, Crime Control and Security. Basingstoke, UK: Palgrave Macmillan, 2016.
Baron, Samuel H. *Bloody Saturday in the Soviet Union: Novocherkassk, 1962*. Stanford: Stanford University Press, 2001.
Beck, Peter. "Britain and the Cold War's 'Cultural Olympics': Responding to the Political Drive of Soviet Sport, 1945–58," *Contemporary British History* 19, no. 2 (2005): 169–85.
Bollsmann, Chris. "Mexico 1968 and South Africa 2010: Sombreros and Vuvuzelas and the Legitimisation of Global Sporting Events." *Bulletin of Latin American Research* 29, no. 1 (2010): 93–106.
Booth, Douglas. *The Race Game: Sport and Politics in South Africa*. London and Portland, OR: Frank Cass Publishers, 1998.
Bourdieu, Pierre. *Language and Symbolic Power*, ed. with an introduction by John B. Thompson, trans. Gino Raymond and Matthew Adamson. Cambridge, MA: Harvard University Press, 1991.
Boykoff, Jules, and Matthew Yasuoka, "Media Coverage of the 2014 Winter Olympics in Sochi, Russia: Putin, Politics, and Pussy Riot." *Olympika* 23 (2014): 27–55.
Breslauer, George. *Khrushchev and Brezhnev as Leaders: Building Authority in Soviet Politics*. London and Boston: Allen and Unwin, 1982.

Brokhin, Yuri. *The Big Red Machine: The Rise and Fall of Soviet Olympic Champions*. New York: Random House, 1978.

Brownell, Susan. *Building the Body for China: Sports in the Moral Order of the Peoples Republic*. Chicago: University of Chicago Press, 1995.

Butler, W. E. "Immunity of Soviet Juridical Persons." *Modern Law Review* 35, no. 2 (March, 1972): 189–93.

Caute, David. *The Dancer Defects: The Struggle for Cultural Supremacy during the Cold War*. New York and London: Oxford University Press, 2005.

Chatziefstathiou, Dikaia. "The Changing Nature of the Ideology of Olympism in the Modern Era." Ph.D. diss., Loughborough, 2005.

Cingiene, Vilma, and Skaiste Laskiene, "A Revitalized Dream: Basketball and National Identity in Lithuania." *International Journal of the History of Sport* 21, no. 5 (2004): 762–79.

Clark, Katerina. *Petersburg: Crucible of Cultural Revolution*. Cambridge: Harvard University Press, 1995.

Cohen, Stephen F. "Was the Soviet System Reformable?" *Slavic Review* 63, no. 3 (2004): 459–88.

Cole, Barbara Carol. "The East German Sports System: Image and Reality." Ph.D. diss., Texas Tech, 2000.

Corthorn, Paul. "The Cold War and British Debates over the Boycott of the Olympics." *Cold War History* 13, no. 1 (2013): 43–66.

Cowan, Geoffrey, and Nicholas J. Cull. "Preface: Public Diplomacy in a Changing World." *The Annals of the American Academy of Political and Social Science* 616 (2008): 6–8.

Cull, Nicholas J. "Public Diplomacy: Taxonomies and Histories," *Annals of the American Academy of Political and Social Science* 616 (2008): 31–54.

Davenport, Joanna. "Monique Berlioux: Her Association with Three IOC Presidents." *Journal of Olympic History* 4, no. 3 (1996): 10–18.

David-Fox, Michael. *Crossing Borders: Modernity, Ideology and Culture in Russia and the Soviet Union*. Pittsburgh, PA: Pittsburgh University Press, 2015.

———. "From Illusory 'Society' to Intellectual 'Public': VOKS, International Travel and Party–Intelligentsia Relations in the Interwar Period." *Contemporary European History* 11, no. 1 (2002): 7–32.

———. "From the Editors: 1930s Studies." *Kritika: Explorations in Russian and Eurasian History* 4, no. 1 (2003): 1–4.

Dichter, Heather L. "Corruption in the 1960s? Rethinking the Origins of Unethical Olympic Bidding Tactics." *International Journal of the History of Sport* 33, nos. 6–7 (2016): 666–682. DOI: 10.1080/09523367.2016.1195374.

Dichter, Heather L. and Andrew L. Johns, eds. *Diplomatic Games: Sport, Statecraft, and International Relations since 1945*. Lexington: University Press of Kentucky, 2014.

Dizard, Jr., Wilson P. *Inventing Public Diplomacy: The Story of the U.S. Information Agency*. Boulder and London: Lynne Rienner Publishers, 2004.

Dobson, Miriam. *Khrushchev's Cold Summer: Gulag Returnees, Crime, and the Fate of Reform after Stalin*. Ithaca, NY: Cornell University Press, 2009.

Dunham, Vera. *In Stalin's Time: Middle Class Values in Soviet Fiction.* Cambridge and New York: Cambridge University Press, 1976.

Dunmore, Timothy. *The Stalinist Command Economy: The Soviet State Apparatus and Economic Policy, 1945–53.* New York: Palgrave, 1980.

———. *Soviet Politics, 1945–1953.* New York: Macmillan, 1984.

Duskin, J. Eric. *Stalinist Reconstruction and the Confirmation of a New Elite, 1945–1953.* Houndmills, Basingstoke, and Hampshire: Palgrave Macmillan, 2001.

Edelman, Robert. "The Professionalization of Soviet Sport: The Case of the Soccer Union." *Journal of Sport History* 17, no. 1 (1990): 44–55.

———. *Serious Fun: A History of Spectator Sports in the USSR.* New York: Oxford University Press, 1993.

———. "A Small Way of Saying 'No': Moscow Working Men, Spartak Soccer, and the Communist Party, 1900–1945." *American Historical Review* 107, no. 5 (2002): 1441–74.

———. *Spartak Moscow: A History of the People's Team in the Workers' State.* Ithaca: Cornell University Press, 2009.

Evans, Christine. *Between Truth and Time: A History of Soviet Central Television.* New Haven: Yale University Press, 2016.

Fainberg, Dina, and Artemy M. Kalinovsky, eds. *Reconsidering Stagnation in the Brezhnev Era: Ideology and Exchange.* Lanham, MD: Lexington Books, 2016.

Fitzpatrick, Sheila. *Everyday Stalinism: Ordinary Life in Extraordinary Times: Russia in the 1930s.* New York: Oxford University Press, 2000.

———. "Politics as Practice: Thoughts on a New Soviet Political History." *Kritika: Explorations in Russian and Eurasian History* 5, no. 1 (2004): 27–54.

———. "Signals from Below: Soviet Letters of Denunciation of the 1930s." *Journal of Modern History*, 68, no. 4 (1996): 831–66.

———. "Stalin and the Making of a New Elite, 1928–1939." *Slavic Review*, 38, no. 3 (1979): 377–402.

———. "Supplicants and Citizens: Public Letter-Writing in Soviet Russia in the 1930s." *Slavic Review* 55, no. 1 (1996): 78–105.

Frank, William D. *Everyone to Skis! Skiing in Russia and the Rise of Soviet Biathlon.* DeKalb: Northern Illinois University Press, 2013.

Gilboa, Eytan. "Searching for a Theory of Public Diplomacy." *Annals of the American Academy of Political and Social Science* 616 (2008): 55–77.

Gorlizki, Yoram, and Oleg Khlevniuk. *Cold Peace: Stalin and the Soviet Ruling Circle, 1945–1953.* Oxford and New York: Oxford University Press, 2004.

Gorsuch, Anne E., and Diane P. Koenker, eds. *Turizm: the Russian and East European Tourist under Capitalism and Socialism.* Ithaca and London: Cornell University Press, 2006.

Grant, Susan. *Physical Culture and Sport in Soviet Society: Propaganda, Acculturation, and Transformation in the 1920s and 1930s.* New York and London: Routledge, 2012.

———. "The Politics and Organization of Physical Culture in the USSR during the 1920s." *Slavonic and East European Review* 89, no. 3 (2011): 494–515.

Griesse, Malte. "Soviet Subjectivities: Discourse, Self-Criticism, Imposture." *Kritika: Explorations in Russian and Eurasian History* 9, no. 3 (2008): 609–24.

Guttmann, Allen. *From Ritual to Record: The Nature of Modern Sports*. New York: Columbia University Press, 1978.

———. *The Games Must Go On: Avery Brundage and the Olympic Movement*. New York: Columbia University Press, 1984.

———. *The Olympics: A History of the Modern Games*, 2nd ed. Urbana and Chicago: University of Illinois Press, 2002.

Hahn, Werner G. *Postwar Soviet Politics: The Fall of Zhdanov and the Defeat of Moderation, 1946–1953*. Ithaca and London: Cornell University Press, 1982.

Harrison, Hope M. *Driving the Soviets up the Wall: Soviet-East German Relations, 1953–1961*. Princeton: Princeton University Press, 2003.

Hill, Christopher. *Olympic Politics*. Manchester and New York: St. Martin's Press, 1992.

Hill, Jeffrey. "Introduction: Sport and Politics." *Journal of Contemporary History* 38, no. 3 (2003): 355–61.

Hixon, Walter L. *Parting the Curtain: Propaganda, Culture, and the cold War, 1945–61*. New York: St. Martin's Press, 1997.

Hoberman, John. *The Olympic Crisis: Sport, Politics and the Moral Order*. New Rochelle, NY: A.D. Caratzas, 1986.

———. *Sport and Political Ideology*. Austin: University of Texas Press, 1984.

———. "Toward a Theory of Olympic Internationalism." *Journal of Sports History* 22, no. 1 (1995): 1–37.

Holloway, David. *Stalin and the Bomb: The Soviet Union and Atomic Energy, 1939–56*. New Haven: Yale University Press, 1994.

Holquist, Peter. "'Information Is the *Alpha* and *Omega* of Our Work." *Journal of Modern History* 69, no. 4 (1997): 415–50.

Hornsby, Robert. *Protest, Reform and Repression in Khrushchev's Soviet Union*, New Studies in European History. Cambridge: Cambridge University Press, 2015.

Hough, Jerry F., and Merle Fainsod, *How the Soviet Union Is Governed*. Cambridge and London: Harvard University Press, 1979.

Huish, Robert. "Punching above Its Weight: Cuba's Use of Sport for South-South Cooperation." *Third World Quarterly* 32, no. 3 (2011): 417–33.

Hulme, Derick L. *The Political Olympics: Moscow, Afghanistan, and the 1980 U.S. Boycott*. New York: Praeger Publishers, 1990.

Hunt, Thomas M. "American Sport Policy and the Cultural Cold War: the Lyndon B. Johnson Presidential Years." *Journal of Sports History* 33, no. 3 (2006): 273–97.

———. *Drug Games: The International Olympic Committee and the Politics of Doping, 1960–2008*. Terry and Jan Todd Series on Physical Culture and Sports. Austin, TX: University of Austin Press, 2011.

Iandolo, Alessandro. "The Rise and Fall of the 'Soviet Model of Development' in West Africa, 1957–64." *Cold War History* 12, no. 4 (2012): 683–704.

Jones, Polly ed. *The Dilemmas of De-Stalinization: Negotiating Cultural and Social Change in the Khrushchev Era*. Abingdon and New York: Routledge, 2006.

Josephson, Paul R. *New Atlantis Revisited: Akademgorodok, The Siberian City of Science*. Princeton: Princeton University Press, 1997.

Kanet, Roger E. "The Superpower Quest for Empire: The Cold War and Soviet Support for 'Wars of National Liberation.'" *Cold War History* 6, no. 3 (2006): 331–52.

Katzer, Nikolaus, Sandra Budy, Alexandra Köhring, and Manfred Zeller, eds. *Euphoria and Exhaustion: Modern Sport in Soviet Culture and Society*. Frankfurt: Campus Verlag, 2010.

Keys, Barbara Jean. *Globalizing Sport: National Rivalry and International Community in the* 1930s. Cambridge: Harvard University Press, 2006.

———. "Soviet Sport and Transnational Mass Culture in the 1930s." *Journal of Contemporary History* 38, no. 3 (2003): 413–34.

———. "The Dictatorship of Sport: Nationalism, Internationalism, and Mass Culture in the 1930s." Ph.D. diss., Harvard University, 2001.

Knight, Amy. *Beria: Stalin's First Lieutenant*. Princeton: Princeton University Press, 1995.

Kojevnikov, Alexei. "Rituals of Stalinist Culture at Work: Science and the Games of Intraparty Democracy circa 1948." *Russian Review* 57, no. 1 (1998): 25–52.

———. *Stalin's Great Science: The Times and Adventures of Soviet Physicists*. London: Imperial College Press, 2004.

Kotkin, Stephen. *Armageddon Averted: The Soviet Collapse, 1970–2000*. New York: Oxford University Press, 2001.

———. *Magic Mountain: Stalinism as Civilization*. Berkeley and Los Angeles: California University Press, 1994.

———. "The State—Is It Us? Memoirs, Archives, and Kremlinologists." *Russian Review* 61, no. 1 (2002): 35–51.

Kozlov, Vladimir A. "Denunciation and Its Functions in Soviet Governance: A Study of Denunciations and Their Bureaucratic Handling from Soviet Police Archives, 1944–1953." *Journal of Modern History* 68, no. 4 (1996): 867–98.

———. *Uprisings in the USSR: Protest and Rebellion in the Post-Stalin Years*. The New Russian History Series. Armonk, NY: M. E. Sharpe, 2002.

Krementsov, Nikolai. *The Cure: A Story of Cancer and Politics from the Annals of the Cold War*. Chicago: University of Chicago Press, 2002.

———. *Stalinist Science*. Princeton: Princeton University Press, 1997.

Lahey, Daniel James. "The Thatcher Government's Response to the Soviet Invasion of Afghanistan 1979–80." *Cold War History* 13, no. 1 (2013): 21–42.

Large, David Clay. *Munich 1972: Tragedy, Terror, and Triumph at the Olympic Games*. Lanham, MD: Rowman and Littlefield, 2012.

Lieven, Dominic C. B. *Russia's Rulers under the Old Regime*. New Haven: Yale University Press, 1989.

Lincoln, W. Bruce. *In the Vanguard of Reform: Russia's Enlightened Bureaucrats, 1825–1851*. DeKalb: Northern Illinois University Press, 1982.

Malia, Martin. *The Soviet Tragedy: A History of Socialism in Russia, 1917–1991*. New York: Simon and Schuster, 1994.

Malz, Arie, Stefan Rohdewald, and Stefan Wiederkehr, eds. *Sport zwischen Ost und West: Beiträge zur Sportgeschichte Osteuropas im 19. und 20. Jahrhundert.* Osnabrück: Fibre Verlag, 2007.

Mathur, Nameeta. "Women and Physical Culture in Modern Poland." Ph.D. diss. Eberly College of Arts and Sciences at West Virginia University, 2001.

Mataxis, Theodore C. "Foreword," *The Soviet-Afghan War: How a Superpower Fought and Lost,* trans. and ed. by Lesster W. Grau and Michael A. Gress. Lawrence: University of Kansas Press, 2002.

Mazov, Sergey. *A Distant Front in the Cold War: The USSR in West Africa and the Congo, 1956–64.* James H. Hershberg, ed. Cold War International History Project. Stanford, CA: Stanford University Press, 2010.

McCagg, William O., Jr. *Stalin Embattled, 1943–48.* Detroit: Wayne State University Press, 1978.

McReynolds, Louise. "Olympic Politics in Tsarist Russia: The Development of a Nationalist Identity." In *Problemy vsemirnoi istorii,* ed. B.V. Anan'ich, R. Sh. Ganelin, and V.M. Panaiekh. St. Petersburg: Vilanin, 2000.

———. *Russia at Play: Leisure Activities at the End of the Tsarist Era.* Ithaca: Cornell University Press, 2003.

Mertin, Evelyn, and Christoph Bertling, eds. *Freunde oder Feinde? Sportberichterstattung in Ost und West während des Kalten Krieges.* Köln: Gütersloh Medienfabrik Gütersloh, 2013.

Mitrohin, Nikolai. "'Back Office' Mikhaila Suslova ili kem i kak Proizvodilas' Ideologiia Brezhnevskogo Vremeni," *Cahiers du Monde Russe* 54, nos. 3–4 (2013): 409–440.

Montagu, Ivor Goldsmith Samuel. *East-West Sports Relations.* Peace Aims Pamphlet 52. London, 1951.

Morton, Henry W. *Soviet Sport.* New York: Collier Books, 1963.

Nye Jr., Joseph S. "Public Diplomacy and Soft Power." *Annals of the American Academy of Political and Social Science* 616 (2008): 94–109.

Osgood, Kenneth. *Total Cold War: Eisenhower's Secret Propaganda Battle at Home and Abroad.* Lawrence: University Press of Kansas, 2006.

Parks, Jenifer. "'Nothing but Trouble': The Soviet Union's Push to 'Democratise' International Sports during the Cold War, 1959–1962." *International Journal of the History of Sport* 30, no. 13 (2013): 1554–67.

———. "Promoting Authority through Sport by States and Societies of Eastern Europe." *Handbuch der Sportgeschichte Osteuropas.* http://www.ios-regensburg.de/service/ios-publikationen/online-publikationen/handbuch-der-sportgeschichte-osteuropas.html (2014).

Peppard, Victor, and James Riordan. *Playing Politics: Soviet Sport Diplomacy to 1992.* Greenwich, CT: JAI Press, 1993.

Péteri, Gyösrgy. "Sites of Convergence: The USSR and Communist Eastern Europe at International Fairs Abroad and at Home." *Journal of Contemporary History* 47, no. 1 (2012): 3–12.

Petersson, Bo, and Karina Vamling, eds. *The Sochi Predicament: Contexts, Characteristics and Challenges of the Olympic Winter Games in 2014.* Newcastle upon Tyne: Cambridge Scholars Publishing, 2013.

Pinkus, Benjamin. *The Jews of the Soviet Union: A History of a National* Minority. Cambridge, New York, and Melbourne: Cambridge University Press, 1988.

Pinter, Walter McKenzie, and Don Karl Rowney, eds. *Russian Officialdom: The Bureaucratization of Russian Society from the Seventeenth to the Twentieth Century.* Chapel Hill: University of North Carolina Press, 1980.

Pollack, Ethan. *Stalin and the Soviet Science Wars.* Princeton, NJ: Princeton University Press, 2006.

Prozumenshchikov, M. Iu. *Bol'shoi sport i bol'shaia politika.* Moscow: ROSSPEN, 2004.

———. "Sports as a Mirror of Eastern Europe's Crises," *Russian Studies in History* 49, no. 2 (2010): 51–93.

Raleigh, Donald J. *Soviet Baby Boomers: An Oral History of Russia's Cold War Generation.* Oxford and New York: Oxford University Press, 2012.

Ratner, Aleksandr. "Vesnoi Piat'desiat pervogo." *Olimpiiskaia Panorama* (1988): 27–35.

Read, Christopher, ed. *The Stalin Years: A Reader.* New York: Palgrave Macmillan, 2003.

Reid, Susan E. "Cold War in the Kitchen: Gender and the De-Stalinization of Consumer Taste in the Soviet Union under Khrushchev." *Slavic Review* 61, no. 2 (2002): 211–52.

Richmond, Yale. *Cultural Exchange and the Cold War: Raising the Iron Curtain.* University Park: Pennsylvania State University Press, 2003.

Rider, Toby C. *Cold War Games: Propaganda, the Olympics, and U.S. Foreign Policy, Sport and Society.* Champaign: University of Illinois Press, 2016.

Riordan, James. "Rewriting Soviet Sports History." *Journal of Sport History* 20, no. 3 (1993): 247–58.

———. "The Rise, Fall and Rebirth of Sporting Women in Russia and the USSR." *Journal of Sports History* 18, no. 1 (1991): 183–99.

———. *Sport, Politics, and Communism.* Manchester and New York: Manchester University Press, 1991.

———. *Sport in Soviet Society: Development of Sport and Physical Education in Russia and the USSR.* Cambridge and New York: Cambridge University Press, 1977.

Roth-Ey, Kristin. *Moscow Prime Time: How the Soviet Union Built the Media Empire that Lost the Cultural Cold War.* Ithaca and London: Cornell University Press, 2011.

Rowley, Alison. "Sport in the Service of the State: Images of Physical Culture and Soviet Women, 1917–1941." *International Journal of the History of Sport*, 23:8 (December 2006): 1326–29.

Ryavec, Karl W. *Russian Bureaucracy: Power and Pathology.* Lanham, MD: Rowman and Littlefield, 2003.

Sarantakes, Nicholas Evan. *Dropping the Torch: Jimmy Carter, the Olympic Boycott, and the Cold War.* New York: Cambridge University Press, 2010.

Schiller, Kay, and Christopher Young, eds. *The 1972 Munich Olympics and the Making of Modern Germany*. Los Angeles: University of California Press, 2010.

Simpson, Pat. "Parading Myths: imaging New Soviet Woman on Fizkul'turnik's Day, July 1944." *Russian Review* 63 (April 2004): 187–211.

Skilling, H.G. and F. Griffiths, eds. *Interest Groups in Soviet Politics*. Princeton: Princeton University Press, 1971.

Solnick, Steven L. *Stealing the State: Control and Collapse in Soviet Institutions*. Cambridge: Harvard University Press, 1998.

Talton, Benjamin. "1960s Africa in Historical Perspective: An Introduction." *Journal of Black Studies* 43, no. 1 (2012): 3–10.

Tarschys, Daniel. "Management by Duplication: Some Observations on Soviet Bureaucracy." *Nordic journal of Soviet and East European Studies* 3, no. 2 (1986): 37–56.

Taubman, William, ed. *Nikita Khrushchev*. New Haven: Yale University Press, 2000.

Tolz, Vera. "'Cultural Bosses' as Patrons and Clients: The Functioning of the Soviet Creative Unions in the Postwar Period." *Contemporary European History* 11, no. 1(2002). 87–105.

Tomoff, Kiril. *Creative Union: The Professional Organization of Soviet Composers, 1939–1953*. Ithaca: Cornell University Press, 2006.

———. "'Most Respected Comrade . . .': Patrons, Clients, Brokers and Unofficial Networks in the Stalinist Music World." *Contemporary European History* 11, no. 1 (2002): 33–65.

———. *Virtuosi Abroad: Soviet Music and Imperial Competition during the Early Cold War, 1945–58*. Ithaca and London: Cornell University Press, 2015.

Tucker, Robert. "Culture, Political Culture, and Communist Society." *Political Science Quarterly* 88, no. 2 (1973): 173–90.

Ulam, Adam. *Expansion and Coexistence: Soviet Foreign Policy, 1917–73*. 2nd ed. New York: Praeger Publishers, 1974.

Ungerleider, Steven. *Faust's Gold: Inside the East German Doping Machine*. New York: Thomas Dunne Books, 2001.

Wagg, Stephen, and David Andrews, eds. *East Plays West: Sport and the Cold War*. London and New York: Routledge, 2006.

Walker, Barbara. "*Kruzhok* Culture: the Meaning of Patronage in the Early Soviet Literary World." *Contemporary European History* 11, no. 1 (2002): 107–23.

Ward, Christopher J. *Brezhnev's Folly: The Building of BAM and Late Soviet Socialism*. Pittsburgh: University of Pittsburgh Press, 2009.

Weber, Max. *Economy and Society: An Outline of Interpretive Sociology*. Vol. 2. Berkeley: University of California Press, 1978.

Westad, Odd Arne. *The Global Cold War: Third World Interventions and the Making of our Times*. Cambridge, UK: Cambridge University Press, 2007.

Wiederkehr, Stefan. "'We Shall Never Know the Exact Number of Men Who Have Competed in the Olympics Posing as Women': Sport, Gender Verification and the Cold War." *International Journal of the History of Sport* 26, no. 4 (2009): 556–72.

Witherspoon, Kevin B. *Before the Eyes of the World: Mexico and the 1968 Olympic Games*. DeKalb: Northern Illinois University Press, 2008.

Xu, Guoqi. *Olympic Dreams: China and Sports, 1895–2008.* Cambridge and London: Harvard University Press, 2008.

Yurchak, Alexei. *Everything Was Forever until It Was No More: The Last Soviet Generation.* Princeton: Princeton University Press, 2005.

Zeller, Manfred. "'Our Own Internationale,' 1966: Dynamo Kiev Fans between Local Identity and Transnational Imagination." *Kritika* 12, no. 1 (2011): 53–82.

Zubkova, Elena. *Russia after the War: Hopes, Illusions, and Disappointments, 1945–1957.* Trans. Hugh Ragsdale. Armonk, NY and London: M.E. Sharpe, 1998.

Zubok, Vladislav, and Constantine Pleshakov. *Inside the Kremlin's Cold War: From Stalin to Khrushchev.* Cambridge: Harvard University Press, 1996.

Zubok, Vladimir M. *A Failed Empire: The Soviet Union in the Cold War from Stalin to Gorbachev.* Chapel Hill: University of North Carolina Press, 2007.

Index

About the Author

Jenifer Parks is associate professor of history at Rocky Mountain College. Her research focuses on sport and politics in the Soviet Union during the Cold War. Her work has been published in the *International Journal of the History of Sport* and a number of edited collections. She lives in Billings, Montana.